Revd. Charles Edward Garrad

Liz Anderson was born in Mandalay, Burma, and came home to England when she was three. She was educated in Bristol at Clifton High School, and matriculated at Newnham College, Cambridge in 1948, the first year in which women were accepted as full members of Cambridge University. She completed her medical training at St Bartholomew's Hospital, London. After retirement from general practice she and her gynaecologist husband Tim worked with Voluntary Service Overseas for two years in Cambodia, where she set up a clinic for sex-workers in a rented brothel. She and Tim have four children and five grandchildren.

UNDER RUNNING LAUGHTER

Burma – The Hidden Heart

Liz Anderson

Matador
9 De Montfort Mews
Leicester LE1 7FW, UK
Tel: (+44) 116 255 9311 / 9312
Email: books@troubador.co.uk
Web: www.troubador.co.uk/matador

ISBN 978-1-848760-677

A Cataloguing-in-Publication (CIP) catalogue record for this book
is available from the British Library.

Original cover design: Simon Francis

Typeset in 11pt Sabon by Troubador Publishing Ltd, Leicester, UK
Printed in the UK by TJ International, Padstow, Cornwall

Matador is an imprint of Troubador Publishing Ltd

To the memory of my father, Charles Edward Garrad, whose story has never been written until now.

PREFACE

This is the story of both my parents. It was only as I was writing it that I came to realise that the one cannot be told without the other, for my father's achievements depended on their union. Although it is written as fiction, it is firmly based on their lives. All the major events and many of the minor ones did in fact take place. All the main characters are real people, called by their actual names. All, that is, except for Matt.

The life of my father Charles Edward Garrad was one of integrity, courage and conviction. Faced with a challenge of overwhelming proportions, he behaved just as he always did; talented and meticulous in equal measure, he tackled it head-on and saw it through to the end and beyond.

By avoiding a factual biography I have been able to be with him alone, to witness his actions and hear his thoughts. This must surely be the best way to share him with my readers.

It is with extraordinary pleasure that I am able to report that as this book is published a new edition of the Garrad Bible is being produced by the Burmese Bible Society, incorporating for the first time the corrections he made so painstakingly right up to a few days before his death.

FEA

FOREWORD

David HW Grubb
Author and Editor

There are many well written biographies and autobiographies, focusing on well known and important individuals. But equally the writer can explore important experiences within more ordinary lives by using a less formal approach, whether it be in a short story, novel, poem or play. This is where Under Running Laughter belongs.

What makes the book so compelling from the opening sentences is that it is a story, there is dialogue, there are numerous cameos and colours and contours and the writing has such a strong sound. By deciding to write in this way Liz Anderson has avoided documentary detailing and restricting herself to the factual and this has a liberating influence on every page.

The story is told as in a work of fiction, some of the events are imagined, there are indeed scenes where nobody else was present. The use of dialogue throughout adds momentum and diversity and the individuals have much greater integrity. Actions, thoughts, feelings and even silences are expressed and as the story builds the reader is caught up in a rich and vibrant narrative.

Under Running Laughter is a story of determination and achievement, struggles and setbacks, impulse and imagination driving a man to reject the more common concepts of duty and scholarship and Liz Anderson has captured the zeal and spirit of her father in a wonderful way.

This book is about important things and the style of the story telling as well as the subject matter lights up the mind in a refreshing and anything but academic way. I think that this book is a remarkable achievement and deserves wide readership in a day and age when celebrities show and tell but have so little of originality and importance to say.

ACKNOWLEDGEMENTS

I am very grateful to the archivist at the United Society for the Propagation of the Gospel for permission to use the frontispiece and the various documents and letters, some written by my father and uncle themselves, stored in the Rhodes House Library section of the Bodleian in Oxford; also to the archivist there for giving me such a great deal of help in finding what I was looking for. All these records have produced vital evidence for what actually took place. One particular letter, ostensibly written by my mother, was in fact written by 'HB' whom I have not been able to trace. My apologies and thanks to HB's relatives. My thanks, too, to the British and Foreign Bible Society for useful information.

I have drawn heavily on *From the Land of Green Ghosts,* published by Flamingo in 2003; my grateful thanks to its author Pascal Khoo Thwe, particularly with respect to the last chapter of my novel. Amitav Gosh's *The Glass Palace*, HarperCollins 2001, and Dr John Ebenezer Marks' autobiography *Forty Years in Burma,* Hutchinson & Co. 1917, have also been helpful for the Burma chapters. *Cambridge and Clare*, Cambridge University Press 1985 by Sir Harry Godwin, was a mine of information. Thank you to all of them.

My heartfelt thanks to all the exceptional people without whose help this book would never have come about. My historian sister Anne has anchored me gently but firmly to the ground with the family records and all the work she has done on them, in particular Fanny's diaries; our brother Douglas's memories have added another solid layer of reality. My mentor and friend David has encouraged me in my efforts to create the imagined links that I believe have made this story more readable. Steering my way between such opposite demands has presented a delicate conundrum. To David, my special gratitude for his patient guidance, optimism and skill in constructive pain-free criticism.

On the technical side, my thanks to my daughter Emily who has wheedled an intransigent computer into doing what was asked of it. And where would I have been without the unwavering support of my husband Tim, who as always is there to lean on?

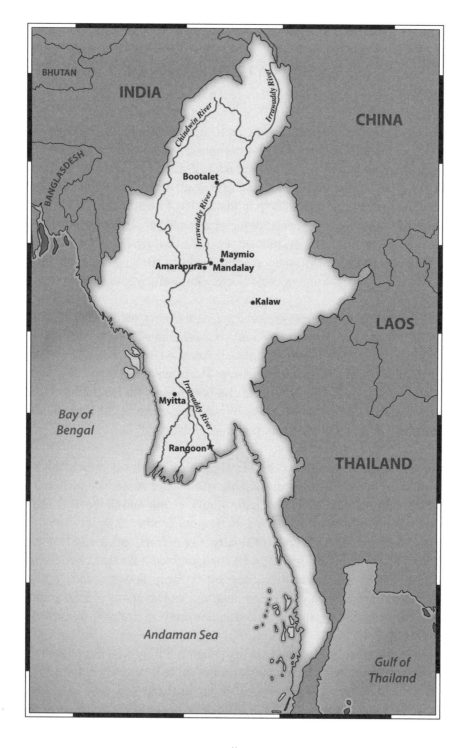

BOOK ONE

ENGLAND

PART ONE

1

ONE SCRATCH ON THE EDGE of the living-room door was much deeper than the rest. My eldest brother made it with a nail when he was eight and now he has gone for a soldier, so you can see how long ago that was. Mother put the Bible on his head as he stood tall against the battered old door, and he marked the place afterwards. Then there was John and then James, and now maybe, just maybe, it was me.

'Ma!' I shouted. 'Can I try for the mark?' Mother was outside at the wash-tub. I could hear the sound of the bristles on the wash-board as she scrubbed the life out of my shirt.

'Just bide a moment,' she said, 'or you'll have no clothes to your back tomorrow.' But she had a soft spot for me, did Ma, and she knew I couldn't wait. So she dropped her brush into the suds and dried her poor chapped hands on the old bit of sacking tied round her. It only just reached, on account of the new baby in there.

'Come on then, take off your boots, and no tip-toe.'

I swear that by squeezing my belly against my backbone I rose up higher and when she was busy balancing the Bible on my hair my heels somehow came off the brick floor all by themselves.

'All right,' she said, 'come out.' I started to scratch the place with a knife off the table, but there was no need. I was scratching away inside Frank's mark. I had arrived!

That was when I was ten years old. My youngest brother, James, had been out to work after school for nearly a year, but now he'd grown too tall for the job. He's my hero, Ma would say, and then she'd laugh. The day before had been Ma's birthday, and I'd heard James's boots clumping up the path to the door. They made a special sound pattern; clonk-slop, clonk-slop, with a gap between, on account of the Infantile Paralysis he'd had three years earlier. He was clinking money in his pocket, but you could see he was trying hard not to cry.

'I'm sorry Ma, but I've got too tall. They don't want me any more up at the farm.'

'Wipe that mud off your boots,' was all she said in reply, but she looked as if she might cry too. James fished in his pocket and brought out five pennies. He held one out to Ma.

'We only did four fields, but Mr Garrad gave me an extra penny because it was my last day. This is for your birthday.' Then Ma did cry, though she tried to hide it by turning away and putting the money in the old tobacco tin on the mantelpiece.

James often talked about Mr Garrad when he got home from the farm; he likes to learn things, does our James, and he got to know all sorts while they walked round the fields. I think Mr Garrad must be a bit like God, except that of course God can see everything, or that's what the vicar said, and Mr Garrad can't see anything. That's because he went blind when he was just a bit older than me, and that's why he needs a boy to lead him round his own farm, so that he can feel how the crops are growing. He likes to walk with his hand on your shoulder, so you have to be just the right height for him to be comfortable.

He tells you where he wants to go.

'Let's start with the Hundred Acre meadow,' he might say. He puts his hand on your shoulder and you walk slowly along the lane, remembering to warn him about the cowpat or the branch that's just about to knock the tall hat off his head. He's quite short so it must be difficult to look grand enough without the hat.

Now perhaps you understand why it was so important for me to reach the mark on the door. It meant I could work instead of James. He could take me up to the farm after school next day, show me to Mr Garrad and see if my shoulder fitted his hand. So as soon as I had been measured against the living-room door I yelled out to Ma and anyone else who might be listening:

'I'm starting work tomorrow! I'm starting work tomorrow!'

But Mother just looked at me and shook her head like she does.

'They won't be wanting you up at Brook House tomorrow,' she said. 'Mrs Cardy told me as how she'd seen the doctor's carriage drive in there three times, and the last time he never came out. And the parson has just arrived. Poor Mrs Garrad must be ever so bad.'

Sometimes I wonder if Mother's a bit of a witch or something, I really do, because she often seems to know about things before they happen. Just at that very moment the church bell started to ring. First off I thought it was just one clang, but then it went again, and again, on and on, but so slow as to make you keep thinking it had stopped for good. Ma went down on her knees just where she was standing on the kitchen floor. 'God rest her soul,' was all she said.

I wondered whose soul for a bit, and then saw it had to be Mrs Garrad's because there was no-one else ill in the village barring old Mrs Bax, who everyone said wasn't ill at all, just cantankerous, whatever that might be (Old Bob, the shepherd, says his dog's ear's cankerous, but I think that must be a bit different).

And then Ma began to cry. To start with, I couldn't really see what the fuss was all about. After all, Mrs Garrad was quite old – 'forty-five,' I'd heard a neighbour say, 'and a truly God-fearing soul if ever there was one' – and so she would have been up in Heaven already, which surely had to be the best place from all the Bible said.

But then I started to think about John and Mary and Edith and Fanny and Katie and Frank and Bob and Charlie and Daisy and Bessie and William, all of them Mrs Garrad's children. I knew what they all looked like and what their names were of course but not much else, and now there was the new baby, George, who they said had been the finish of her. I began to think about our Ma and I just couldn't imagine her not being there, and I reckon I began to understand.

2

Bures, England 1885

'OH MAMA MAMA, what am I going to do without you?'

The silence in the house was absolute. It was difficult to believe that just one short week ago everything was as it had always been. Doors banged, feet clattered, the baby cried, snatches of song and children's laughter filled the rooms with the welcome sounds of a family in full flood. And now, nothing. The blackbird still sang in the weeping willow and the clump of men's boots and the clanking of pails still came in through the open windows, but even these familiar sounds seemed muted and sad.

Mary slipped silently upstairs and eased her tall, slim frame round the edge of the open door into her mother's room. The village nurse had done her job well. The body lay stretched out down the centre of the bed, covered with one of the best embroidered linen sheets folded down at the top. Mother's face belied her forty-five years; there were tiny crows'-feet at the corners of her eyes, but the serenity that had been her hallmark in life had remained with her through her last illness and her dying, and the two women could have passed for sisters.

At seventeen, poor Mary was already marked by the passage of years made busy and burdensome by so many young brothers and sisters. She took her responsibilities very seriously, and the signs of frequent laughter remaining even now on her mother's face were absent from her own.

She flung herself down on her knees by the pillow, and the fair and the dark strands of long hair mingled across the crisp white linen.

Mary's words seemed forced out of her by their own intensity and the silence that followed was even denser than before. Then, at last, it was broken by sobs so deep that the whole bed shook, the brass knobs on the sturdy iron frame shimmering and quivering in the shafts of April sunshine that found their way between the drawn curtains. In every house in the village blinds were pulled down and shutters were up in the windows of every shop, for on this day the whole village joined the family in their sadness. For a long time Mary's poor thin body was convulsed by her grief until, worn out at last, she subsided almost into sleep.

Her reverie was broken by the squeak of the hinges ('that door was never hung quite right,' she remembered her mother saying often) and she looked up to see her brother John standing uncertainly in the doorway. Taller than his sister, but with the same dark wavy hair and the family's prominent eyes, he was just a year her senior. He, too, conscious of his father's blindness, took his duties doubly to heart. Brother and sister would spend hours closeted together in private discussion.

'John and Mary are at it again,' the other children would sigh, rolling up their eyes in mock despair and carrying on playing without them.

Now, in their mother's room, Mary rushed at him. 'Oh John, I'm so glad you've come.' She threw herself into his unaccustomed arms. Exhibition of feeling was not the Suffolk country way.

'Whatever shall we do?' she asked him. 'However are we going to manage? What about baby George? And Charlie? The only person who can – could – cope with his tantrums was Mama. Sometimes I think he really hates me, and he just gets worse when I try and help. And poor, dear Daisy; why, she's almost an imbecile, and little Bessie's miles behind for her age. Ever since Mama's been ill everybody's been saying how wonderfully we've all been managing, but it wasn't that at all. All through these last fearful days we've been numb. We just could not believe what was happening. We'd always been a big, happy family, and we always would be. Mother was so tired after little George was born but I thought she was getting better until last week and now ...'

'Steady, steady!' John stroked her hair and tried to get out his handkerchief at the same time. But it was no use. Mary had hardly spoken since her mother's death the day before and now she couldn't stop.

'She was wanting to dress and Jenny even came up from the village and did her hair. And then, suddenly, everything seemed to go wrong again. She kept fainting and she wouldn't eat. And then Father talked for ages to the doctor and wouldn't let us listen, but he said no expense was to be spared and those useless specialists were sent for. These last few days were a nightmare. You know I hardly left her bedside. I just sat and watched her fading away before my very eyes. My own dear mother was actually dying and it seemed as if no-one was doing anything to stop it. It didn't seem possible, she was always so full of life.

More than any of us. And then, last evening, she just slipped away. And she'll never come back.'

The tears and bone-shaking sobs redoubled. It seemed that their father had shut himself in his study and wouldn't come out. Downstairs the baby was screaming now and the younger children were starting to whimper. Edie, next in line and forever practical, was trying to shepherd them into some sort of comfort but even she had to own defeat and came searching for her older sister. Exhausted though she was, at that moment it dawned on Mary with extraordinary force that now, as the eldest daughter, everything was up to her and John. Though, to be sure, they were not quite alone. There was always Cook; and Father, of course.

In the kitchen, beyond the green baize door, Cook took the blackened kettle off the range and poured boiling water into the fat teapot, its cheerful brown glaze glinting in the morning sunshine. There were cups and saucers on the scrubbed table, and, as Mary burst into the room, Cook poured the tea.

She took one look at the wild tear-stained figure.

'Now Miss Mary, it's no good your making yourself ill as well as the Mistress, God rest her soul. You just sit yourself down here close to the stove, and get this nice hot cup of tea down you. It looks to me as if you could do with a drop of brandy, but we can't get at that until the Master comes out and unlocks the cupboard.' Cook's fat, comforting arm went round Mary's shoulders and steered her into the waiting chair.

'Oh Cookie' was all that was said; there was no need for more. Gradually a little colour came back into Mary's face, and she made a manful effort to take control.

'Do you know whether Father has started to make arrangements for the funeral, or if anything at all has been done?' she asked.

'The vicar's in with Mr Garrad now', Cook replied. 'I think they've sent for Mr Bollingbroke and Mr Steed, but you go in there and join them and you'll find out for yourself. That is, if you're up to it, Miss Mary. Don't you worry about the children; me and Violet'll see to them.'

❧

'CHAR! CHAR! HAS ANYONE SEEN Charlie?' It seemed that no-one had noticed the little boy since early morning, when he had crept out of the room he shared with Bob, his elder brother by two years.

The 'where are you off to, Char?' from the semi-conscious Bob had received no reply; or perhaps the eleven-year-old was asleep again before the answer was given. Bob, like most of the household, had tossed and turned for much of the night, so that the dawn slumber, when at last it came, was all the more profound.

Charlie was still young enough for sleep to encompass him utterly. He woke with the blackbird in the weeping willow, and, grabbing clothes and shoes and choosing to ignore Bob's question, tiptoed out of the room. He knew exactly what he wanted to do. There was a tall tree that overlooked the yard at the back of the house. It was a sort of pine, and the branches were spaced so that even he, far the least agile of all the brothers, could climb it. He pulled on his shirt and shorts. He'd forgotten his socks, but at least he'd brought gym-shoes instead of boots; he couldn't have managed in those.

Slowly and laboriously up he went, higher and higher. Once, for a fraction of a second, he looked down. The familiar landmarks beneath him set up a sickening spin and he shut his eyes; always look upwards, he remembered someone telling him. As he strained skywards for the next branch, it suddenly twitched out of his reach. A squirrel, as frightened as he was, leapt past his ear and up, up and away to the very top of the tree, where it clung perilously, peering scornfully down at the clumsy boy.

'All very well for you,' Charlie said out loud, his heart racing. 'You've got four legs and anyway you're used to it. But I do wish you could give me a tow.'

Never one to give up easily, he struggled on, always with just one, and then one more, branch to grab and pull on, hand, foot, hand, foot, until at last he could go no further. His perch, like the squirrel's, swayed in the breeze; never before had he climbed this far, and he knew that no-one would think to look for him up there.

'See?' he said to the squirrel, 'you're not the only one!'

He almost smiled at his conquest. He could just picture the admiration in the family's eyes, hear the awe in Fanny's 'Oh, Char, how brave you are!' and the 'Well done, old fellow – I didn't know you had it in you!' from big brother Bob. And then he remembered why he was there.

It was certainly an excellent lookout post. He could watch not just the yard below but right over the house to the front gate. He would see all the comings and goings, for today was the day of his mother's funeral. He wouldn't go to the church with the family, of course; he would hide up there till bedtime if necessary, but he was not going to watch them dig a hole and put his mother in it, like they'd done with that poor dead thrush just the week before. That was unthinkable and anyway his mother wouldn't allow it. She would stop them from making him go – but no, that wouldn't work because she wasn't there. She was up in Heaven, and that was the real reason that he'd dared make this terrifying climb. He knew the older ones would laugh at him, but somehow he felt nearer to her at the top of this tree. After all, Heaven was supposed to be in the sky, though he could never see how that worked; surely it would come crashing down to the ground. So if it was right up there, say beyond that little cloud, why then, balanced on his perch even higher than the blackbird, surely he must be a little bit nearer to Mama.

For a while, it was quiet. Then he heard the cowman calling the cows in the Top Meadow, and he watched as the procession crossed the yard.

'We'd best get the milking done quick this morning,' the man remarked to his young assistant as between them they deftly drove the herd of Dairy Shorthorns into the milking shed. Charlie could picture it all; many times he had been there with them, taken part in the twice daily ritual. Each cow knew her own stall and would make her ponderous way there until she stood, docile, with her wet muzzle under the painted notice bearing her name. The two, man and boy, would put on their aprons and milking caps, wash down each udder, grab a bucket and a stool, and set to work. Sitting by the animal's flank just out of reach of irritated heels and pressing their foreheads into her warm cow-smelling side, their strong, skilful fingers would pump out the steaming milk, the sound changing from a clang as the two long, powerful jets hit the metal pail to a bubbling hiss as the bucket filled.

The back door opened and Cook came out.

'It's a mercy it's a fine day,' she remarked through the open door to an invisible presence behind her.

'That'll be Violet she's talking to,' thought Charlie. 'Cook always drags her out of bed before the others.' Violet was the kitchen-maid; 'flighty', sister Mary called her. Charlie thought she was nice. She had pretty hair that sort of wound round like a corkscrew and she had a habit of tossing it, to make you notice its gingery colour, he reckoned.

'I always thinks a funeral's got a lot more spirit to it when the sun's shining, if you know what I mean,' went on Cook. Charlie couldn't hear whether or not Violet did know what she meant. He certainly didn't, but he too was extremely glad that it wasn't raining. He might have got washed out, like that old bird's nest in the storm last month.

Before long, a delectable smell began to make its presence felt. It started slowly, a mere sensation in the air, but, rapidly gaining in strength, became almost unbearable. Bacon. Cook was frying bacon for breakfast. Suddenly,

Charlie was ravenously hungry. What should he do? He couldn't come down, not yet, not for ages and ages. Nothing had even begun to happen. Anyway, he couldn't come down because he simply couldn't get down. The yard looked tiny, a uniform grey, the cobbles merged into one another by distance. But for the moment that wasn't the problem. He still had almost a whole day to sit through, on this exceedingly hard and scratchy branch. He just was not going to go to the funeral.

The cows came out and were driven back to the field. They were comfortable now, udders flapping emptily against hind legs. The wonderful aroma grew less. So did everything else. There didn't seem to be anything remotely cheerful to think about and there was nothing to do. A passing insect flew into Charlie's ear, but by breaking off a twig he managed to fish it out quite quickly. So there was still nothing to do. He tried a bit of recitation. Their governess had been teaching them a poem, Shakespeare he thought, but although he usually came top in most things, he didn't seem able to remember a single word of it. It was a stupid poem, anyway. His eyes began to prick and he cautiously let go with one hand to rub at them.

And then, at last, things really did begin to happen. A carriage and pair drove in through the gate, the horses a gleaming black. Charlie didn't know who they belonged to, and was so high up that at first he could only see the top of the driver's head. But then the man looked up, so quickly that the boy, swaying dangerously, hardly had time to dodge behind a sprig of pine. He held his breath; had he been spotted? No; the visitor was merely looking to see if the weather was set fair, and Charlie had time to recognise him as the gentleman farmer from the next village, a friend of his parents who had doubtless come to offer help and sympathy.

Big brother John came down the steps from the front door to greet the visitor.

'I don't know how you are planning to transport the family to the cemetery, but the carriage is not in use today and I thought it might be helpful to you.' The man's voice was loud and important, and Charlie could hear it quite clearly. Not so John's reply, but evidently the offer was accepted for one of the farm lads came to hold the horses and Mr Edwards was ushered into the house.

Soon, a few of the villagers started to collect opposite the front gate, just a couple of children at first and then, gradually, several of the people that Charlie knew. He occupied himself in trying to put names to all of them and picturing the house that each lived in. On the edge of the group he spied the lad who led Charlie's father round the fields. They had exchanged a few words now and then, and he seemed a pleasant enough fellow, though with a bad limp.

Standing next to him was a smaller boy, perhaps his brother. Now, why did he look so familiar? Ah, that was it. It was the boy's suit that Charlie recognised, his own old one that he'd just grown out of. It was too patched and shabby to be passed on to the next in the Garrad line. One of his sisters, probably Fanny, must have given it to the boy's family. Its wearer was too far away for Charlie to see him very clearly, but he felt curiously drawn to the boy. 'It would be good,' he thought, 'if that fellow were to take over as Father's guide, and then perhaps we could make friends.'

One after another, several more carriages turned into the drive, their drivers dismounting to stand at the heads of the restless horses. The noise down below was mounting and it was some time before Charlie picked out his own name being called above the hubbub.

'Charlie! Charlie! Wherever are you, Char?'

At first he took no notice. He was not coming down for anyone. But the cries were getting more desperate. He was used to being yelled at by John and Mary, but when he realised that Edie and even the gentle Fanny were joining in, he began to doubt. There was no question but that he was exceedingly hungry. There were other bodily functions that needed urgent attention too, to which he had been giving some increasingly uncomfortable thought. Birds manage, he had decided, and squirrels too; but then they were not so big as him. His behind was numb, and despite the spring sunshine he was extremely chilly. An unwelcome thought began to tickle the very back of his mind; perhaps, just perhaps, he would after all have to give up his vigil.

But how? Apart from the sheer horror of the descent, his limbs, stiff from disuse, felt as if they would never function again. He moved, very cautiously. The tree swayed. He froze. After a few moments, he tried again and this time he nearly fell. He let out a cry of sheer terror; there was nothing he could do to prevent it, and it seemed as if the world's spotlight had been turned on him. Every face in the crowded forecourt looked up at him as he clung there, too terrified now to do anything except hang on for dear life

It was the farm foreman, Mr Cardy, who came to his senses first.

'Hang on, Master Charles,' he shouted. 'I'll get the big ladder and we'll have you down in the twinkling of an eye. Just you hold on tight and don't try and move.'

And suddenly the crowd was in uproar as Mr Cardy led a stream of running men to the barn and pulled out the long ladder used in autumn for building the corn ricks. Willing hands carried it to the tree and set it up, and Cardy himself ran up it like a cat until he was within easy reach of the frightened boy. Out went the big, strong arms and encircled him, and it seemed only seconds before Charlie was back on the ground, shaking and tearstained but totally unhurt. He was safe.

POOR CHARLIE; HIS PLAN HAD FAILED utterly. Despite his efforts, he was after all in time for the funeral. With a bowlful of hot broth inside him and knees and hands well scrubbed, he found himself packed into the carriage, squashed between his father and two sisters. All the fight had gone out of him. The girls were crying, but his eyes were dry now, his young face tense and pale. He leant back on the cracked leather cushions and gave himself up to his own private grief. It seemed as though the bitter cold had crept inwards from his hands to his heart and frozen it solid, a weight so heavy that he could scarcely breathe. He could no longer avoid the bleak, terrible truth; that the one person who really loved him, and he loved most in the world, was dead and he would never see her again.

For once he envied his father, sitting beside him with, surprisingly, a hand on Charlie's knee. In Father's blindness, he was spared the sight of the procession ahead, with the frightening black-coated officials leading the way. He would not be able to see the polished oak coffin, borne high on the shoulders of six of the men from the village, disguised in their Sunday best. He would not be able to see, either, the wealth of flowers that covered it.

To Charlie at that moment the glorious yellow of the bunched daffodils, shining out in the early spring sunshine, seemed a mockery; everything surely should be as black as the undertakers' coats. But then he remembered how much his mother had loved the spring; how excited she had been each year when she heard the chaffinch, silent for the long winter, sing his first song, and then, later on, the chiffchaff as it arrived from faraway places. He remembered how she always asked him to come and help her gather great armfuls of the daffodils that meant so much to her, and how he and the others had done their best to brighten her sickroom with the cheerful blooms. And then the tears did come in a flood, so that by the time the party arrived at the church three out of the four handkerchiefs in the carriage were sodden and useless.

The little boy drifted through the ceremony in a dream. His legs took him through the familiar church door, his ears heard the organ's melancholy chords, his tongue twisted itself round the funeral service's frightening phrases, but his mind was empty of everything except a boundless pain. He knelt down, stood up and sang the hymns with the rest. He felt no discomfort as he sat on the hard pew while the rector spoke, and he heard not a single one of the comforting words.

He walked with his family behind the hearse as it was carried up the winding lane to the new cemetery, a bleak windswept field with only one other grave for company. Buffeted by a squall of rain but unaware of cold, he stood beside the grave, its blackness made more awful by the cut edges of bright turf surrounding it, and watched as the coffin was lowered into the ground. The churchyard would somehow have been more welcoming, with so many of the family buried there for company, but only a few weeks before the last space had been taken.

He shook hands with a great many people with tears running down their kind faces. But somehow none of it seemed real. He had faced the blackest of his demons during those few minutes in the carriage; such strength of emotion was impossible to sustain and was never to return with quite so much venom. This terrible day was almost over, and tomorrow, somehow, life would start again.

As he lay in bed that evening, sister Fanny tiptoed in to say goodnight,

'Are you asleep?' she asked, When he shook his tired head she gave him a kiss in exactly the same spot as his mother had always chosen. 'We shall be all right, you'll see,' she said. 'Whatever happens, Charlie, you and I will always stand together.'

At that moment, it seemed merely a tender ray of comfort from a much loved sister. But later, much later, he had reason to remember it.

Bootalet, Burma, 1885

THE BUNDLE WAS ONLY THE SIZE of a large watermelon, but it unbalanced her. She supposed it was because she was used to carrying the weight in front; now that he was born and slung across her back she was frightened of drowning him. The mud was slippery, and twice when she had stood up to stretch her aching back she had almost tipped backwards and fallen on to him, into the water.

The throbbing ache in her breasts was becoming almost unbearable, but she had nearly finished now. Just those few paddy seedlings to be planted out and she could go back to the shade of the palm leaf roof of her house and put him to the breast.

What did he feel, riding on her back, she wondered? No doubt the heat; in spite of her wide straw hat it must be hotter there than in her cool, dark womb. Could he see the bright scarlet of his binder? After all, he wasn't like a kitten, born with his eyes shut. Was it too bright, after the darkness? Perhaps the sound of her thudding heart was a comfort to him – he was used to that. And her smell, he was used to that too, though the milk was new. It was only just coming in, flooding through her thin blouse in two big wet patches.

There had, of course, to be a name. The discussion had lasted all through the pregnancy, with two mothers, two fathers, seven grandparents, thirteen brothers and sisters (between them), not to mention an infinite number of cousins, nieces and nephews, all giving advice. There still had been no final decision.

She finished the seedlings and stretched up for the final time that day. At home at last, she unslung the baby, opened her blouse and put him to the breast. As the milk began to flow into the tiny vigorous mouth, she asked:

'So what, in the end, are we going to call him?'

'Pyau,' said her husband. And that was that.

3

EIGHTEEN FEET CLATTERING DOWN the staircase almost drowned the sound of the little brass gong in the hall. A bottle-neck in the dining-room doorway resolved itself as the room filled and eighteen hands pulled the nine stiff mahogany chairs from their places and swivelled them with their backs to the breakfast table. Each child stood to attention by his or her place as the servants filed in and lined themselves up respectfully against the wall. The tap-tap of his stick announced the arrival of the *paterfamilias*. Mr Garrad, his sightless passage rendered faultless by familiarity, edged his way to his own seat at the top of the table.

'Let us pray.' As one man the assembled company dropped to its knees, eyes closed and elbows on horsehair seats. The routine of Family Prayers had begun.

Today, Charlie didn't mind. In any case, he quite liked the soothing poetry of the old-fashioned verses, though the hymn-singing with his father on the little organ in the hall was quite beyond him. Unable to produce a single note in tune, he had long since learnt simply to mouth the words, if only to escape the others' nudges and withering glances. But this morning, the longer he could keep the day waiting the better; the longer he could spin out prayers, breakfast and the usually boring household chores, the happier he would be. On his way down to the dining-room he had met Mary on the landing. As soon as she had spoken to him he had known there was real trouble. She had only to say 'Charles,' a name kept for important strangers and the vicar, and he realised that something quite out of the ordinary was afoot.

'Charles,' she had said, though with a curiously kindly look on her tired face. 'We have something very important to tell you. After breakfast I have to go visiting in the village, as it is Tuesday and I shall be expected. But once lunch is over Father, John and I shall expect you in Father's study.' This was almost unprecedented. Whatever could it possibly be about? A whisper of impending doom lodged itself in his ear and would not be displaced.

So once breakfast was finished and they were outside, Frank's cheery 'Come on, Char – how about a stilt race to the barn?' was more than welcome. The two boys scrambled on to their long homemade legs and set off across the cobbles. It had been raining and the clumsy wooden feet constantly slithered and slid down the smooth stones into the valleys between. It was a hazardous journey. Frank, always the winner in these desperate trials of strength, was for once trailing behind his younger brother when the inevitable happened. In his excitement Charlie took too big a step, his stilts flew out from under him, and he sprawled face down on the hard muddy ground.

'Are you hurt?' The unfamiliar voice surprised the boy into forgetting the pain in his knee and he scrambled to his feet. Who could have come into their yard? For a moment, he didn't recognise the speaker. And then he placed him. Surely he was the lad whom he had spied at the edge of the crowd on the day of his mother's funeral, wearing his own cast-off suit. He remembered thinking he would like to get to know him, that perhaps somehow they could be friends one day. The village children and the Garrads of Brook House on the whole did not mix, so this meeting at his own home was an opportunity not to be missed.

'No, just a bit muddy,' he answered as he glanced ruefully down at his clothes. Evidence from eyes and nose certainly suggested that one of the carthorses had very recently passed that way and he could picture only too clearly what Mary's reaction would be. Jolted back into reality, his stomach took a fearsome lurch towards his muddy boots. Whatever was of such importance that he must, after lunch, go to his father's study?

But the boy was still talking.

'My brother, you know, James, the one with the limp, used to lead Mr Garrad round the farm. But then he grew too tall and Mr Garrad found it tiring, so I stood against the door and Mother said I'd reached the mark, so here I am.' Poor Charlie was completely at a loss, but as Matthew expanded his enigmatic statement the light began to dawn.

'So you are Father's new boy?' he asked. Matthew nodded, his whole face lighting up with delight.

'James brought me up yesterday and showed me to your Pa, I mean Mr Garrad, and said would I do instead of him, and when your P... er, Mr Garrad, tried me on he said I fitted him beautifully but was I strong enough because he likes to walk very quick. So I said I was, so here I am.'

INEVITABLY, LUNCH CAME AND WENT. Charlie had little idea what he was eating, but he was a boy with a normal appetite and his plates were clean when they went back to the kitchen. And then the moment came. As he stood uncertainly by his chair at the end of the meal, his eldest brother John came up to him.

'Father wants to see you in his study straight away,' he said, and uncharacteristically patted the younger boy on the shoulder. More alarmed than ever, and racking his brains for the umpteenth time for some crime that he had unwittingly committed, Charlie followed his tall brother down the passage and waited while John knocked on the study door. In obedience to the peremptory 'come in' the two boys found their father sitting as usual at his desk with Mary already beside him in an upright chair.

They took the only empty seats. There was a long, long pause, seemingly endless to the younger of the two. What could be going to happen?

At last, his father turned towards Charlie. His sense of direction, his 'third eye' as he called it, was uncannily accurate and he seemed to be fixing the young boy with his unseeing gaze as he spoke.

'Charles,' he said. 'I have some very good news for you.' Charlie's heart crept up half-an-inch from the soles of his boots as he waited. But what good news could there possibly be?

'I have been talking to your governess, and she confirms what your mother and I had already suspected, that you have an unusually high intelligence. She tells me that she has little more to offer you in terms of education; that in almost all subjects, but particularly Latin, you are already surpassing her. She also says that you should by now be starting on the study of Greek, in which she cannot help you as she has no knowledge of the language.'

Charlie by this time was beginning to feel rather pleased with himself. His father had never praised him before; in truth he had had little personal contact with so aloof a figure. Mother had always been there to act as intermediary between the clamouring children and their father, isolated in his study by both blindness and a binding sense of duty. So preoccupied was he with farm and village matters that he found little time to spare for his own family.

There was another pause. Mary looked at her father. John looked at Mary, shifting uncomfortably in his seat. Charlie looked at all three in turn and carried on waiting.

'So,' said the stern figure 'I have decided that you should go to school.'

Now this really was a puzzle. Charlie had talked several times to the village boys when he had gone visiting with his mother or one of his older sisters and had been shocked at what he had heard. Most of them, even those several years older than himself, could scarcely read or write, let alone learn Greek and Latin. What was the point of going to school with them? And anyway, social mixing of the gentry and the villagers was taboo. It simply was not done.

Baffled, he turned to Mary for enlightenment. She had read his thoughts.

'Father means that you are to go to a different school,' she said, 'a school where the masters are very clever and can teach you all sorts of new things. It would be much better for you, and there would be a great many other boys of your own sort for you to play with.'

Charlie found his tongue. 'But there aren't any schools like that anywhere near here. I suppose there might be one in Ipswich, but how would I get there? Even if Cardy took me in the trap every day I should arrive just in time to turn round and come home.'

Come home. That was it. They were all looking at him, and at last the truth dawned. He would not come home. The two sons of the neighbouring squire, Frank's friends, had one day simply disappeared. They had been sent away to boarding-school, in the eyes of the Garrad brothers a fate worse than death itself. But surely he must be mistaken. Surely they, his own family, would not do this to him. But already he was feeling guilty for his mother's death so this must surely be his punishment. Perhaps he hadn't looked after her properly. Perhaps he should have run more errands, got up sooner, gone to bed the first time he was told. Perhaps ...

His father broke in on his thoughts.

'The school to which you will go is in Crowthorne, a small town in Berkshire. The headmaster is a friend of the vicar; they met at college and have kept in touch ever since. I understand he's a wise and clever man, and a number of his pupils have eventually gone on to Oxford and Cambridge.'

Mr Garrad turned his head in John's direction.

'I know you are concerned about the expense, but although we lost almost the entire barley crop in last summer's rain and many of the early lambs from that unusually cold snap at the beginning of February, the farm's finances are sound. You need not worry on that score.

'So, Charlie, you are a lucky boy. You seem to be unusually clever and we are sure that this will be the best for you in the long run. If you work hard, there could be a great future ahead of you.'

An enormous chasm seemed to open up in front of Charlie, and a deep darkness hovered about him. To his dying day he was not sure whether he actually fell or whether the blackness before his eyes simply spread and enveloped him. His stomach rose and the sour taste of vomit filled his mouth.

Through the mist, and at that moment as blind as his father, he somehow gathered himself together and groped his way out of the study and up to his room.

4

IT WAS THE SAILOR SUIT that was to blame.

That spring, one of the three bow windows of Sudbury's Gentleman's Outfitter was devoted entirely to a nautical display in preparation for summer seaside holidays. Two starfish lay on the sandy floor and a decrepit stuffed seagull hung suspended in mid-flight on a piece of string attached to the sky-blue ceiling. There was no mistaking the pirate in his red bandana and black eye patch, but it was the child-sized model in a sailor suit standing proudly on the other side of the cut-out palm tree that caught Mary's eye.

'Oh Char, do look! Doesn't the sailor-boy look smart?'

Mary knew that all well brought up children wore sailor suits for best. She also knew in her heart of hearts that this particular child would be as obstinate as a donkey on the subject. But by some miracle it seemed that help was at hand; surely even Charlie could not fail to succumb. There stood the gallant sailor, his hand resting on the barrel of a painted canon as he faced the deadly pirate threat. His uniform was perfect in every detail: the big square collar, the wide buttoned cuffs, the open V-neck revealing an anchor embroidered on the white shirt beneath. And then the trousers with their blue stripe down each leg, ending in plenty of time to show off the white stockings and shiny black button shoes.

Poor Mary. Far from winning her charge round to her way of thinking, the display had clearly had the opposite effect. She saw from Charlie's face that all the joy had gone from his day, and she hurried him inside in the forlorn hope that not too much damage had been done.

This was the first time that Charlie had shown any animation since that awful day three weeks before when he had stumbled from his father's study and shut himself in his bedroom. He had pushed his bed against the door and abandoned himself to such a hurricane of grief and anger that the family, listening outside and trying to reason with him had actually begun to fear for his sanity. At first they had simply looked at each other and shrugged their shoulders. They were all used to Charlie's tantrums; it would surely pass, even though Mother was not there to work her magic on him. But the hours went by, and it was only when it was getting dark that, at last, Fanny pushed her way into the room and led him out, grey faced and sodden with tears.

But his father was adamant. Charlie was to go away to school. He must learn to be a man.

So preparations for his departure continued. It was to be this very next summer term, and there were only a few weeks left. At first, the boy took no interest. The future was too terrible to contemplate. He was simply an observer, unable to take any part in the general commotion. And then, one day, a chance meeting opened the first tiny crack in his defences. He met his father coming back from his daily tour round the farm, one hand resting on the arm of the new boy from the village. Matthew winked at Charlie and, when he had delivered his charge safely indoors, came and spoke to him.

'I hear you're not too pleased with your Pa,' he said. 'He's been saying as how he wants you to go away to school and learn things, all sorts that you'd never get to hear about at home. Then, when you're grown up, you can do anything you like. But he says as how you don't want to go – that true?'

The first inkling of doubt crept into Charlie's mind.

'Well, yes. How would you like to be sent away from home?'

'I'd miss Ma and our James and that, of course, but my word I'd grab at the chance. There's not much round here, you know. I been reading in a book our teacher lent me all about Africa and India and suchlike – you might even get to go to some place like that one day.' And Matthew climbed over the gate and ran back home across the fields.

Charlie watched the boy disappear. 'I wish I was like him,' he said out loud.

From then on, despite himself, he gradually got caught up in the excitement, so that when Mary suggested they go shopping in Sudbury to buy some of the things he would need, she was pleasantly surprised at his reaction. Cardy took them in the trap and, setting out straight after breakfast, arranged to meet them in the afternoon. And so it was that they found themselves outside the gentleman's outfitter, gazing at that sailor suit.

A young man in his twenties, with his hair stuck to his scalp as if he'd used machine-grease all over it – 'it was disgusting,' Charlie would later recall – greeted them at the door.

'Good morning, Madam,' he said. 'And good morning, Sir,' he added in the special sugar-sweet voice he used for children. He fancied himself as being good with children. Charlie cringed.

'Good morning. My brother is going to boarding-school and needs suitable clothes. I should like you to start by showing us an everyday jacket and trousers.'

The assistant led them to the appropriate racks and in no time at all Charlie had been suitably fitted up.

So far so good, but Mary could put off the moment no longer. She had to buy a sailor suit; in her opinion, it was the only fitting wear for a gentleman's son.

'I am sure you must have a great deal of experience,' she said, and the young man bowed and smiled his ingratiating smile. Mary took a deep breath.

'So you will know,' she went on, 'that the only proper wear 'for best' is a sailor suit like the one in the window.'

Charlie tugged at her sleeve.

'Mary, I can't. I wouldn't be seen dead in ...'

'Shush, dear, and listen to what he has to say.'

The shop assistant turned to the boy.

'If your Mama had come with you today I am certain that a sailor suit is exactly what she would choose.'

Charlie looked at him.

'My Mama is dead. And anyway, she wouldn't make me if I didn't want to.'

The assistant began to wonder if he was as good with children as he had thought. Charlie's short span of patience had run out; the day that had started off so well threatened disaster as his face set and his whining reached crescendo pitch.

Mary knew the signs of an oncoming tantrum only too well but she could be as obstinate as Charlie. A sailor suit in the same size as the other purchases was rapidly found and wrapped. Her purse was emptied of its guineas, and they made their way out to the waiting trap, Cardy standing patiently at the head of the restless horse. On the way home not one word was spoken. Cardy kept his questions to himself.

⚜

IN CHARLIE'S YOUNG MIND, the events of those next few weeks ran together in an indistinguishable blur; excitement, apprehension and, at times, downright terror swirled in a mixture of emotions, their colour constantly changing with his changing moods. One thing, though, was certain. A train of events had been set in motion which would march inexorably forward and could have only one possible outcome. Boarding-school.

The day arrived, as was bound to happen. In the care of his brother John he was to travel by train. Even to the senior members of the Garrad family, trains were a newfangled invention. Charlie's father had been twelve when their local line opened, four years before he had lost his sight. Behind his blind eyes he could still see the great puffing monster with its shining paint and gleaming brass that had dominated Marks Tey station on that great gala day in 1849. Never again would the little station platform, bedecked in red white and blue, see such crowds, or such a waving of little paper Union Jacks, on sale at a farthing each at the brand-new ticket-office. Never again would the centuries-old village be safe from the world outside.

Charlie had not been on a train before the fateful day so this in itself was a mighty adventure. The tears and hugs on that little station platform affected even the burly station master, who had a lot to say to his wife in the privacy of their parlour that night on the subject of the gentry and their strange habits.

And so the boy was transported at the speed of light from his quiet village backwater into the noise and bustle of the great city of London. If only there had been more time! Horses pulling carriages, men pushing barrows, nursemaids with perambulators, policemen in helmets, soldiers in busbies, children in rags, parks full of flowers, streets full of rubbish; and people, people everywhere. How could so many be crammed together in one place?

Houses and hovels, shops so large and grand that surely no-one would dare to enter, rows of carcasses in the butcher's, rows of suits in the tailor's, piles of hats, pink, purple, green, yellow, in the milliner's, pyramids of cakes in the baker's; it was hard to distinguish one from the other. With nose pressed against the cab window and eyes, and brain, aching from their efforts to absorb so much, it was almost a relief to arrive at the coaching inn.

There was little more to be done and, after sharing a meal and a bed, John waved goodbye to his brother. He would not find it easy to forget the pinched white face, desperate for one last glimpse of home, pressed once again against the window, this time of the coach that would deliver him to his final destination.

Boarding-school.

AMONGST CHARLIE'S FELLOW PASSENGERS there were just three others on their way to the school. The four new-boys, all starting their school career in the last rather than the first term of the year, had been asked to arrive a day late. So it was not until they had gone through the tall wrought iron school gates and the horses' hooves had clattered up the long, winding brick driveway that they caught their first glimpse of their established fellow pupils. It had been raining and the tangled mass of small boys, liberated on wet days from the eternal boredom of cricket, was busily kicking a football round the slippery field. Plastered from head to foot with mud, they looked to Charlie like nothing so much as a group of small Red Indians without their feathers.

'The coach! The coach!'

A shrill voice soared above the clatter of arrival. Engrossed in their game, a few moments had elapsed before the footballers had noticed the stagecoach, time enough for the sailor-suited Charlie to wish he were dead. He had hoped against hope to be able to slip unseen into the school before anyone had noticed him. The only hope now was to jump down into the biggest puddle he could see; surely at least he could saturate the horrible white stockings with decent mud.

'Look – new boys! Come on!'

The cry, rising from fifty throats in fifty different treble tones, and the thundering footsteps of a hundred booted feet as every man-jack of the players rushed at the new arrivals, seemed to the exhausted quartet a battle charge of terrifying ferocity. The attackers screeched to a halt a yard from the newcomers, and the staring silence that followed was, by contrast, of such intensity that the last shred of courage in Charlie's tender bosom vanished, to leave him totally defenceless.

And then the laughter started. First one, and then another, and another pointing finger was aimed at him, just him, until in his bewildered mind the semicircle of jutting arms turned into a forest of spears held aloft by Indian braves amidst such a din of jeering and caterwauling that he turned and ran for his life.

The mob gave chase.

'Sailor suit! Sailor suit!'

The battle cry rang ever louder in his ears as he desperately tried to make his escape. But it was of no use. These were bigger boys, fleeter of foot and to his overstretched nerves by now numbering in their hundreds. In his hurry he slipped and fell flat on his face, slap into the thickest of the mud. The wretched sailor suit, now nothing but the filthy pelt of a quarry run to earth, clung to his skin. His last hour had come.

Then came the miracle. A deeper voice, cracking a little on the high notes, rang out above the rest:

'Hold on, you fellows. Give the chap a chance.'

A muddy hand in his armpit hoisted him gently to his feet and he found himself gazing up into a dirt-splattered face that to his dying day he would never forget.

'I say, thanks awfully!'

The stuttered words came out as a shrill squeak, and Charlie found himself being steered back through the crowd, now silent and backing away to make a path for the ill-matched pair.

'Come on,' said the older boy. 'We'll go and find Matron and see what she can do to clean you up a bit. It really isn't as bad as it looks, you know.'

And the two of them walked in through the door of Charlie's very first school.

<h1 style="text-align: center;">5</h1>

'GARRAD IS A TOTAL SWOT.'

'I don't want Garrad in my team.'

Cricket, football, gym; the plea from all the captains was the same.

'Oh no, not Garrad – he'll just spoil everything. We'll never beat them with him messing things up!' It was not really personal; the competitive instinct simply overshadowed finer feelings. They wanted to win.

That, as far as the other boys went, was the long and the short of it, and Charlie was left alone and confused; if only he could talk to Mother everything would be so much easier.

One thing, though, he did understand, and that was that he had been sent all this way to learn. So learn he would, and to his amazement he found pleasure in the process. It didn't take the masters long to see that here was someone well beyond the common run of things. One or two of them came to realise all too soon that this quaint little boy would come to challenge them to their limits, and even, heaven forbid, well beyond.

'HOW DO YOU PLAY THAT GAME?'

One wet Saturday afternoon, a boy in the next form up found Charlie sitting in the corner of the classroom, a chessboard in front of him on the desk. He had learnt the rudiments of the game at home, and was enjoying the feel and familiarity of the pieces, found at the back of the games cupboard.

'Do you want to play? I'm not much good at it, but I could show you...'

'What do you have to do?'

'Well, to start with you set out the pieces like this. You be black, I'll be white. This one's called the White Knight – this midget's just a stupid little pawn.'

'Who's this one?'

'That's a Queen.'

'But what's the actual point of it?'

And so the lesson went on. By the end of it, Charlie had made his first friend, and more were to come, slowly but surely attracted by his kindness, self-effacement and, most of all, by his quiet sense of humour. He found, to his supreme joy, that sometimes he could even make them laugh.

THE DAYS CREPT BY. For a few nights each month the moon shone through the dormitory window, illuminating the sleeping, dreaming humps that barely swelled the flimsy bed-covers. Charlie took great comfort from the moon. He could see the Man and knew he was looking down at his own empty bed at home and onto the dear face of his sister Fanny.

At last, the third full moon was on the turn, and packing was in full swing. Trunks were brought out from store and Matron and her helpers were kept busy filling them with their young owners' treasures. This very night, the waning moon would be shining on each boy in his own bed at home.

JOHN WAS WAITING for Charlie at the coaching inn. As the boys tumbled out of the stagecoach, the young man wondered whether he would be able to recognise his little brother amongst the tidal wave of small forms that poured ceaselessly out into the inn yard. He need not have worried. The sailor suit, washed and ironed, was back in place on the thin frame; not another soul was wearing anything remotely resembling it. Matron had dealt kindly with Charlie during the term, limiting the public appearances of the detested outfit to the absolute minimum. She had found him other clothes in her 'outgrown' cupboard, but, despite his pleadings, on this one point she was adamant.

'Your father paid a lot of money for that suit, young man. You are to wear it home, and no arguing.' She was a stickler for correctness; parents, whatever their failings, which in her private view were all too many, must be shown due respect and appreciation. Come what may, the young Garrad would don the despised article before he left her care. (In her heart he was Charlie. But decorum prevailed).

As the two brothers formally shook hands they eyed one another. Both saw changes. Charlie thought John looked a bit like the headmaster's assistant and correspondingly felt momentarily even more distant from him. John saw a new expression on the other's face, a glimpse of what he had been through in those last few weeks, and perhaps of an emerging maturity that had not been there before.

But 'welcome home!' was all he said. And 'come on ... the old coach was a bit late, and our train goes in two hours.' There was no time to talk as they each grabbed an end of Charlie's box and manhandled it into a waiting cab.

Once settled in the cab, Charlie found himself unexpectedly tongue-tied. John was obviously waiting for Charlie to tell him all about his new school. But how could he? Where could he start? Until a few weeks ago, he and his brother had been in the same house together every day of their lives. How could he begin to articulate the myriad of new experiences that had battered at him almost every minute of every day since he left home?

'Well, how was it?'

'All right.'

'What was the food like?'

'Not bad.' Charlie was astonished to hear such a downright lie coming from his own mouth. That was not at all what he had meant to say. Quite unexpectedly, he felt a surge of loyalty to this extraordinary new life that, in his sudden and total immersion, had initially threatened to drown him.

John persisted.

'The masters? Are you learning anything?

'They're all right. A bit.'

To the younger boy's relief, a sudden jolt brought the conversation to an abrupt end. He was not prepared to be subjected to a catechism on something that was entirely his, not John's. He would tell them as best he could, but in his own good time. Not now. Not to John. So the cab driver's altercation with the barrow-boy whose cart had just scratched his shiny new paint came as a welcome interruption, and from then on the two boys stuck to astonished comments on the strange goings-on in the London streets.

John bought a newspaper at Liverpool Street station and, handing the middle pages to his brother, settled down to read in a corner seat of the compartment.

Suddenly he broke the silence.

'Just listen to this. Apparently, there's this famous architect in America called Jenney and he's actually built a building in Chicago that's nine storeys high! They're calling it a sky-scraper – trust the Americans to think of a fancy name.'

Charlie got a pencil out of his pocket and drew a picture in the margin of a sheet of John's paper. He simply couldn't imagine why it wouldn't blow over in the first strong wind that came along. He must keep an eye on the news, just in case.

Perhaps the other boys at school wouldn't have heard; what a sensation he would make when he told them!

6

TEA WAS ON THE LAWN, next to the weeping willow. Fortunately for the village, the gentle summer breeze was blowing in the opposite direction; otherwise no inhabitant would have been spared, for the noise was almost deafening. They were all there. Father in the seat of honour, dark glasses on his nose, Daisy ensconced in her little basket chair, baby George in the big old pram that had known, intimately, each child in turn.

All but one of the other nine had formed themselves into a rough semicircle, some on garden chairs, most sitting on rugs spread on the grass, and everybody was talking at once. Edie was scolding George for throwing his rattle out of the pram. George was responding in kind. Father's bass voice penetrated the general treble from time to time as he tried to keep some sort of order.

'... one at a time, then I might just be able to hear.'

'... think there's enough sandwiches?'

'Katie, where are those scones you promised? I can't see ...'

'Anybody got a pick-axe ? Those rock-buns do look a bit ...'

There were two small tables with clean embroidered cloths covering their everyday shabbiness, one holding plates with mountains of sandwiches; the other, a huge fruitcake.

Right in the centre of the circle sat a small figure in a smart sailor suit, grinning from ear to ear and with little Bessie on his bony knee. Cook and Violet were there too, but standing respectfully, and much more comfortably, for it was a hot day, in the shade of the willow.

'HONESTLY CHAR, WE CAN'T WAIT a second longer. You simply must have had enough to eat by now. PLEASE tell us what it was like.'

'My mouth's completely full and Mama always ...'

'For goodness sake put that great bit of cake down then. Tell us from the very beginning. What happened when John left?'

Charlie didn't want to think about when John left, about his arrival at the school, and about the awful episode of the sailor suit. Not ever again. He wasn't going to relive that even for them.

'Oh I just met some fellows and one of them took me into school and I saw Matron and she was jolly nice.'

'Did she take you and show you your bedroom? Do you have to share?'

'Of course I do, stupid. It's a boarding-school. You have dormitories in boarding-schools. I thought everybody knew that.' Had he known, though, before he went? He couldn't remember. 'There's twenty fellows in my dorm and they're always playing tricks. I had a hard time of it when I first arrived, I can tell you.'

His adoring sisters were gazing at him, admiring him. This was a totally new sensation and Charlie was definitely warming to his task.

'Why? What happened? Tell us!' They were all shouting at once, and the boy had to wait a moment before he could go on. He took the opportunity to cram in another mouthful.

'First of all, because I'm new, I have to be tossed. The four biggest fellows in the dorm grab a blanket and you lie on it and then they toss you up to the ceiling. They're supposed to catch you again in the blanket but sometimes it doesn't work. The fellow who was done before me got dropped and cracked his head on the floor and went a bit funny. Luckily, I was all right – because I was such a shrimp, they said.'

'Are the others nice? Who's your best friend?'

Now it was Charlie's turn to look adoring.

'Well, there's this chap called Fairbairn. He's head boy and captain of football and he's been really, really nice to me. He's rescued me from all sorts of scrapes.'

'What sort of scrapes?'

He looked uncomfortable.

'I'm no good at games, you see, and you have to be, for people to like you. So some of them take it out on me, and report me for doing things that really they've done. Mostly things they'd get into trouble for if they were caught. So I catch it instead and get a beating. But Fairbairn found out about this and gave them what for, so now they leave me alone. But soon he'll be leaving, and then I don't know what will happen.'

The bright face clouded. Little Bessie on his knee gave him a hug and a slobbery kiss. There were no words yet; tiny in stature and late in development, she was a worry to all of them, particularly Mary. But at least, Mary would say, at least she isn't a mongol like poor dear Daisy.

'Have you been beaten lots of times? Does it hurt?'

'Of course it hurts, specially when they make you take your trousers down. Yes, I've been flogged a good few times.'

Charlie blushed. That really was a whopper. Flogging, to the other boys, was a true badge of manliness. He had really only been beaten once, when bullies had trapped him into a false confession. Luckily, the interrogation moved on, to firmer ground.

'We haven't heard anything yet about the purpose of your schooling,' said his father. John had thrown him a quick glance during Charlie's account and had been amazed to see the flicker of a smile below the big black spectacles.

'Are you studying hard?'

'Yes Father, but you don't get much of a chance with all the other fellows laughing at you.'

'Laughing at you? Why is that? No, don't tell me now. It would be better if you come to my study after prayers tomorrow morning, and give me a proper account of your progress.'

Edie rose to guide her father back into the house.

Then the questions came thick and fast, the children shouting across one another in their efforts to get as much information out of their brother in the shortest possible time. The upshot was that the school food was disgusting, the weekly half-holiday really jolly when it wasn't raining, and ball games a purgatory. It soon came out that there was a great deal of teasing for being such a swot, and that undisguised hero-worship of that paragon of boys, Fairbairn, was almost universal. The family learnt about the two ushers, who weren't proper masters and didn't know anything, but who took it in turns to umpire cricket and take them out into the country on half-holidays. One of them was quite decent; the other was apt to turn on you for no good reason, with dire consequences.

And so it went on until bedtime. Charlie shared a room with Bob and went first as the younger of the two, and so was alone in their room when Fanny came in to say goodnight. She, perhaps only she, had not been taken in by her brother's bravado.

'What's it really like?' The question came without preamble and caught Charlie off guard.

'Oh Fanny, I don't want to go back, ever again. If only I was good at cricket it would be different. But I can't do it – they bowl so fast I just don't see the ball so I hardly ever make any runs, and you know I can't catch to save my life. It would be all right if they just laughed at me, but sometimes I think they really hate me.'

'No, Gar dear, they don't. I know they don't – they couldn't. But why ...?'

Gar. If only they were back then, when Fanny was too little to say Char and Mama was alive. It had been a private name, just between Fanny and him – he hadn't heard her use it for a long time.

'Well, once after games, Jones shut me in the games cupboard – it was pitch dark, except the cricket pads glowed a bit, like ghosts all round me, coming in on me. Old Fisher heard me yell and let me out, and they all laughed because I was blubbing. I couldn't help it – tried to pretend the dust in there had made my eyes water. But they weren't having any –'

And he rolled over, hiding the fresh tears in his pillow. But Fanny, so gently, turned him back and put her arms around him.

'They were only teasing, you know. They're just like you inside – they're only bullies because there's a gang of them all together, and they don't know any better. Mama would say tease them back – let them see that you don't mind, even if you do.'

As brother and sister sat together, the sobs slowly subsided. Outside, the blackbird in the big sycamore sang the last few notes of his song and Edie's voice called out to the chickens as she shooed them into the hen-house for the night.

Fanny smoothed her brother's forehead and kissed him.

'Go to sleep now. It'll be all right, you'll see,' and the door closed quietly behind her.

7

FAIRBAIRN WAS DEAD.

Following behind the giant shoebox borne on the shoulders of four prefects, Charlie knew for certain that once again the death was his fault. The carriage windows were tight shut, but still the showers of milk pudding hurled by the jeering throng of schoolfellows outside flew at him through the glass, reducing his sailor suit to an unrecognisable pulp. It was hot, so hot, in that tiny box-like space. He must get out, but the walls were closing in on him and he could not move. Sweat mixed with the semolina, and his ears thrummed with the horrible sound of screaming. Now he was falling, falling -

'Char! Wake up! Wake UP!' Someone was shaking him, pulling him out of bed. He tried hard to obey the voices, but his whole face seemed set in concrete, a gaping hole letting out those awful rasping screams, eyelids stuck fast.

Char? Nobody at school called him that.

'STOP it, Char, for goodness sake, shut UP It's all right, dear, it's only a dream.' The jumble of meaningless words slowly parsed itself in his overwrought brain and, as he shut his mouth, the screaming mercifully ceased. Released, his eyelids parted and revealed to the confused boy a ring of assorted shining angels standing round his bed. He closed his eyes and cautiously tried again, and now the heavenly beings had transformed themselves into his own brothers and sisters, the early morning summer sun gleaming on their white nightclothes.

It was Bob who was shaking him, and of course it was Fanny who was smoothing his sodden brow. More and more of the frightened family were pouring into the room, gazing at him wide-eyed. Only little Bessie, in her tiny nightgown, seemed to know what to do. Hardly able to see over the edge of the bed, she reached up and, taking his sweaty hand between her two tiny ones, gave it a kiss.

Speech was still beyond her grasp. In any case, nobody knew what to say.

Nightmares were no strangers to their brother. Dear Charlie had always been a little odd, a little different. There were the temper tantrums; and there was something else, something intangible, something they did not fully understand as yet. Perhaps they never would. Like the time that Charlie, as a very small boy, had got lost wandering through the fields and had not shown the least surprise when, asking the way of a passing hen, he had found his way home without further trouble. Yes, there was a great deal more to this brother of theirs than met their youthful eyes.

The dream faded, as most dreams do. But there remained behind a cobweb of anxiety to haunt the dreamer. Was Fairbairn dead? There was no practical reason to suppose so, but it had all been so very vivid. Perhaps this was a portent, an omen of things to come?

And, at a more practical level, there still remained the problem of the sailor suit, now doubly abhorrent, the initial disastrous incident tinged with the overtones of nightmare.

BUT THESE WORRIES WERE INSUBSTANTIAL, pushed out by the glorious reality of the great escape from school. It was the very beginning of the summer holidays, which to Charlie stretched far away into the future, a future that could for the time being be totally ignored. He was too late for haymaking and the hide-away burrows to be made in the piles of sweet-smelling grass as they lay drying in the June sunshine. But the weather had for once been good and the corn would ripen early. He would be able to help Cardy and the other men with the harvest.

He went out into the yard.

'Pleased to see you home, Master Charlie.'

The cheerful voice came from inside the barn, its doorway open wide in the sunshine and ablaze with a myriad sparkling, dancing points of light as the breeze caught at the dust within.

For a moment, Charlie was puzzled.

'Who's that?' And then, as the speaker loomed through the dusty air, he remembered. Of course – it was Matt, Father's boy. Suddenly shy, he added

'Pleased to see you too, Matthew.'

'How long have you got home then?' When he heard, Matt's face almost split open in one of the biggest grins Charlie had ever seen. 'What a time we'll have! I've got lots to show you, and we can go fishing with the maggots off a dead rabbit I found, and you can tell me all about that grand school you're at.'

This was new. Charlie had never had a real friend all his own before, someone who really wanted him for himself. Matt didn't have to be welcoming. He just was.

Not waiting for a reply, the younger boy disappeared back into the dust.

'Come in here and have a look. Don't suppose your Pa's had time to tell you about our new reaper yet.'

Charlie smiled at the 'our' and followed him into the barn. As his eyes got used to the dim light, he saw that Matt was pointing at a new piece of farm machinery, its shiny pillarbox red paint picked out by darts of the sunshine that fought its way through the vast assortment of objects filling the cavernous space.

'What's happened to the old one, then? It was working all right last year.'

'He sold that to Farmer Gissing over Sudbury way and bought this instead. He read about it in the *Farmer's Weekly* – well, I read it to him – and then there was no stopping him. It's a brand new invention and saves ever so much time. When the corn comes out of the side here, all nice and neatly cut, you don't have to bundle it up and tie it no more like you used to. The machine does it for you, with string! Then you just have to do the stooking.'

There followed the intricacies of machine talk, of knife-boards and 'fingers' and cranks and revolving rakes and all the paraphernalia of modern-day farming. Both boys were intensely interested, and it wasn't until he heard his name being called that Charlie remembered that his father had asked to see him in his study after breakfast.

This time, Charlie entered the room alone. This he presumed was to be an inquisition on his progress in his first term at school. He was not particularly nervous, for he knew that academically he had performed well and assumed that this was all his father was interested in.

So, when he'd settled himself in the second chair and found to his joy that the tips of his boots actually did at last reach the floor, he wasn't prepared for the opening sentence.

'It seems, Charles, that you have a few problems at school.' His father felt for and picked up a letter lying on his desk. 'This letter arrived by post a few days ago, and John has read it to me more than once so that I am fully aware of its content.'

There was a pause; clearly, his father was having difficulty in finding the right words.

'The Reverend Carter is happy, very happy, with your work. Latin and Greek, and mathematics, all seem satisfactory. In fact, you are almost always top of your class in all three. I congratulate you.'

Another pause.

So? thought Charlie, sitting as still as a mouse.

'But it seems that the matron is concerned about you.'

What, thought Charlie, had Matron to do with anything? He had thought she was his friend. Not a whisker stirred.

'It seems that the whole problem stems from some unfortunate clothing that you arrived in on your first day and that you have had to continue to wear on high days and holidays since – that the other boys make fun of you, and that you are not always man enough to bear it – that there have been a great many tears and that this, of course, makes matters worse. In short, it seems that you are very unhappy at the school.'

The expression of deep concern and kindness on the face that his father turned towards his son utterly unnerved the boy, and, to his own astonishment, he began to cry. It was just three months since his world had been overturned by his mother's death; the awful nightmare was still terrifyingly close; there had not been time to make the emotional transition from school to home.

Of course, he thought of none of these things, but the sum of them produced an overwhelming and totally unexpected outpouring which his father was hard pressed to follow. But behind his dark glasses and his stern manner was a heart, hidden by custom and circumstance from most of his children, full of sympathy and the countryman's practical wisdom. He listened and tried to follow and to understand, his arm round the shoulders of the small son who had somehow found himself on his knees by his father's chair, his head on his lap.

And so they remained, for as long as it took for them to reach an understanding that was probably as deep as it would ever go.

'Right!' said Charlie's father, at the end of it. His son went back to his chair.

'Point number one: we will somehow dispose of that dreadful sailor suit. You can give it to your new friend, Matt if you like. I can't imagine what Mary will say, but I suppose I must try and handle that.' His left cheek creased upwards in an otherwise invisible wink. Charlie could scarcely believe his own eyes.

'Point number two: Crowthorne is of course only a prep school, and you will need to move on at some point. I had been making enquiries anyway about Haileybury, a public school in Hertfordshire, and had decided that you should go on there in due course. The only change that we must make is that they take you there at the earliest possible date. I shall find out, but I think you will have to stick it out for a bit longer. I hope that after this talk together you will feel able to do that?'

'Yes Sir. I'm sure I will.'

'Now off you go. The sun's shining. Get outside.'

'Father?'

'Yes, Charlie?'

'Your new reaper-binder looks really good. But I don't understand how the knot gets tied in the string.'

'Come on then. Let's go out and have a look.' And off they went, father's hand on son's shoulder.

'You know, Charlie, you are the perfect height for me now,' he said as his son deftly guided him down the steps to the yard.

8

England 1885-1889

Brook House
Bures
Suffolk

The Reverend J. Robertson   August 19th 1885
Haileybury School
Hertfordshire

Dear Mr Robertson

I take the liberty of writing to you with regard to my son, Charles, now nine years old. To put the matter simply, although he seems to be of high intelligence and is performing very well in the academic field at his present school, he is not happy there.

I know that at one time you took boys as young as eight. I am aware, however, that in many Public Schools the age of admission is greater, and perhaps your own rules have changed. If, however, there is still a younger entry, I should like formally to ask that he be admitted to your school, known for its excellence, as soon as possible.

Yours sincerely
W. Garrad

The reply from Haileybury arrived after the beginning of term and was in the negative. Charlie's father wrote to his son and the next letter-writing session produced the following answer:

Crowthorne Preparatory School
September 14th 1885

Dear Father

Thank you for your letter. I am alright now, so don't worry. As you can see, I got here alright after John left me. There are crowds of new boys this term, at least eight that I can think of, and one of them, Monk Minor, is in my dorm. We call him monkey, becos he really does look like one. He dont mind. He might be my friend.

Cricket is over. Now theres just football, which is a bit more fun.
Your affeckchunit son
Charles

꿎

Brook House
Bures
Suffolk

December 3rd 1885

Dearest Char

How wonderful; you will soon be home for Christmas! We have been to the plantation to choose a tree, and Cardy will cut it down for us a few days before you come so that we can have it all ready for you. We have made lovely decorations from fir-cones and brightly painted paper which we've been very busy cutting into all sorts of funny shapes. Frank's speciality is animals – there are red cows and green horses and even a bright purple hippopotamus!

A wonderful piece of news; Bessie has said her first word; well, that's what Cook says. She says she distinctly heard her say 'Violet', which does not have a great ring of truth about it! We must wait and see.

Are you very cold at school? We have had to pile the fires high with wood, and poor Cardy spends a lot of time keeping the log-baskets and coal-scuttles full. Poor Father feels the cold very badly, though of course he does not complain. Outside, everything looks so beautiful. The pond is freezing over, and the ducks look so funny slithering about all over the place! They seem mortally offended that their world has shrunk to the tiny space that the men keep open for them! By the time you get home I should think there will be skating, if Jack Frost holds. When I woke up this morning, there was such a strange light coming through the cracks in the curtains, and everything was so quiet. Then I remembered what it was like last winter when it snowed so hard and when I drew back the blinds sure enough the fields were all covered with snow! Now the sun is shining, and the whole world seems a-glitter. It is so very beautiful; I wish you were here to see it. But I daresay it is just the same at school.

John is just about to drive the trap into the village with some food for the poor Mitchells. Joe Mitchell has consumption and can't work. I must catch him, John I mean, and ask him to post this for me.

It will be a strange Christmas without dear Mama, but I know she is looking down from Heaven and will be happy for us so we must be happy too.

Your very affectionate sister

Fanny.

P.S. Father says your spelling is atrocious and at least by now you should be able to spell a-f-f-e-c-t-i-o-n-a-t-e.

Christmas and then Easter came and went and soon the long journey from Bures to Crowthorne and back again three times a year became an established fixture in Charles's life, managed without an escort and very much a part of his growing up.

Certainly, by and large, matters did improve. Anything 'bookish' appealed to him, and he started to take an interest in world affairs. Some of his sparse pocket money came to be spent on *The Times* newspaper; partly, it must be said, to improve his rating in the termly current events test set by the headmaster.

In *The Times* of November 10th 1886 there was a particular article that caught his fancy. Apparently, Queen Victoria had just presented Mount Kilimanjaro to her grandson, the future Wilhelm II, as a birthday present and Charlie tried to imagine being given a mountain, any mountain, let alone an African one, for his own birthday. He failed. Flicking back to the front page he scanned the usual lists of births, marriages and deaths. The death of his own mother had been posted there the previous year, and he had got into the habit of glancing down the list each day, just in case there were any special entries. He loved odd names; a Mrs Hyde-Parker was a family friend and made him giggle whenever he thought of it. But that day none stood out. Rawson was evidently not sufficiently unusual to catch his eye. A pity, because there it was:

'On 7th inst. at Marston Vicarage, Northwich, Cheshire, to the wife of the Rev. Edward Octavius Rawson a daughter ...'

The paper should have burst into flames in his hand. The school chapel should have rung joyous peals on its non-existent bells. At least there should have been a half-holiday, with free access to the tuck-shop. But none of these things happened.

It was, after all, just an ordinary day.

٭

Haileybury School
Hertfordshire
January 14th 1889

Mr W. Garrad
Brook House
Bures
Suffolk

Dear Mr Garrad

Thank you for your letter reminding me of our previous correspondence and applying once more for a place in our school for your boy Charles now that he is almost thirteen.

We are now taking names for the Autumn term of this year, and shall be pleased to add his to the list, subject of course to the usual formalities. It is usual to receive a report from the boy's previous headmaster and I should be grateful if you could send me details of name, school, etcetera.

I will be in touch again shortly.

Yours sincerely

J. Robertson, Headmaster.

❧

Crowthorne Preparatory
May 15th 1889

Dear Father

Thank you very much for your letter. It is good to hear that you have written again to Haileybury and that I have been accepted. Lots of the fellows from here go there and say it is a very jolly school and the food is a lot better than here. As always, I wish I was better at games, as there are wonderful playing fields. But they say you don't have to play cricket if you don't like it, at least when you get up the school a bit, so that's good too.

I am almost sad to be leaving here now! It is quite different when you are a prefect. The other chaps look up to you a bit. But I shall be glad to go somewhere new, with different masters and a good library.

We have final examinations coming up soon, and I have a great deal of revision to do. So I must end this letter,

remaining ever your AFFECTIONATE son

Charles

P.S. You see I have even learnt to spell!

Bootalet, Burma 1889

It was surely an earth-shaking discovery and Pyau was entranced by it. Just to make sure, he tried it again – and again, and again. Yes, it worked every time and he chuckled with glee. He looked across at his mother, stooping over the paddy seedlings. She had that red binder on her back, and for a moment a shadow fell across the sunshine of his perfect world. Well, it had been perfect, until the new baby had turned up and tried to spoil things. But, after all, his little brother couldn't do what he could do, and to prove it he jumped into the water yet again and sent that magical fountain of sparkling gems up into the air. His mother was so beautiful, and he wanted to collect a whole potful of jewels in every colour of the rainbow and cover her from head to foot. He tried to catch the iridescent drops of water as they fell, but somehow they slipped through his fat little fingers every time and disappeared into the muddy sludge round his legs. It was frustrating. He pictured his jewels glistening in Mother's hair and tried again. She was so beautiful.

PART TWO

9

England, 1892

THE SILENCE IN THE HOUSE was absolute. It was difficult to believe that just one short week ago everything was as it had always been. Doors banged, feet clattered, the baby cried, snatches of song and children's laughter filled the rooms with the welcome sounds of a family in full flood. And now, nothing. The gulls still screeched in the windy sky and the clump of fishermen's boots coming home from the sea still came in through the open windows, but even these familiar sounds seemed muted and sad.

Annie struggled wearily up the winding stairs. A cheap seaside hotel is no place to die. Her husband's body lay stretched out down the centre of the bed, the sheet pulled up over the week's growth of black stubble on his chin. The young contorted face, muscles pulled tight, held a blueish tinge; the desperate struggle to breathe had made him a stranger. It was here, in this room, that the air screamed its silence, so great was the contrast with what had gone before. No need for the doctor's stethoscope; the rasp of Edward's breathing had, at the end, filled the whole thin-walled house.

And then, quite suddenly, it had ceased.

Downstairs, the children looked at one another.

'Stop rocking that cradle, Jo – I can't hear a thing.'

Transfixed, for a long moment no-one moved. And then little Heather clapped her podgy hands.

'Papa better!'

Her happy voice cut across the silence and the spell was broken. Agatha and Marjory hugged each other; Heather rushed for the door.

'Want to see Papa!' she shouted.

'Wait!' said Josephine, one hand still resting on her baby brother's cradle. 'Mother said we were to stay here and not move.' Of them all, only she looked puzzled.

Could it be that Papa, far from recovering, was dead?

FOUR BRIGHTLY COLOURED TIN BUCKETS, one brand-new and painted with a gaudy mermaid, were shaken free of sand and stacked neatly into one another; the little wooden spades, tied together with string, lay beside them. Two suitcases stood ready on the step, waiting for the undertaker's cab that would take the coffin to the railway station; there would be ample space beside it for their sparse belongings.

Their landlady, not one to put herself out as a rule, was suddenly being as helpful as could be. No doubt she wanted to get rid of them as soon as possible. A gentleman, and a parson at that, dying in your hotel was not much of an advertisement.

'The parson's wife said as how it was my damp sheets that gave him the pneumonia,' she told her neighbours afterwards. 'The cheek of it! But then you had to feel sorry for her with all them little children, and her seeming so helpless somehow.'

JOSEPHINE SAT WITH THE OTHERS in the front pew of her father's church. She simply could not take in that he was really dead, that she would never see him again.

'If I blink and make a wish, a special one as it's in church, Papa might, just might, push up the lid of the coffin and walk over to our pew.' Whether or not she spoke her thoughts out loud she neither knew nor cared. But there were no miracles.

She remembered how, just a week before, the two of them had been paddling in the sea, their long legs taking them farther out than the younger children could manage. He had been coughing that day; if only she had known she would never have pulled at him to go further out into deeper waters, she would have dried his poor, thin white legs, she would have tucked him up in his hotel bed, she would ...

Little Heather's stage-whispered 'that man's not Papa!' brought Josephine back from her reverie. The smaller child was pointing at a strange parson in her father's pulpit and Jo made a supreme effort to take in what the preacher was saying. Words, only words, always words; that was not what she wanted. Eyes swimming with tears, she glanced along the choirstalls; the flock of black-clad priests that had come to honour her father seemed to merge, split up, and merge again in a macabre dance that threatened to engulf her. She gave herself up to her thoughts and emotions, and at last the long, dirgeful service came to an end and they could all go home. All – except for Papa.

AS THE TRAIN BEARING ITS TRAGIC BURDEN had puffed into the railway station, she had had no special part to play. Kind neighbours had taken the heavy coffin from the guard's van and lifted it into the waiting carriage. Their wives and daughters had clucked around the bereft family. Cries of 'come along, you poor, poor dears' had wrapped them round as they clambered into a second carriage. Surrounded by friends and neighbours, they had driven to their house and found it full of flowers and the welcome smell of food in preparation.

But there had not been much eating over the two terrible days since the funeral, for things were changing. Josephine was only eight years old, but as the parson's eldest daughter a great deal was expected of her. Now, when her world was tumbling about her ears, for she had loved her father very dearly, the burden was almost more than she could bear. Irritation with her mother's near total collapse was replacing the anxiety she felt about her, and she simply did not know what to do.

At first, the two of them had sobbed together, arms around each other's necks. Few words were spoken, words of comfort and of love. To her mother's 'Oh Jo, Jo, how are we going to manage?' she had made the automatic reply of 'We'll be all right, Mother, things will work out, you'll see,' for she knew that this was what her beloved Papa would have said. But, as the days went by and Mama withdrew further and further into herself, as the housekeeping fell into ever deeper confusion, as meals failed to appear at the appointed time and became less and less appetising, Joe's worries grew. What, indeed, would become of them?

One young servant lived in the house, a girl from the village only four or five years older than herself. A few days after the funeral, she came running to Jo.

'Oh please miss, there's a parson gentleman at the door, and he says he's got something special to tell your Ma, only I don't like to disturb her. She's shut herself in her room again and says she's got a headache and to stop banging on the door.'

The visitor, a young curate from the next parish, shook Josephine warmly by the hand. But her 'Can I help you?' received short shrift.

'I fear my business can be conducted only with your mother as it is of a very personal nature.' If only Josephine had been a little more mature she would have seen him for what he was, a shy young man trying to cope with a highly sensitive situation. But in her eight-year-old eyes he was being just plain obstinate, and there and then she made up her mind to dislike him intensely. This however made no impression upon his demands to see her mother. He was clearly going to stand there with his shiny clerical foot in the door until she did what he asked.

'Mrs. Rawson,' said the young man, when at last they were seated formally in the vicarage drawing-room. 'I have something to tell you – to give you – that I think – hope – will be of some help to you at this sad time.'

At the same moment, another part of the young curate's mind was deciding that sitting in such a freezing cold room was completely ridiculous, and that, when he had a living of his own, he would make sure that good coal fires burned in all the grates. He would never be able to write sermons with his own breath hanging about his face like a shroud.

The visitor held out an envelope. Annie Rawson took it and opened it.

'It worked wonders,' he told a gathering of the villagers later that evening.

'She'd come into the room looking so pale and sad, and so drab, as if she simply didn't care about anything any more. Then, when she opened the envelope and read the letter, she coloured right up and looked quite jolly for a moment. She looked at the cheque, and then at me. 'I don't know what to say,' she said. 'I really don't know if I can accept this. I'm not sure that my husband would have wanted me to.'

'Of course,' the young curate's account continued, 'I said that he would, and finally she got up and took my hand in both of hers, and just said "thank you." So I explained again that the money wasn't from me, but that all the parishioners had been so fond of him that, now he was gone, they wanted to do something to help his family. So they had passed the hat round, and this is what they'd collected, rounded up to the nearest guinea.'

THE MONEY DID NOT LAST LONG and, after a few well-nourished weeks, the family found themselves in exactly the same predicament as before. The young maid did her best, but a diet of undercooked mutton and overcooked cabbage did nothing for the children's tempers, and passers-by shook their heads at the noisy arguments bursting from the vicarage windows, their poor mother's mood too low for her to keep them occupied and happy.

Their father's stipend, enough for a comfortable existence, had ceased with his death. Annie's parents, still very much alive, had owned a thriving business but times were hard and the receivers had arrived. Struggling themselves, they had nothing to spare for the daughter who had been brought up in luxury and with no thought for a future where she must fend for herself. Letters went to and fro, but bankruptcy and death make cruel partners and the future grew ever bleaker.

Annie was 31 years old and accustomed all her life to being the one who was cared for. She had never for one second contemplated the possibility of loneliness. And, as for penury, why, that was a word that belonged only to the obscure world of unfortunate beings for whom one felt vaguely sorry in a scornful sort of way, but who undoubtedly could do better if they put their minds to it.

Or could they? Faced now with exactly that situation, what could Annie do? What was she able to do? Through no fault of her own, she was fit for nothing. Cleaning, cooking, washing clothes – these were all skills way beyond her. In different circumstances perhaps she might have come up with something, even an idea for making a little money. But she was shocked by the sudden death, and she was very tired. Her confinement a few months earlier had been a difficult one, and she was still draining all her energies into feeding her son, who was always hungry. Sometimes she felt he sucked the very marrow out of her bones. Above all, her heart was broken, and with it her will. It seemed that nothing, absolutely nothing, could be done.

Until someone came up with an idea.

There was only one thing to do. And Annie was the only person who could do it.

10

THERE WERE THE FIVE OF THEM; Josephine, Marjory, Agatha, Heather and baby Edward. All beautiful, all healthy. It was a perfect summer's day, and the whole family was on the vicarage lawn. The croquet hoops were set out and the three older children were struggling with the heavy wooden mallets as they attempted to knock the balls through the metal arches in some game of their own. Little Heather sat on the grass, plump legs wide apart as she collected flowers for a daisy chain. Daisies were her passion. She gathered them by the handful, leaving little dying bunches of them all over the house and pestering anyone and everyone to help her stuff them into jam-jars of water. Perhaps it was a passion that lasted all her life, for Daisy was the nickname given her by her own nephews and nieces. But that, of course, was later, much later, after a lifetime of experiences she couldn't even have begun to imagine as she played on the vicarage lawn in that summer of 1892.

Annie sat by the pram on a garden chair in the shade of a sycamore tree, the wood-pigeons in its branches repeating their soothing mantra of 'take TWO cows, Taffy, take TWO' over and over again, the sun for once exactly the right heat. The previous night's sleep had been interrupted by Edward's crying, and at any other time she would have been soothed into a gentle slumber by the perfection all around her.

But this was no perfection. This was the nearest to Hell that Annie had ever been. This was the day on which she had set herself to choose.

Or perhaps that other day, a week or so ago, had been even worse, if such a thing were possible. When the maid had told her she had visitors, she had dragged herself down to the drawing-room; only a remaining shred of politeness took her there, for she had lost all interest in everything. She had been surprised to see such a large gathering. There were local friends, several parsons from neighbouring parishes, and the village school teacher. The Rural Dean was there too, a senior colleague much respected by her husband. Even from the doorway she could recognise her father's large clear writing on the letter he held in his hand.

It had been the Dean who spoke first.

'We apologise for this intrusion, Mrs Rawson, but we have something very important to discuss with you and thought it best that we all come.'

He pushed forward a chair for her, and, as she sat, they all found themselves somewhere to perch, on the piano stool or the arm or cushion of one of the many chairs that furnished the large, bleak room.

'As you know, we are all deeply sorry for your tragic loss.' A sympathetic murmur went round the room. 'The Reverend Rawson was an excellent priest, and a good friend to many of us here, especially to myself.' Another murmur.

'We are equally sorry to find you in this serious predicament, with five lovely children and no longer a husband to help you bring them up, and also, if I may touch on a delicate subject, in very straightened circumstances. You have made no secret of this; otherwise I should not be so bold as to mention it. As you know, a collection was made on your behalf, but in the long term there will clearly have to be more permanent arrangements.'

A long silence. Feet shifting. Throats clearing.

At last he went on.

'Your parents are of course in touch with you over this thorny subject, but your father has also thought fit to write to me. Again as you know, they are in considerable financial trouble themselves; otherwise they would clearly have taken you all in. A certain suggestion has been made, and it seems that your mother and father, and all your friends gathered here, are of one mind that you should take it up.'

Another, longer, silence. Someone stood and then sat down again. Glances were exchanged.

Annie Rawson's attention was by this time riveted on the speaker. What on earth was he going to suggest? What possible remedy for this irredeemable situation could there be?

She, and all those in the room with her, waited.

Why the mystery? Why don't they get on with the job and tell me what this is all about? Her mind was buzzing, but she did not have long to wait before the speaker started again.

'I have recently been visiting my brother, who lives in Staffordshire, near the Welsh border.'

What had that got to do with her?

'He too has several young children, and the conversation turned to your –

er – situation. After a few moments, he became quite excited – you have heard, no doubt, of Chadwick sewing-thread?'

What sort of a question was that? Of course she had; everybody had. The words cotton and Chadwick were synonymous. There were at least two reels of it, one black, one white, in her work-basket at that very moment.

'The Chadwicks live in a magnificent house called Hints Hall, near my brother's town of Tamworth.'

The Dean swallowed, and looked desperately round the room as if seeking support. Then the words came with a rush.

'My brother has heard that Mrs. Chadwick, though married for a number of years, has not been able to have a child. She is therefore looking round for a suitable baby to come and live with her, and to be brought up as her own. The suggestion that has been made, and that we are all of the opinion you should take up, is that you continue to look after just four of your children, and that you give the fifth away to someone who is better able to care for him – or her, for of course it does not have to be the youngest child. It is for you to choose.'

That had been a week ago. Some matters are too awful to contemplate, and for the last few days the merciful shutter that had come crashing down held back her agony. She had thought that her heart was broken when her beloved Edward died, but as she looked at her family playing so happily on the lawn she felt once again the sharp-edged pieces knotting in her breast, making her catch her breath and clutch the sides of her chair. For now she must take a scalpel and cut away yet more of her own flesh.

She must choose.

Edward had been so desperate for a son and, when at last he arrived had christened him with his own name. The little baby cooing in the pram beside her looked just like his father; the same high forehead, the same bright blue eyes. It had been this likeness, those sky-blue eyes gazing trustingly up at her as she put him to the breast, this feeling that Edward Octavius lived on in little Edward Douglas, that had enabled her to retain a scrap of sanity in those last weeks.

No, she could not part with Edward.

She looked again at her four daughters, all of them now sitting in the shade, the bigger ones helping little Heather make her daisy chain. As she watched, Josephine ran inside and emerged precariously balancing a tray with five glasses on it. She put it down on the grass and came over to her mother, slopping a little water from the tumbler with every careful step.

'For you, Mama,' she said.

No, she could not part with Josephine. She relied on her too much.

Marjory, Agatha, Heather. Agatha was the tomboy, liking her own way and already showing skill at the sports her father had loved. She was only four years old, but the two of them had spent much time together with a soft ball and a cut-down cricket bat.

Could she part with Agatha?

Marjory, too, clearly had an eye for the ball, but was beginning to show other talents. She was always singing, her tuneful little voice even on these grey days raising the family spirits. At six, she was an avid reader and story-teller; for the last few weeks, it was often she who sat by little Heather as she lay in her cot at bed-time, telling her the old fairy-tales and making up new ones of her own.

No, she could not part with Marjory.

Agatha and Heather. Oh, how hard it was. She knew she should not have favourites, but Heather was such a sunny child, and such a pretty one with her fair curls and happy smile. Agatha, though, had come first, and there was a determination about her that her mother greatly admired. Agatha would not in any way take kindly to a different family. Indeed, she might be so difficult that it was more than possible that she would be sent home again. She would not be loved as Heather would. In any case, the Cotton King, or rather Queen, had apparently specified a baby. Agatha, she felt, despite her tender years, was almost as grown-up as she herself.

No, it could not be Agatha.

MR AND MRS CHADWICK came in their carriage all the way from Hints Hall. They seemed to the impoverished family to be very grand; everything about them reeked of the money that they themselves were without.

But they were very charming too, and were enchanted by little Heather, who bestowed on them a non-stop series of her most winning smiles. Of course, at two years old she was incapable of understanding the situation, a prospect so bleak for her wretched mother that Annie could only shut her mind to it and get through the day as best as she was able.

For the Chadwicks had laid down their own conditions. Heather and her mother were to have absolutely no contact; the separation was to be total and complete.

11

'HOW COULD YOU, MAMA? How could you do such a wicked, wicked thing? I'm never, ever in all the world going to speak to you again.' Josephine banged out of the room.

It was not until the carriage had disappeared out of sight that Annie had told her three remaining daughters that they might well never see their beloved little sister again. The resultant storm, the thunderous anger, the torrent of tears, the jagged lightning of their fury, all these things perhaps, just perhaps, Annie could have handled. But it was the expression of utter despair on Marjory's sensitive young face that was her undoing. First, the child had lost her father; now, she had lost too the little sister to whom she had grown so close, particularly in the last few weeks when Mama had seemed so distant and unapproachable.

Marjory wanted above everything to follow Jo from the room and seek solace in her own private hideaway, behind the rubbish heap in the garden. But, looking back with her hand on the doorknob, she caught sight of her beloved mother's face, her own expression exactly mirrored on it. She stopped in her tracks, and, running back, put her arms round her mother's waist and gave her a hug.

' Love you, Mama,' she said, and ran from the room.

BEFORE MANY DAYS HAD PASSED, the Rural Dean was back.

'I feel sure you understand, Mrs Rawson, that we shall shortly have to appoint a successor to your late husband. We have several candidates for the living, and each of them would like to see round the vicarage before making a decision as to whether he would be happy here should he succeed in his application. I shall be in touch again when the first man will be coming.'

Galvanised into action, Annie realised that she must find somewhere else for them to live. And so a third loss was to be added to the list, loss of the house and garden where for six years they had played at happy families, with no idea of the bombshell that was to explode in their faces.

But where could they go? How should she set about looking?

The very next morning a letter arrived. Marjory took it from the postman, sitting high on the driving seat of his delivery van.

'Morning, Miss,' he had said, his face almost as red as the braid that edged his cap. 'Letter for your Mama. Let's hope it brings some good news, after all your troubles.'

Marjorie liked the postman. She liked his smile and the way he geed-up the horse. And she liked the look of this particular letter, for it was Grandma's sloping handwriting that was on the envelope.

Annie opened it at once.

> My dear Daughter. You will be now be searching for somewhere to live and I felt my Duty to write straight away with news that has just come my way of lodgings in Bedford. Mrs. Brindwell's Housekeeper has moved there to be near her Daughter, and is setting up rooms to let. Mrs Brindwell speaks well of her, and has already spoken to her about you and the Children. It seems she would be happy to have you, and her terms are very reasonable. I can arrange all for you if you wish.
>
> Yr. Loving Mother.

Good news at last, thought Annie. A true answer to prayer.

THE MOVE WAS DULY MADE. As matters turned out, it was questionable which of the spiritual powers was responsible for that particular answer, though nobody from such a God-fearing vicarage family would have dared to put such a thought into words.

Except for Josephine.

'I cannot stand Baggy,' she said one day, when things were particularly bad. 'I really do hate her.' The remarkable contour of the housekeeper's voluminous and wind-filled drawers on the very first Monday's washing-line could scarcely have failed to draw the attention of the younger Rawsons, particularly Edward, and the nickname had stuck firmly ever since.

Jo's maliciousness towards Baggy was getting worse, and Marjory didn't know what to do. The older girl's tongue was sharp, and the butt of her remarks was too slow-witted to stand up for herself. Like a tormenting wasp, Jo never missed a chance to sting.

12

ANNIE LAY AWAKE A LONG TIME that night taking stock of her family. Edward Octavius was dead; Heather too as far as Annie was concerned. Nothing she could do would bring either of them back.

But Josephine; now she was a different matter altogether. Her eldest daughter seemed to be developing traits that were beyond her mother's understanding. If Annie were honest with herself, these were not new. For some time she had been aware of feelings towards her eldest daughter which were not those that a mother should harbour.

Increasingly, time that Annie's late husband had previously spent shut away in his study with his religious tomes and sermons had come to be shared with Josephine. To begin with, it would be restricted to bad weather, when the children were cooped-up indoors. On those days, he would say to her: 'Come into the study for a bit. My books are mostly very dry, but you might be able to pick out something that takes your fancy.'

Jo would take one down and settle herself on the stool by the fire with it on her knee. It would not be long before she came across a word she did not know. Then the use of the dictionary had to be explained, or one of the twenty-five volumes of the *Encyclopædia Britannica*, too large and precious for Jo to handle, pulled down and its beautiful India paper pages carefully turned until the relevant article came to light.

This, thought Annie as she lay in bed with cold feet and the sheets all rucked up around her, this was all very well. But soon it had become a habit, and Jo would go to the study most days, and read and discuss and, in Annie's opinion, waste too much of the time that Edward should have been spending on his work. On the rare occasion that Annie herself knocked on the study door and crept in to discuss some important household matter, her husband, with the utmost politeness, would say:

'Not now, dear. I am too busy. We will talk about this after lunch.'

Then the time Edward and Josephine spent together had spread to the afternoons. Edward always took a walk in the afternoons, 'to air my brain,' he would say, and often to visit parishioners. Josephine took to going with him. Sometimes, in the summer, she would wander about outside while her father went into the stuffy house to comfort a bereaved parent or to discuss wedding plans. But often, and especially when the weather was bad, she would go in with him and sit quietly while he went about his business.

There was one particular cottage that she specially loved. It belonged to two old sisters, the Misses Bax. The room where they sat, one on either side of the range which in winter was always alight, was dark and very hot. They looked rather like book-ends, she decided, each in charge of one of the two ovens that flanked the Zebo-ed grate.

It was the one on the right, the old bread oven, that held the most interest for visiting children. Although occasionally in cold weather it would deliver a delicious hot scone for the youngest generation, it was only in the summertime, when the fire was not lit, that it came into its own.

The game, always the same, went like this:

'What's in the oven today, Miss Bax?'

'Do you know, I can't remember! And my rheumaticky old hands won't turn the handle. Would you be so kind as to do it for me?'

And, at a touch of Jo's, or Marjory's, or Agatha's small hand, the oven would fly open and there would be humbugs and toffees and chocolate bars in such profusion that they had even been known to fall out on to the mat.

ANNIE PULLED HER THOUGHTS BACK TO THE PRESENT.

'Yes.' Her own voice startled her, for she had spoken aloud. But there was no-one to disturb. The other side of the big double bed lay cool and unslept-on, the sheet as smooth as when the bed had been made that morning. 'I must not go mad,' she thought, 'I must keep my thoughts to myself.

'Yes, I do believe I used to be jealous of my own little daughter. I resented my darling husband spending so much time with her. I understood it, because she is so bright and quick. But I was jealous, and showed it, and she hasn't forgiven me ...'

She felt the familiar prick behind her eyelids and her nose began to run. 'No, I simply will not cry. I have to think things through.' Where had she got to? Ah yes, Josephine. 'She is beginning to give serious trouble, and somehow I must help her. She was all right until little Heather – and now, naturally, she blames me for that too. Oh how I wish I hadn't listened to them – if only I could put back the clock and go into her bedroom and see her little curly head on the pillow! – but I had to do it, I had to. There was nothing else I could do ...'

And she pulled her own pillow over her face to stifle the sobs that would not be contained.

Exhausted now, her thoughts turned to her remaining three children, Marjory, Agatha and Edward. She loved thinking about Edward, with his good looks that were so like his father's, and his sweet baby ways. He was still uncomplicated; his mother was still the source of everything he wanted, and he was the one person whom she could satisfy completely – for the moment. For a little while she luxuriated in her thoughts of Edward. He seemed bright enough, cooing at the leaves as they fluttered above him in his pram, sitting up at the right age, hearing her when she talked to him. Yes, he seemed to have his wits about him. Her mind wandered forward to his schooling. Edward Octavius had often spoken about his plans for his only son.

'I want him to go to a really good public school.' he would say as they sat together after the children had gone to bed.

'I want him to be inspired, to have teachers that will not just teach him Greek and Latin and mathematics, but about the whys and the wherefores, about the spirit, about the soul. I want them to bring out his whole personality, to find the good in him and nurture it. Yes, I must work hard, and try to better myself so that there will be enough money to send him to such a place.'

Like all good fathers, he had wanted his son to be happy. But there was something more. There was no doubt that Edward Octavius was ambitious for Edward Douglas. Now it was up to her, his widow, to set the child on his way, a responsibility that lay heavily upon her shoulders.

Suddenly, she shivered. Her mother would say that a ghost had walked across her grave.

She turned her thoughts away from Edward. What about Marjory? Poor little Marjory, always second to Josephine, already with so much sadness in her short life. Marjory had suffered just as much as Josephine. Perhaps she had not been so close to her father, but oh how she had loved her baby sister. What had Annie done to her? She pictured her daughter's elfin face, not classically pretty but vivacious and nearly always smiling. She too had the family's bright blue eyes, full of light and sparkle. Annie knew she really must give some thought to Marjory, but not now, not this minute.

Her daughter's face spun up up and away as, at long last, sleep overtook the exhausted woman and, for a short time, released her from her cares.

13

'MAMA, WHEN CAN WE GO and see Grandmama and Grandpapa again?'

Marjory could not remember her mother's parents very well, for she had not seen them for a long time now. But Annie liked to talk about them, and she always started in the same way. She would sit Marjory on her knee, and begin.

'You won't remember this,' she would say, 'because you were too young.'

And then would come stories of visits with the whole family to the seaside or the zoological gardens, when Grandpapa owned his own coach and pair. There would always be a sumptuous picnic, with Grandmama's maid laying out a cloth on the beach and covering it with mouth-watering delicacies from the picnic hamper.

But those happy shared moments were getting fewer, and Marjory, from wondering when she would see her beloved grandparents again, began to think that they too had gone from her life altogether.

Until that wonderful, happy morning. It was a moment photographed on her mind forever. She had on her best clothes, for it was a Sunday, underdone-boiled-egg-for-breakfast day, and they would soon be off on the long dreary trail to church. Her pink jersey was clean, but it was too tight from endless washing; besides, she had had it for a long time, and as it shrank, so she got bigger, with uncomfortable consequences. The green skirt was all right, though. She liked its new shorter hemline as her legs grew longer, and her shrinking middle adapted well to its narrow waist-band. The sun, undeterred by the dirty windows, glistened on the cheap cutlery, turning it, if you half shut your eyes, into the finest, grandest sterling silver, just like Grandmama used to have. And the room was warm.

Her mother had been silent as she sat at the head of the table. Before she had even finished, she got up and left the room. The children looked at one another. She had been so odd lately. What now?

They did not have long to wonder. Within a minute she was back with a letter in her hand.

As she sat down again, she pulled the flimsy sheet of paper from its envelope, and once again Marjory recognised Grandmama's elegant sloping hand-writing. Her stomach lurched. On a beautiful day like this, the news surely could only be good. Or could it?

The wait while her mother re-read the letter seemed endless. But   at last she looked up and glanced round the table at each of them in turn.

'I received this letter from your grandmother by yesterday's post, and since then I have been thinking about what it says.' Pause. There was a collective holding of breath, for whatever it was, the news the letter brought was clearly important. Always impatient, Josephine was the first to break the silence.

'So what does it say, Mama?'

'As you know, your grandparents live in a town called Knutsford, in Cheshire. Grandmama has written to say that she has found a small house near their own that is up for rent. She doesn't know any details yet, but she wonders whether we would consider another move.' Annie looked up from the letter and round the table.

But all three places were empty. The girls had left their seats, their feet dancing, their hands clapping, their voices reaching to the rafters. Baggy came rushing in from the kitchen to see what on earth all the fuss was about. As soon as she put her face round the door, the uproar increased.

'We're going, Baggy, we're leaving! Isn't it wonderful?'

One startled glance was enough and the poor woman turned and fled.

After a few moments, Marjory went after her. If any of the others had bothered to follow they would have found her in the kitchen with her arm round the housekeeper, the apron over Baggy's face hiding the flooding tears.

14

'WHAT DO YOU THINK OF IT, JO?' The two girls lay side by side in the big double bed, with just room enough between it and the shabby wallpaper for an upright chair.

'I think it's awful.' Josephine rolled over irritably, flinging out an arm and catching her sister painfully on the side of the neck. 'You'd think that at least we'd have our own beds here. It was bad enough sharing at Baggy's – you kick like mad when you're dreaming and I'm always covered in bruises. But we knew we'd move from that awful, awful place. Now it looks as if we're stuck for good in this hole. I don't know what on earth Mama was thinking of.'

'But you know she can't help it. It's not her fault.'

'Oh, for goodness sake stop being so nice about everybody. You drive me mad. Why can't you be bitchy even for once?'

'Jo! That's a terrible word! What would Mama say?'

Secretly, Jo was a little ashamed of herself. Never mind her mother; it was Papa that she was worried about. He would, she knew, have been deeply shocked. These days she always seemed to be coming out with things she didn't really mean. 'Sorry, Papa – I'll try not to do it again.' But she knew she would. Somehow she didn't seem able to help herself.

৵

THE MONTHS PASSED, and all five of them settled down to their new life. It was, despite Josephine's misgivings, a huge improvement on the old one. School for the three girls; a quiet little garden, well fenced from the road, where Edward learnt to walk. And above all, frequent visits to and from the grandparents, who, after initial misgivings, found great joy in their increasing involvement with the family.

The visit from Uncle Evie, though, was quite another matter. Their mother's brother lived in Cambridgeshire, a long way from this little family nucleus, so that when he wrote to say that he was coming to see them it seemed that the older generation's excitement knew no bounds. For weeks before his arrival, there was talk of no-one and nothing else; from all accounts he was perfect, and the children grew sick and tired of hearing about him.

'What an incredible fuss!' Josephine slashed at the hedge with a stick as she dawdled beside Marjory on their daily walk. 'I really cannot believe he's anything like they make out. Anyway, he sounds the most unutterable prig.' And secretly they all agreed.

Until he actually arrived. Who knows what each of them expected; what they saw was a tall man, young, much younger looking than their mother, with a kind face and a dog-collar round his neck.

'Why do parsons always have to wear those things?' It was Josephine again. 'For goodness sake, he's on holiday. Can't he take it off for once?'

But all of them, even Josephine, had to admit that as uncles go, and churchy ones at that, he won first prize. Laughter had been rare in their young lives; and how he made them laugh. At best, in the children's experience, adults were dreary, or old, or both; at worst, plain unbearable like Baggy. But here was a grown-up who was none of these things, who actually seemed on the same planet as themselves, who actually seemed to understand.

In the end, his visit was all too short. To their endless cries of 'please, please, stay just a few more days!' he always smiled and shook his head.

'Not this time. I have to get back to your Aunt Beatrice and to my parish. But I'll see you again soon, I promise.'

And with that they had to be satisfied.

BED WAS THE EASIEST PLACE TO TALK. Josephine lay in the middle; Marjory balanced her thin body on the very edge of the springs.

'Jo,' she said, 'don't you think Mama's a bit more cheerful these days?'

She felt the bedclothes move as her sister shrugged.

'Can't say I've noticed much change. I suppose p'raps she doesn't go on at us all so much.' She grabbed hold of the blankets as she turned away, her back clearly announcing resistance to further confidences.

Marjory sighed; it simply wasn't worth her while struggling either with her sister's mood or with the covers. Both problems would vanish as Jo slept; she could reclaim the eiderdown and she would be rid for a while of the bad temper imprisoned in the body beside her. She would have precious time alone.

'DO YOU LIKE LIVING HERE IN KNUTSFORD?'

Marjory was with her mother in the garden, picking peas; she had a summer cold and had been kept home from school. They walked down the row, one on either side, and before long their baskets were full. The weather had been kind and it was a good crop. Sitting together at the kitchen table, with the colander and the full pods on a sheet from yesterday's *Times* between them, her mother began the questions.

'But what about Jo? I have a feeling she's not very happy.' And then, surprisingly, 'you liked Uncle Evie when he came to stay, didn't you?'

Marjory suddenly felt very grown-up. Somehow it seemed that her answers were important.

'Why are you asking, Mama?'

Annie just smiled. 'Wait and see,' she said, and for the rest of the time there was no sound save for the ticking of the kitchen clock, the pop of the opening pea-pods and the rustling newspaper as they gathered up the last green stragglers.

Marjory duly waited, but nothing seemed to happen and, as the weeks went by, she forgot the strange question and answer session at the kitchen table. And then one morning the postman brought a letter, an event so rare that the whole family ran to receive it. As little Edward gave it to her, Annie glanced at the handwriting, flushed and tore it open with trembling hands. After what seemed an eternity, she looked up and, gathering them all in a bunch, her arms just long enough to encompass them, spoke at last.

'Thank God!' was all she said, and the tears ran down her cheeks. She fell on her knees, and the three younger children, looking at each other in total bewilderment, slowly followed suit. Josephine remained on her feet. She could not be sure in her own mind of the source of whatever it was that had happened, and while doubt remained, she preferred to hedge her bets.

PART THREE

15

Hertforshire, England 1889

CHARLIE ARRIVED IN A THUNDERSTORM. As the train had pulled in to Hertford railway-station the clouds had been gathering. But it was not until he had climbed with churning stomach into a waiting cab and set off on the short drive to Haileybury that the rain began. To start with, it was a gentle, soothing patter on the roof. But just before the road twisted and he would have been able to see his new school at last came the first tremendous thwack as the thunder burst straight overhead, so terrifying that he felt his guts tearing and his throat tighten to the point of pain.

The cosy little cab was transformed into a boat in imminent danger of shipwreck, rocking this way and that as the horse skittered and bucked with every ear-splitting crack and crackle. Now it was the sea that seemed to thunder on the thin roof and deluge down the windows; though it was early afternoon, the only light that penetrated Charlie's enclosed and waterlogged world came from brilliant flashes of the summer lightning that made the ensuing darkness even more impenetrable.

The thunder passed; the rain did not. The driver, drenched to the skin, got down from his cab and comforted his terrified horse, and soon they were on their way once more. But Haileybury, the school for which Charlie had waited so long, had completely vanished, washed out of sight by the torrents of water that were still flooding down the carriage windows. For a moment, as the cab finally came to a stop, the years fell away. Glancing down as he opened the carriage door, Charlie, blinkered and disorientated, almost expected to see the knee breeches and long white stockings of that never-to-be-forgotten sailor suit. His legs, clad instead in uniform black trousers, were certainly longer, but inside he felt exactly the same as he had done five years previously, arriving for the first time at Crowthorne Preparatory School.

'Don't be silly,' he whispered to himself as he ran for the school entrance. Every night for the past weeks he had told himself that this would be different. There were bound to be lots of other fellows like him. Fellows who came to school actually to learn. Other boys who didn't always have to be throwing or kicking or hitting some ball or other. People he could talk to about things that mattered. Real things. Surely there would – wouldn't there?

Poor Charlie; he had so much to learn. His allotted guide, a boy a year or so senior to himself, confused him utterly on that first tour of the school. It was all so big; he would never find his way.

'This is your House, it's called Batten,' he was told. Why? he wondered, but didn't dare ask.

'This is your dorm. That'll be your bed at the end, as you're a new gov.'

'A new what?'

'A new gov. – you know, governor.'

Charlie certainly didn't know. A governor, even a brand-new one, was the last thing he felt like, and he was much too timid to ask. A long time later, he discovered that the boys had inherited their nickname of 'governor' from their predecessors in this building. He already knew that, at the beginning of the century, this had been the East India College, where up-and-coming young hopefuls had been trained as district officers destined for the Far East. But the college had fallen on troubled times and in 1857, at the time of the Indian Mutiny, it had closed.

'Aren't we all new-boys – I mean, new govs – in here then?' asked Charlie, as he walked down the row of beds, each with a four-foot partition between it and its neighbour. He counted as he went; twenty-four down each side.

'No, silly. If you were all put together just imagine the jinks you'd get up to. No, there'll be fellows from all different forms in here, same as in the other dorms.'

Charlie sniffed, and pinched his nose. 'Pretty smelly, isn't it?'

His guide felt somewhat affronted, but had to agree.

'Probably the Toby hasn't had time to empty the jerries,' Both boys stooped down to look under the beds. When the older boy pulled out one of the offending articles, urine slopped on to the floor and Charlie winced.

'Oh, you don't want to worry about that, it happens all the time.' Looking at the stained floorboards, misused for nearly a century by a succession of sleepy young men, Charlie could only agree.

The boys looked at each other, simultaneously stricken with the same pressing need. They chose one each and, mission accomplished and two of the chamber-pots now dangerously full, discovered a new bond.

So Charlie felt able to ask:

'Who's Toby, then?'

For a moment his companion looked puzzled.

'Toby? Toby who? We don't use Christian names here, you ... oh, not Toby, a Toby, you goose. Don't you know anything? They're the sort of college servants – clear up, make the beds and all that. And they wait at table in the dining-room too. Some of them are jolly nice – the one in my dorm is. But some of them are beastly, out to make trouble for people all the time. Take Smith Minor – he's my best friend. His fellow ...' and off he went into a long and troubled tale.

But Charlie's brain was reeling, and the story did not seem so very interesting. After a restless night in his own bed at home and an extremely early start to catch the train, he suddenly felt very tired indeed. He liked his new companion and didn't wish to offend him, but he simply could not hide the enormous yawn that almost split his face in two.

In any case, time was up. It was almost a quarter to seven, and the next activity on the agenda was tea. Unpunctuality was a heinous crime and the two of them reached the dining-room only just in time.

CRIMES THERE WERE IN PLENTY, roughly proportional to the huge number of school rules. Not long before Charlie's arrival, a booklet called *Haileybury Customs* had been published, covering everything from the cost of private tuition in electricity to who could cane, flog or otherwise punish whom in the presence of which observer. The exact times of all five meals in the day (four in summer) were laid down, as well as the days on which the boys could get their hair cut. No brush was to be used, the comb and scissors would be dipped in disinfectant between each boy.

But, despite the disinfectant and the five meals a day, the boys were often sick. Not so many years later, with the progress of science, things would improve. But these were unenlightened days and it was not long before Charlie fell a victim to a method of washing-up which he had initially thought splendid in its time and labour-saving efficiency.

His downfall came about on a Friday; he remembered that because it gave him a wonderful let-out from games on the Saturday. There were always two sittings for the midday dinner. Usually he tried to get into the first one; there had been nothing to eat since breakfast five hours previously, and he was always ravenously hungry. But that Friday there had been visitors to the school, and the younger boys were banned entry until the newcomers had been fed. As usual, on an enamel table by the door into the dining-room stood a large bowl of water.

'What's that for?' he had asked his guide on the first day.

'Just do what I do.' The boy plunged his hand into the clean, steaming water and pulled out a gleaming knife, fork and spoon. Charlie obediently followed suit, sat down at the long table, and ate his meal.

'Don't forget your knife and fork,' said his friend as Charlie got up to go. As the two of them left the room the dirty implements were dropped back into the rapidly cooling water, covered now in scum of congealed grease and soggy crumbs. Out of general interest, Charlie stirred it up a bit before he deposited his cutlery; on balance he rather wished he hadn't but otherwise gave it no more thought.

But on that Friday, attending the second sitting, it was a very different matter. There on the table was the familiar bowl. A boy came out as Charlie went in, carelessly dropping his cutlery into its now murky depths; and the dreadful truth dawned. The knife and fork that he needed for his dinner were at the bottom of that unspeakable soup, and he, Charlie, had to fish around and catch them. Not only that, but then he must eat with them too.

The earth-closet nearest his dormitory saw a lot of him for the next few days and, although the local top-soil may have benefited from the large number of buckets that were emptied on it, the lettuces growing there can only have compounded the problem.

CHARLIE SETTLED QUICKLY to his new routine. He worked hard and took part in sport only when it couldn't be avoided. He found football bearable; with forty players on the field, it was not difficult to avoid contact with the ball for most of the time. True, he was never picked for the House Twenty, but he was only too aware that such fame was well outside his reach. Cricket would not start for two more terms; he would worry about that when it happened.

His favourite room in the school was the library, and whenever he could he escaped to its welcome peace. He loved the smell of the books and the feel of them in his hands. Next to the shelves of Dickens and Kingsley was a collection of volumes on climbing and mountaineering. Idly wondering why there were so many, he pulled one down at random and found between its pages an old torn newspaper cutting dated July 1865. The headline caught his eye. 'Dr James Robertson Helps in Search for Missing Victims of Matterhorn Disaster.' He read on. 'On 15th July 1865, the world awoke to the news of the conquest of that great and terrible mountain, the Matterhorn. Excitement at this mighty feat by Edward Whymper and his team, however, was sadly tempered by the tragic loss of four of the seven climbers who ...' and there it ended, the paper, frail from age and much handling, torn right across. No amount of flicking through the book's pages revealed the rest.

To Charlie, Dr Robertson was a remote and alarming figure. He had only spoken to his headmaster once, when he had first arrived and like all the other new-boys had had his hand shaken by the great man. Now he felt a stir of excitement. Kicking a stupid ball about was one thing; tackling a mighty mountain quite another. He thought back to the handshake, and felt proud.

'What happened?' he asked his neighbour at tea that day.

'Oh, I dunno. Ask Scott – he's interested in that kind of thing.'

Scott was a prefect, and so almost as unapproachable as the Headmaster himself. But, running to catch up with him on his way across the quad, Charlie plucked up all his courage.

'Please Sir, I read something about Dr Robertson and the Matterhorn. Can you tell me what actually happened?'

The older boy laughed. 'You don't have to call me Sir, you know. That's just the masters. Yes, I can tell you a bit about it. Mr Robertson's certainly quite a climber. Obviously you know Whymper finally got to the summit of the Matterhorn. Well, on the way down there was this terrible accident, and one of the Swiss guides and three English climbers fell down the mountain and were killed. There was a lot of talk about the rope being cut or something – I don't think they ever got to the bottom of that. Anyway, Whymper asked Robertson and a couple of others to climb up to find the bodies. Which they did. And Robertson had a hand in the wording on the Swiss guide's tombstone – he writes poetry, would you believe?'

Charlie would. From then on, he looked at his headmaster with new eyes.

THE YEAR WORE ON, and all went reasonably well. Charlie was neither particularly happy nor unhappy. Like most of the others, he was hungry most of the time and, like most of the others, he wasn't averse to grubbing up the odd potato in the field next door to add to the school's frugal meals.

However, he never quite dared go as far as some of the senior boys. Following a sixth-former into early chapel one morning, he was puzzled by his contour. A slender, fit games player, he seemed suddenly to have developed a curiously bulgy outline. Charlie nudged the young boy beside him and pointed, eyebrows raised.

'Tell you later,' whispered the boy, and in they went. On the way out, his companion pushed him away from the crowd and gave him the explanation.

'A gang of them sometimes set rabbit traps overnight and have a feast the next day. I reckon Jones overslept, and that he's got a brace of bunnies in those huge poachers' pockets he's sewn into his jacket. Lucky it's black is all I can say.'

THE SUMMER TERM was finally nearing its end and all minds turned to home. But at Assembly just a week before, Dr Robertson strode on to the platform looking unusually grim.

'Got out of bed the wrong side this morning,' whispered Charlie's neighbour.

But there was more to it than that.

'I have news for you this morning, boys, which gives me great pain, though I daresay will please some of you.' He forced a smile. 'After this week, we will not meet again, for I shall not be coming back next year. I have offered the school governors my resignation and they have accepted it. I am not going to make a speech, nor am I prepared to discuss the reason for my decision, though some of you older ones will I think have guessed. As usual, I shall be available over the next few days to talk to any of you who wish to come to my study. Please make appointments in the usual way.

'We will now sing hymn number 203.'

And that was that.

WHEN CHARLIE GOT HOME, he asked his father if he knew why Dr Robertson was leaving. No-one at school seemed able to tell him. The boys' parents had all received letters giving the explanation, so the farmer was able to enlighten his son.

'It was all in *The Times* a couple of years ago. Dr Robertson expelled a boy called Hutt for suspected pilfering and his parson father sued the school governors. At the trial, the boy put up such a good performance that the judge ruled that there was insufficient evidence to convict him, though reading between the lines it seemed almost certain that he had really done it. He left, of course, but the whole thing had done a lot of damage to the school, and numbers were going down badly. That's why your brave headmaster has decided it's only fair to the school to resign and let somebody else pick up the pieces. I'm very sorry.'

'And so am I,' thought Charlie. 'He was a bit gruff, but I liked him. He was all right.'

16

WHEN HE HEARD THAT HIS NEW headmaster's aunt was married to Mr Gladstone, Charlie thought it might all be all right. He rather liked the sound of Mr Gladstone. As far as he could make out, he'd had a go at being Prime Minister several times, but seemed to have to take it in turns with Mr Disraeli and now someone called Salisbury. But he might have another chance, at the next General Election. Perhaps Mrs Gladstone would help him. And perhaps her nephew was nice.

But right from the start his hopes were dashed. Charlie simply did not like him. The Reverend Canon the Honourable Edward Lyttleton was the perfect *Boys Own Paper* choice. He was young, handsome, go-ahead and, above all, a keen sportsman. In his Cambridge days, he had played for the university and had bowled out the famous W. G. Grace twice, as well as making a century for his own team.

The brother of this paragon was a national sporting hero and Charlie's friends were deeply shocked at his ignorance.

'He played football for England – everybody knows that. And he won the Royal Tennis Trophy no end of times.'

'So does he play your famous cricket as well?'

Heads shook in disbelief.

'He's only the best all-rounder there is, that's all. Wicket-keeping, bowling, batting – you name it, he can beat anybody at all of them.'

What a brother. No wonder the boys thought the world of him, of both of them. No wonder the school numbers went up by leaps and bounds.

The new school year started well, especially as, now Charlie had gone up a form, he no longer had to fag for 'his' three prefects. Actually, they had been rather nice to him, this quaint little new gov who treated them all as if they were gods, made toast like a Trojan, and ran every errand under the sun without a word of complaint. But not having to do all that did give Charlie more time to himself.

The first thing that happened was the posting of a new school rule on the noticeboard.

'From now on, each boy will take a cold bath every day. This, whilst inculcating a spirit of self-discipline, will teach manliness and fortitude under conditions of hardship.' By Order of the Headmaster.

Not many days later, Charlie was nearly knocked over by one of his friends whose nose was buried in a letter.

'Mind out you twerp. Can't you look where you're go...?'

But the other was not listening.

'I say,' he burst out; 'my governor has just heard from Lyttleton that they're not to send any more food hampers, as too much grub makes us soft. I shall die from starvation, and then perhaps he'll be sorry.'

Charlie never got food parcels anyway. At Bures, they would have been considered an unnecessary luxury and he had never asked for them. But sometimes others were generous. This was not good news.

Gradually, as time went by, other things became apparent. Clearly games, particularly cricket, were billed to play a much larger part in the life of the school. By the time the summer term came round, cricket mania was taking over. And cricket was Charlie's anathema. He simply could not do it, any of it. He couldn't hit the ball, he couldn't throw the ball, he couldn't stop it even if it almost ran into him.

Provision for such boys was, reluctantly, made. Regularly at first, he would be approached by the captain of cricket or one of his team;

'Are you going to play for the next month, Garrad?'

His inevitable stuttered 'n-no, thank you, Smith,' or Jones or Robinson would be received with increasingly ill-concealed scorn, until at last they stopped asking him altogether, and he was clearly consigned to the outer circle of the totally disgraced.

Then problems began to creep into his work, hitherto his lifeline. A rumour was going round the classics department that Dr Lyttleton wanted to enlarge the school curriculum at the expense of Latin and Greek, that he thought the classics had little to offer. 'It sharpens their thinking – but gives them little to think about,' he was reputed to have written. Nothing came of it, but behind the scenes it had been a hard-won battle and had left its mark on the department.

That the masters and keenest students found this totally unacceptable does not need to be said, and lessons went on as before. But it was a depressing atmosphere in which to work and it took its toll on all of them.

HOLIDAYS CAME AND WENT. Each time Charlie went home, back to Brook House, to his father, his brothers and sisters and his dear friend Matt, it seemed to him that he loved it more. Everything and everybody welcomed him for what he was, not for what they thought he ought to be. It didn't matter that he couldn't play games, that he hadn't enough money to be generous with tuck bought at Grubbers, that he had few social graces. When he went back to school and heard about the grand holidays enjoyed by his rich friends, visiting their important relatives in their important houses, he felt no envy, none at all. None of them had a home like his. Of course, he still missed Mama, but even that loss was fading; sometimes he even had difficulty in picturing her face.

He supposed that, on balance, school was not so very terrible. Despite Dr Lyttleton's neglect of the classics, he was learning, learning, learning. To his surprise, he found that he was excelling in mathematics. Like Latin, it was immensely logical, and logic made sense. He liked things to make sense; that was the way his mind worked. And he liked to learn.

Two of the masters who taught him had been to Cambridge and encouraged him to try to gain a place there.

'You'd love it, Garrad,' they would say. 'It would be right up your street. No compulsory games, wonderful libraries with more books in them than you can imagine, fellow undergraduates who feel the same about things as you do. Plenty of time and space to think, write, learn, discuss – oh, you'd be in your element.'

One day one of them brought in some photographs to show him.

'Look, this is a picture of my college, Clare.' He took it to the window and held it close to his face. 'If you look carefully, you can just make out my window.' Pointing at a tiny spot, almost invisible on the dark grainy print, he added: 'My rooms looked over the main court, as you can see. I shared them with a chap called ...' And off he went.

But Charlie's mind was far away, floating above the River Cam. In his mind's eye he lay back on the cushions of a punt, his skilled and capable friend (he would have lots of friends) effortlessly guiding them along the river as it flowed behind the colleges. Then, casually, he would say 'my turn now,' and would steer the boat every bit as well, if not better, and ...

The harsh sound of the school bell nearly made him jump out of his skin.

❧

DAYDREAMING HARDENED INTO RESOLVE.

Charlie's father thought that, in principle, it was a good idea. But of course there were questions and one of his own answers took Charlie himself by surprise.

'What will come of all this studying?' he was asked. 'Of course your chosen subject will be classics, but what do you intend to do with your life?'

Charlie took a moment to answer, and then said slowly:

'Actually, I'm not sure about classics – theology might be better. You see, I might want to be a parson. You and Mama've always made sure we go to church, and lots of important people seem to have started off as parsons.' He smiled as he added, 'mind you, I can't exactly see myself at the moment rushing off to darkest Africa to convert the natives. But I might surprise myself.'

What he didn't say would have surprised his father even more.

It was his English master who had started it, a short plump man in a rather too tight sports jacket. On his very first night at Haileybury, Charlie had learnt an interesting piece of school lore about Mr Roland. His next-door neighbour at supper, a frighteningly superior person who was a whole year his senior, had given the awestruck new boy a thumbnail sketch of each master in turn.

'S'pose you came down from Mars and landed at our school, and the first person you met was Old Roly. How would you know without speaking what term it was?'

'I dunno. How would you?'

'Well, you'd just look at the buttons on that old jacket he always wears. Middle one latched in the autumn term, top two in the spring term, none in the summer. You mark my words.'

Charlie did. His informant was unfailingly right.

It had been in their first poetry lesson that it had happened. The boys had been playing marbles on the floor between their desks when, surprisingly light on his little feet, Old Roly came tripping into the room, his middle button straining dangerously at its moorings. He said nothing, wrote a title on the board, sat down at his desk and began to read out loud. The effect was both immediate and total. Stunned into silence by the deep sonorous voice, every boy crept, despite himself, to his own desk and listened spellbound as the compelling syllables unfurled.

THREE PASSAGES FROM THE POEM were given to the boys for prep that night. They were to learn them by heart, and it was there that Charlie kept them for the rest of his life.

I fled Him, down the night and down the days;
I fled Him, down the arches of the years;
I fled Him, down the labyrinthine ways
Of my own mind; and in the midst of tears
I hid from Him, and under running laughter.

But with unhurrying chase
And unperturbed pace
Deliberate speed, majestic instancy,
They beat – and a Voice beat
More instant than the Feet -
'All things betray thee who betrayest Me'.

For, though I knew His love Who followed,
Yet was I sore adread
Lest, having Him, I must have naught beside.

Charlie had found the poem terrifying. If only Mama had been alive, he would, he thought, have talked to her about it. But, much as he respected and loved his father, theirs was an altogether different relationship. So he hugged it close to his chest. Old Roly had planted an uncomfortable seed; he above all people would have been astonished at the fertile soil in which *The Hound of Heaven* had taken root. Francis Thompson's words had struck a rich seam, deep in the soul of this quiet child.

BUT CHARLIE'S FATHER KNEW NONE OF THIS. His was a practical interest; he had twelve children, one of them weak-minded and another slow to reach maturity; the rest must find their own way in the world. So when his son talked in an airy-fairy way about going to Cambridge, there was another all-important question to ask.

'There is of course the problem of money. Have you any ideas as to how you can help finance this dream of yours?'

Charlie had thought about that too.

'My Latin master thinks I should be able to get a scholarship. Of course it'll mean an awful lot of hard work, but he seems to think I could do it if I try. I have the two years of the sixth form to come, and that should give me time to work everything up to the necessary level.'

His father patted him on the shoulder.

'I'm very proud of you, you know, my boy,' he said, and, unbeknown to the blind father, his boy blushed.

17

Hertfordshire, England 1894

IT WAS HIS LAST YEAR, THE HAPPY culmination of a successful school career. As Charlie sat in the train, for the first time he actually looked forward to his arrival at Hertford station and the cab drive to the school, smiling to himself as he remembered the thunderstorm and his agony of apprehension five long years ago. Now he would be a prefect, he would have a study, and he could work in peace. Certainly, he would have to share the study with a couple of others, but there were very few fellows that he really couldn't get on with. He would keep a low profile; he was used to that. He would manage.

There were several new-govs in his carriage. Perhaps emboldened by his smile, the smallest of them, who looked no more than ten despite his thirteen years, turned to Charlie and said:

'Excuse me Sir, but how long will it take us to get there?'

Now he laughed out loud. He remembered the first time that he had addressed a prefect, how impossibly distant and grand that boy had seemed, and how he too had addressed him as 'Sir.' He remembered Scott's exact words in reply and repeated them to the little boy. 'You don't have to call me Sir, you know. That's just for masters.' The rest of the journey passed pleasantly enough, a question-and-answer session that grew more and more animated as the newcomers' shyness diminished and Charlie got into his stride.

Already conscious of his new authority and boosted by the unfamiliar admiration of his companions, he strode into school and straight to the notice board. The list of prefects had already been posted and, halfway down at the top of the Gs, he found his own name. So far, so good. Next to it was another notice, this time detailing the names of the boys' studies and, against each, its occupants for the coming year. And now Charlie's blood froze. There were only three senior boys in the whole school that he simply could not stand, and his own name was bracketed with two of them.

Looking back, the start of this year that should have been so great and glorious was one of the worst periods of Charlie's life. Up to now, he had learnt that by keeping his head down he could almost disappear. Wearing a cloak of what to most boys was dullness, priggishness even, he could be invisible. But to his horror, that time was over; his anonymity was at an end.

Of course he had known that prefects had responsibilities, that they must maintain discipline, ensure the keeping of school rules. The new-boys were no problem; he had already made firm allies with several on the train and they remained faithful, grateful perhaps for his kindness and lack of 'side.' Most of the rest of the school still tolerated him. It was a small gang of the older boys who became the bane of his life, teasing, mocking, tripping him up at every turn. Time and again he had to go to one or other housemaster to report insolence or downright disobedience. Canings and even floggings became more frequent as a result, and the vicious circle rotated ever faster. It was a bad time.

IN DESPAIR, HE WROTE A LETTER to his friend, Matt – he who had been his father's guide round the farm fields and had persuaded him that going away to school might be a blessing in disguise. His friend Matt, who had worked so hard at his own reading and writing and schooling, and knew so much now about so many things. As Charlie put pen to paper, he wondered for a moment about his friend's future. Matt had so many qualities. He deserved the very best.

> Dear Matt,
> I was pleased to hear from Father that he has promoted you to Cowman. You always were brilliant with animals, and Papa will probably have to invest in extra milk-churns as I am sure the yield will increase under your care.
> Well, at least the cows are happy, lucky things. I am sorry to say that I am not. In fact, far from it. I told you that I would probably be a prefect this term. Well, I am, but I am absolutely hopeless at it. No-one will do anything I say, and it's getting worse and worse. This wouldn't happen to you, I know; you're such a positive sort of fellow, and they would all like you. I am so miserable that when I went for a walk the other day and stood on the railway bridge as a train came under it, I thought what an easy way out it would be. Of course I wouldn't really do anything like that, and please please don't say anything to the family.

But you are my only real friend, so I am telling you and asking you what you think I should do. Please answer quickly.

Yr. Affectionate friend

Charlie

Dear Charlie.

What on earth are you thinking of. Youve nearly finished at that wretched school. Then you can do anything you like. Whats happened to that famous temper of yours. You could frighten them to death if you let fly, like you did to me once. Remember? I thought you were going to kill me. Who do they think they are anyways.

Matt

THE NEXT TIME CHARLIE WAS TAUNTED, he lost his rag. Perhaps it was Matt's advice; perhaps he was about to snap in any case. He happened to have in his hand a confiscated cricket bat, and the world watched in amazement as, with an astonishing turn of speed, he chased his tormentors down the corridor, flailing the bat and making eminently satisfactory contact every time. The thwacks and ensuing yells penetrated to the far reaches of the house, and with every corner negotiated the crowds grew, boys of all ages turning out through every door along the way.

At last, as the caravan crashed past the housemaster's room, a strong hand came out and caught hold of Charlie's coat-tails. He tried to wriggle out of the imprisoned jacket, but the fight was already going out of him, and he subsided suddenly on to the stone floor, panting and bleeding from a scraped hand.

'Garrad! What do you think you are doing?'

But the eyes that looked down on him were twinkling and, instead of the telling-off that he expected, he found himself being helped to his feet by a number of willing hands, dusted down, and offered a rather grubby handkerchief to stem the flow of blood.

'S-s-sorry Sir. I don't know what came over me.'

'I think you should come straight into my room so that we can sort out this disgraceful behaviour at once' came the reply, and prefect and housemaster disappeared behind closed doors.

The crowds waited, agog. What would happen? Would Garrad be expelled on the spot? Good for him. Didn't know he had it in him. Whatever will the gang do to him now? Maybe we should look out for him ...

There was not long to wait. He emerged, red in the face but smiling. The door closed behind him. He stalked off to his study. No more was said.

OF COURSE, THAT WAS NOT THE END OF IT. 'The gang' continued to taunt him, but in a more circumspect manner. The two other prefects in his study went on trying by all sorts of cowardly and insidious means to make his life as miserable as they could. But even they gradually grew tired of it and began to leave him well alone. The younger boys, especially those from the train, eyed him with awe. Life for Charlie was definitely looking up.

༈

UNTIL THAT HOT JUNE NIGHT. The school clock had struck twelve times, but still the air outside seemed solidified by the heat. Not a breath trickled through the window into the gas-lit oven that was Charlie's study.

The owl on her usual perch outside waited impatiently, encased in the stillness. That single square of light affected her night vision and her chicks were hungry. The only movement came from the figure inside as he turned the pages of his book.

The unexpected noise startled her, and as Charlie suddenly flung his Latin Grammar across the room, he saw the great white shape swoop past his window. He knew her habits, as she knew his. He knew where her nest was, and many times he had watched her as she flew with a mouse or small bird in her great claws to feed her growing babies. But their friendship was soon to end, for in three days' time he would sit the Cambridge scholarship and the endless period of studying would be over. Nights would at last be for sleep once more.

But on this particular night he was at the end of his tether. He knew nothing, nothing at all, and there were only three days left. It was hopeless. He laid his weary head on his desk and abandoned himself to despair.

There was a patter of huge claws on the wooden floor. The panting grew louder by the moment and hot breaths seared the hairs on the back of his neck. He tried to raise his head but it was glued to the table; he tried to run, but his feet were frozen to the floor. And all the time the sound of those great snapping jaws grew closer and closer; sharp teeth nipped his ankles and he was surely done for.

It didn't seem the least bit surprising that Old Roly was there, middle button straining, reading aloud from his poetry book. Charlie had to listen hard to make out his words above the din. And then – of course!

It was the Hound of Heaven, and it had him by the heels.

WHEN HE AWOKE, dawn was filling the little room with coolness and a gentle light. The frustrations and fears of last evening had evaporated with the darkness. He felt confident and calm.

Then he remembered. The Hound of Heaven. It had been a dream, of course, a nightmare. It meant nothing, nothing at all, except that he'd been overworking, and he tried to banish it from his mind.

But it would not go, and part of him was glad. Something inside him seemed to have snapped, some resistance broken, a conflict resolved. But as the dream faded, shreds of doubt still niggled in his mind. One line in the poem went round and round in his head; 'lest, having Him, I must have naught beside.' He, Charlie, had so much beside. Must he really give it all up? Must he go into the Church?

Final exams came and went. In mathematics, Charlie finished third, and won the overall school maths prize. In classics too he did well but, in his private view, not well enough. He couldn't help feeling that he should have come top, that he would have come top, if only he had been good at cricket.

But none of that was important. He had achieved his heart's desire and won a scholarship to Clare College, Cambridge.

'WHAT SUBJECT WILL YOU READ?'

The question seemed to be on the tip of the whole world's tongue and he could put off his choice no longer. He would read theology. After all, it didn't necessarily mean that he would become a parson, did it? There were all sorts of other ways he could earn a living with a good degree in his pocket. He could teach, he could do research; the possibilities were surely endless. No final decision had been taken.

Or had it?

Bootalet, Burma, 1894

The wind got up so suddenly that it could only mean one thing. In a few seconds, the great black clouds that seemed almost to be sitting on the ruffled tree-tops would burst like over-ripe figs and spill out on top of them. All that water must be so heavy and Pyau almost felt sorry for the clouds, until that marvellous moment of release. It was like a long, cold, delicious drink and a dive into a deep cool pool, all in one. He took his little brother's hands and the pair of them whirled round and round, faster and faster, until boys and water were a blur of spinning, splashing wetness.

They were late for school. The three-mile walk from Bootalet to the next village had taken longer today, and the pagoda was steaming like a pan of rice from wet longyis and sodden saffron robes when they finally crept in. But nobody minded; it was a day of rejoicing for all living creatures, for the dry season was over at last and the rains had begun.

PART FOUR

.

18

Chevely, England 1895

THE REVEREND EVELYN DOUGLAS, recently returned from the visit to his sister Annie in Knutsford, could be a man of few words, but even for him this one-letter sentence was unusually brief. His sister Beatrice, in the act of sinking into a comfy chair in the Rectory drawing-room, was in dire need of a cup of tea. She had just got in from a duty call on one of her brother's sick parishioners in the little Cambridgeshire town of Chevely, and she was tired. But there are many ways of enunciating 'B' and she recognised at once that this time she must pay attention.

'B,' he had said again. 'I have something to ask you. It is a huge thing, and I want you to think about the implications of it before you answer.'

The somewhat stout woman took out her hatpin and removed her hat.

'Yes, brother,' she said, as she gently eased large and awkward feet from their restraining lace-up boots. 'Ask your question, and I promise I won't reply until I'm sure of the answer.' She was used to acting as sounding-board for her unmarried brother's thoughts, but here, she felt, was something out of the ordinary and a premonition sent a barely perceptible quiver through her ample frame.

'You know I've just been to visit our sister Annie.' He paused. She waited. 'And you know that we have four – no, three, now Heather's gone – three little nieces and one nephew, all living with Annie in a tiny house and without money or any male guidance.'

Now B realized exactly what was coming, and she did not want to hear it. She had watched Evie struggling with his conscience over the last few days, for she knew her dear brother very well indeed. After all, they had lived here together for several years, and even as children had been very close. She understood perfectly what he had been thinking, for she had thought the same herself. She knew that neither of them wanted this, but equally that, without question, they would do it.

To spare him further difficulty, she finished his little speech for him.

'So you want them to come and live with us in this big old house, which of course should be full of children and noise and muddle instead of just two fuddy-duddies like us, and turn our lives inside out and help us all to live happily ever after.'

Evie looked at her affectionately, but without surprise.

'What an amazing woman you are. Yes, that's exactly what I was going to suggest, but only suggest, because you must have time to think about it. If you have any hesitation at all, we'll leave them where they are. After all, they have our mother and father nearby, and they will undoubtedly manage somehow.'

'Evelyn Douglas, you're a goose. Of course we must have them, if you think that's best and that you can cope with them with all your parish work as well. And don't forget the doctors say you mustn't take on too much, with your weak heart.'

And that was that. The letter was written and, with her own heart in her mouth, B posted it in the pillar box just around the corner. There was no question in her mind as to what the answer would be.

Nor was there any question in any of their minds when Annie finally managed to master herself sufficiently to tell the children what was in the letter. To her, it had not come as a complete surprise. Her brother Evie had asked some guarded questions while staying with them which had made her wonder, though she had tried her best to push such thoughts aside.

But to the children, it was a miracle. Up went the cry every bed-time for the next week 'Mama, Mama, tell us a story about Uncle Evie,' or Aunt B, or the big old rectory where they were to live.

And Annie would have to rack her brains and launch forth into what was, to her too, largely unknown territory.

'Once upon a time, when our Queen Victoria was young and pretty instead of old and fat like she is now, there was a great big house out in the country, its red brick all shining and new. At the bottom of the long drive were tall iron gates, with a man to open them when you tugged the bell-pull. There were ...'

'But who lived in the house, Mama?'

'In it lived a clergyman, like your father and your Uncle Evie. Except that this one was fat, with lots of money and lots of children.'

'How many? Were they boys or girls? Where did they all sleep?'

And so it went on, until the avid listeners had learnt that there were bedrooms galore, huge half-empty attics to play in, and cellars full of cobwebs and spiders and ghostly racks for the hundreds of dusty bottles from which the portly clergyman had entertained his friends; that there was a large garden where you were actually allowed to play cricket and football, with room to spare; in short, that there was everything that any self-respecting person of whatever age could possibly desire.

'Does the fat parson still live there?'

'No, he got old and went away, so Uncle Evie moved in to be the rector of the parish.'

Every story ended the same way.

'And what's best of all, Mama?'

'And best of all is that soon we shall all be there. Uncle Evie will be like Papa, and dear Aunt B, who everyone says is so kind, will look after us.'

Though doubtless her stories were exaggerated, the gist of them was true. Here at last was space, space to grow, to play, to read, to think. It was indeed a miracle. Surely from now on life would be perfect for all of them.

SO BEGAN A PERIOD OF CALM in the Rawson family's tempestuous life. It was almost like old times, for suddenly the children found that they were once again moving in clerical circles, but – dare they say or even think it? – in a rather lighter mode than before. Mama's brother was good fun; for a parson, that is. Even church was an improvement. There were actually jokes in the sermon that you were allowed to laugh at out loud. Uncle Evie didn't seem to mind if you wriggled a bit or dropped your prayer-book by mistake. The children knew all the hymns and sang along with the choir at the top of their voices, and were delighted when heads turned to smile at them as word of the new family arrangements got round.

But it wasn't just church. Their uncle had evidently been a great hero in his Eton days. He was very reticent about his achievements there, but dear, proud Aunt B was only too ready to tell them of his successes. He had been Senior Keeper of the football field, which seemed to mean he had captained the school team. He had excelled himself at cricket, and had been Master of the school beagles pack.

'So you can see he was a great swell there,' Aunt B told them. 'And then he went on to Oxford. But that was rather a sad time because the college doctor discovered he had a bad heart, and stopped all his sport. But they couldn't stop his studies, or his kindnesses to other people. And they couldn't stop his lovely laugh.'

THE EXPERIMENT WORKED OUT better than anyone had dared hope. The brother and his two sisters knew each other well enough to walk away from conflict most of the time. The children, with enough food and space, and suddenly almost too much tender loving care, were each developing his or her own life, able at last to concentrate on the serious and self-centred business of growing up.

Marjory, Agatha and Edward were happy; Josephine was not. She was not 'sporty', like the others. She felt suffocated by the kindness and goodness that seemed to smother her. 'If I have to play one more game of cricket on the lawn, I shall die,' or kill myself, or run away, according to mood; Marjory grew more than tired of her endless complaints. 'I just don't understand you, Jo,' she would say, and would turn her back and talk to Agatha instead. Agatha, despite her place as the youngest of the girls, was definitely emerging as the sportsman of the family, and an ever increasing amount of time was spent in searching for lost balls – 'boundaries' – whacked into the bushes by the miniscule budding cricketer.

Josephine was the only one who really remembered her father, and she missed him more rather than less as time went by. One day, in despair, she turned to her uncle. Warned never to disturb him when he was in his study, she nevertheless plucked up her courage and, secure in the knowledge that Mama and Aunt B were out in the village, tapped on the forbidden door.

Accepting the invitation to 'come in,' she sat herself down on the edge of one of the hard upright chairs ranged against the wall. Her uncle turned towards her. With the usual twinkle in his eye, and extending to her the courtesy he would have shown to any one of his parishioners, he asked what he could do for her. Truth to tell, he was a little frightened of his sister's oldest child, with her moods and her sulks and her approaching adolescence.

Josephine suddenly wondered why she was there. She wanted to say to him:

'I wish you could treat me as my father did. I wish I could come in here whenever I liked and read your difficult books, and discuss the difficult things they talk about. I wish you would treat me as an adult, not just one of your sister's children. I wish I could learn from you, as I did from Papa – I wish my father had not died ...'

In fact she said none of these things; if only she had matters might have turned out differently. But she could not; neither could her uncle, for all his perceptiveness, penetrate the depths of her mind.

Because she was unable to voice her real thoughts, she said nothing, nothing at all, and just sat and looked at him, the tears starting to prick. Alarmed and taken by surprise, her uncle too was momentarily struck dumb. Clearly the child was troubled; how could he reach her?

He tried to take her hand, but she hated to be touched and pulled it roughly away. Leaping suddenly to her feet, she rushed from the room and, leaving the door wide open behind her, tore up the stairs two at a time to the sanctuary of her own bedroom. This door was hers to bang and, once inside, she threw herself face down on the flowery eiderdown and filled the room with sobbing.

Evie was deeply troubled. Up to the present, things had gone so well and now, suddenly, everything seemed to have turned sour. When his two sisters came back from the village, he asked them straight into the study and told them what had happened. Annie was flustered and full of apology. Beatrice, angry at first, soon realised there was something deeply amiss with Josephine.

'We must try again to talk to her.' she said, 'but I think it would be best to leave it to tomorrow.'

Tomorrow came, but Josephine, now outwardly fully composed and back to her slightly scornful self, would not be budged. She was sorry, she said, to have disturbed her uncle when he was working, but no, there was after all nothing that she wanted to say. Yes, she was quite happy, and no, there was nothing wrong.

And back she went upstairs, head held high and more unapproachable than ever.

19

JOSEPHINE MUST GO AWAY to boarding-school. They all thought so, including Josephine herself.

'Anything would be better than staying here,' she confided to Marjory in one of her more mellow moods. 'You all seem so happy, but I can't stand everyone being good all the time. I simply can't breathe – I must get away and be my own person,' and she was sensible enough to see that, for the moment, boarding-school was the only option. A suitable school was duly selected and off she went.

After she had gone, there was a unanimous sigh of relief at the rectory and the next couple of years passed peacefully enough. There were school holidays, of course, but they seemed to go by without too much disruption. Josephine's reports were full of praise for her academic ability and of blame for her disruptive behaviour, but on the whole the good seemed to outweigh the bad.

The only small disappointment was Edward.

'He's a nice enough little fellow.' Evie was snatching a rare opportunity to talk to B alone.

'I know he's only six, but so far it doesn't seem very likely that he will be the brilliant brain his father had hoped for. And he's more likely to fall over the ball than kick it.'

'Give the poor boy a chance!' But secretly Beatrice agreed. He had none of the spark that made his sisters so special – and so difficult. They must just wait and see.

༄

NOW THE MOMENT HAD COME for Marjory to join her sister at boarding-school; there was to be no discrimination between the girls. So her trunk was packed with her new school uniform and off she went. This time there were a great many tears for, unlike Josephine, she loved her home. But an unexpected adventurousness was sprouting in Marjory's budding bosom that came as a surprise even to herself, one that would eventually lead her along unimaginable pathways. Now, it simply meant that, despite the terror that Jo's school stories had instilled in her, it was excitement that was her overwhelming emotion. She was amazed to find that she really wanted to go.

It wasn't so very exciting after all; apart from Josephine. Jo was constantly in trouble, and Marjory constantly suffered as a result. As the sister of the Bad Girl of the School, she was unable just to merge into the background as she would have wished. She was a good scholar and worked hard, but she never shone as Jo did; when she put her mind to it. The comparisons were constant and unrelenting; good or bad, they were the background against which the two children alternately limped and sprinted up the school in an everlasting obstacle race of Jo's making.

It was the school performance of *Twelfth Night* that was the beginning of the end for the older girl. Dressed as Cesario, her heartfelt rendering on her master Orsino's behalf of the romantic ...

Make me a willow cabin at your gate,
And call upon my soul within the house;
Write loyal cantons of contemned love
And sing them loud even in the dead of night ...

took the collective breath away. There had never in all the annals of the school been a performance like it. She was a tall, good-looking girl, with already a following of younger girls who thought they had a crush on her. In her man's clothing, she was too much for them, and after each of the three performances she was mobbed by an adoring crowd of children.

There and then she made up her mind. She would be an actress, and she would be famous. This was the life for her. None other would do.

On the way home for the holidays, Marjory did her best to dissuade her.

'Jo, you can't, you simply can't. It's the worst thing you could possibly do to Mama, and to Uncle Evie and Aunt B, too. Don't you remember that talk we had at school about a charity for Fallen Women? I'm still not exactly sure what they do, but I know it's something terrible, and I'm sure Mama will think that going on the stage means being one of them. It'll kill her.'

'Honestly Marjie, d'you really mean to tell me that you don't know what fallen women get up to? You really are completely pathetic.'

'Well, what do they? You tell me.'

'They go with men, of course.'

'Go where with men? I wish to goodness someone would tell me what exactly happens. Bet you don't really know.'

'Bet you I do, but I'm not telling you. You're too young and innocent, my dear little sister.'

And with that Marjory had to be content.

NOTHING HAPPENED until the end of the holidays, when Josephine finally plucked up courage to confront her mother, her aunt and her uncle with her decision. The row was even worse than the two girls had anticipated. Marjory was banned from the room, but even through the thick oak door she could hear the storms of weeping, the raised voices, the long spells of murmurings. The four of them remained incarcerated together for the entire morning. Lunch was eaten in total silence, apart from whimpering from Edward, still too young to pretend.

It wasn't until they were in the train going back to school that Marjory had the chance to ask Jo what had happened. Sitting side by side in the corner of the carriage, the clatter of the wheels on the track covering their conversation, Marjory dared to ask her question.

'What did they say?'

'They all took it in turns to say everything and anything to try and make me change my mind. Mama even said she'd disown me if I did. But I don't care. I've made up my mind. I'm going on the stage. And when I'm famous and people are paying pounds and pounds to come and see me act, then they'll be sorry. You'll see'.

What Marjory saw at that moment was her own sister, so like herself in many ways, a sister whom she loved and who was about to make a mistake big enough to spoil her entire life. And there was nothing she could do to stop her.

Each of the girls had her own pigeon-hole, arranged in alphabetical order, where their letters were placed every morning. As the term went by, Marjory couldn't help noticing that Jo's box next her own was filling more quickly. She got into the habit of having a quick glance at the envelopes when no-one was looking, and was puzzled to see from the post-marks that they were coming from all corners of the country, and that most were in different and unknown handwriting.

So now what was happening? There was only one way to find out.

'Who are you getting all those funny letters from, Jo?'

Even for Jo, the reply was unusually angry.

'I'd thank you to mind your own business, and not to poke your nose and your horrid little hands into my private affairs.'

So that was that. Until that memorable morning, the day that Marjory found a letter in her own box addressed to her in her sister's handwriting.

July 2nd 1903

Dear sister,

I have run away. I have got a part in a play with a repertory company in the north of England. It is a good part, and I shall be paid enough for me to live on until I find something even better. I have saved up the money for my train fare and shall be well on my way by the time you receive this, so do not try to find me. I am, after all, seventeen years old, and am perfectly capable of looking after myself. I simply cannot face going back to Chevely, ever again.

I will write to you again, to tell you how I am getting on.

REPEAT. Do not try to find me.

You are the best of the bunch, Marjie, and I shall miss you.

Your loving sister

Jo.

20

Everything had started so well. The other occupant of her study-bedroom was a deep sleeper and for once Jo was grateful for her snoring. The two separate flights of creaky stairs were easy to negotiate, once you knew that you must keep close to the wall. It had been a simple matter to climb out of a downstairs window, the one with the broken lock. The walk in the dark to the station had been the worst part, but Jo had chosen a night when she knew the moon would be almost full, and although it was cloudy she had no difficulty in finding her way along the country lanes. She kept to the middle, avoiding the dense darkness at the foot of the high hedges on either side.

The station seemed so different, a ghostly parody of its daytime workaday self. There was no sound, no sign of any activity. She had never imagined it like this. Of course she was very early; there was nearly an hour to wait for the milk train, and for safety's sake she stayed out in the station yard, keeping well into the shadows. Wisps of the early morning mist that was gathering over the flat landscape moved silently about her, spectral shapes wafted hither and thither by the breeze that often comes at dawn. Jo thought longingly of her cosy, warm bed; there was plenty of time to get back to school before anyone would be any the wiser.

But all of a sudden such feeble thoughts were banished by the cheerful sound of clanking milk-churns as one after the other the local farmers drove their carts up the rough lane and unloaded on to the single platform.

'Morning Bill.'

'Morning Fred. Looks like it'll be a warm one.'

Her fears dispelled together with the silence, Jo put her mind to her next task. Buying her ticket.

It wasn't long before she could just make out the arrival on a bicycle of a portly gentleman in a peaked cap. He disappeared into the station building, and in a few moments a gradually increasing light appeared in one of the windows. In her mind's eye, Jo could see the oil-lamp's glass chimney being replaced and the wick turned up. There was still a quarter of an hour before the train was due, but supposing it was early? Supposing the timetable had been changed? Supposing...?

This was the moment she had been dreading. The stationmaster or whoever he was might guess her guilty secret; he might refuse to sell her a ticket. But she must try.

Gathering up all her reserves, the tall young woman strode confidently into the room where she had seen the light.

'I should like to buy a ticket to Scunthorpe, please.'

The official didn't seem to show any particular surprise. Jo felt better.

'Would that be a single or return, Miss?' was all he said.

'A single, please.'

That seemed to bring him up short and Jo's heart missed a beat. Looking at her more attentively, he saw an attractive girl, about the age of his Lizzie. She definitely wasn't from around here; he knew all Lizzie's friends, at least by sight, and she spoke like the vicar's wife. So where had she sprung from, in the middle of the night like, and why wasn't she coming back?

'I was that puzzled, I can tell you.' He was enjoying his moment of glory in the Fox and Goose that night. 'But she knew where she wanted to go and she 'ad the money to pay 'er fare, so I didn't reckon I 'ad the right to stop 'er. So she got 'er ticket and some instructions about 'ow she 'ad to change twice, and off she went on to the platform. Soon after, George arrived, and 'e went out and took a good look at 'er as she walked up and down the platform.

'Then the train came in and she got on it, cool as a cucumber like, and off she went. That was when George sent young Will off to the school.'

As the train pulled out of the station, Jo had breathed a huge sigh of relief. But could she really have got away with it? She hadn't liked the way that man had looked at her when she bought her ticket. And then, when the other one had arrived and stared at her as she waited for the train, she had feared the worst. But nothing had happened; surely they couldn't stop her now?

She achieved the two changes, and got ready to alight at her final destination. She pulled down her small suitcase from the rack and, as the train puffed its way through the suburbs of Scunthorpe, struggled with the thick leather strap that would release the window-glass. With her head out of the window, she watched the approach of the platform ahead with its sprinkling of would-be passengers and of friends waiting to greet arrivals. Alas, there would be no-one looking for her. She had the address of her lodgings on a scrap of paper in her pocket, and though she knew it off by heart, backwards and forwards, she took it out once more.

As the train squealed to a halt she leaned out again and turned the heavy handle. The door swung open, almost hitting a uniformed policeman.

'I'm so sorry ...' But it is doubtful that he even heard her, for her words were drowned by his own.

'Miss Josephine Rawson?' She nodded a speechless 'yes.'

'I have orders to arrest you as an escaped minor.'

POOR JO. IT HAD NOT TAKEN them long to find her.

The headmistress had come to the railway-station in person, with the Latin master and Josephine's housemistress in support.

The stationmaster had ushered them into his bleak little office.

'I ain't usually 'ere for the milk-train,' he had said, taking off his cap to scratch his bald head and putting it on again. 'Today, though, I particularly needs to speak to the driver, so I gets up early and comes in. And there she is, all by 'erself, walking up and down the platform, up and down, ever so worried-looking. My Ticket Officer 'ere said as 'ow she fumbled the ticket money, and got ever so flustered when 'e told 'er she'd 'ave to change trains twice. There was only one place round 'ere she could've come from, a posh young lady and all alone, and that's why I took the liberty of sending young William to the school.'

Young William had run all the way. Even so, it had taken him so long to wake anyone up that it was nearly half past five before he had heard the squeak of the bolts sliding back and the door had flown open.

'Whatever is the matter?' Two teachers – 'that young pretty one, and the old 'ag with the glasses, both of 'em in their night clothes,' he had said to his friend later – stood looking at him.

'Has there been an accident? Is there a fire? What ...'

'No, miss. But there's one of them young ladies 'as just caught the early train from our station, and Reg – that's the stationmaster – reckons as 'ow she comes from 'ere.'

'Good gracious! Whoever ...?' The two women looked at each other. By now, a strange assortment of sleepy figures was gathering on the doorstep; shawls, dressing-gowns, overcoats, even a bath-towel, had been hastily thrown over a variety of night garments. 'A rum looking lot, I can tell you,' Will was later to tell his friend.

The headmistress arrived, decorously clad in full daytime attire. After surely the strangest staff meeting ever held, there and then and to the music of a dawn chorus so deafening that the discussion was almost, but not quite, lost to the open-mouthed Will, a plan was rapidly made and equally rapidly put into action. The motley crowd dispersed; each girl was to get back into her own bed, while the staff would come round and search until the empty bed revealed the identity of the missing girl.

Marjory had been desperately looking round the crowd for her sister, and an awful possibility dawned. No-one seemed to have seen Jo. The possibility hardened into probability, and then, horror of horrors, into near certainty.

There was not long to wait.

It was Josephine Rawson's bed that was found empty. By six o'clock, the emergency committee were at the station. By a quarter past, the telegram had been despatched on the railway telegraph to Jo's destination. And at ten-twenty-seven, Jo found herself a prisoner in the ladies waiting room at Scunthorpe station, a railway porter at the door, miserably awaiting events.

JO COULD NOT BELIEVE HER misfortune. At first she blamed her sister.

'The little sneak.' She thought of the letter she had left in Marjory's pigeon-hole, of the trust she had shown her in writing it. And now Marjory had betrayed her. But, sitting there, a prisoner, her mind went over and over the events of the last few hours. There would not have been time for Marjie to have found the letter; it could not be her little sister that was to blame.

After half a day's wait for an escort in that smutty, dirty waiting-room, with its hard shiny seats and the taste and smell of fumes from the huge steaming monsters that shunted endlessly up and down outside the open door, a great many things seemed to happen in quick succession. The journey back to school with the Latin master as prison warder was a mere prelude to a torrent of blame. Interviews with the headmistress, the housemistress, the school chaplain and, finally, with Annie and Uncle Evie, followed one another in quick succession. No-one seemed to think she might be hungry or tired. Her disgrace was total, made worse by her seeming indifference and lack of any sign of shame or remorse.

Forced to stand throughout, it was only when she started to sway and nearly fell that the barrage ceased and she was allowed, still without food or drink, to go to bed.

JOSEPHINE WAS KEPT ON at the school for a final year. With privileges removed and fellow pupils increasingly unable to find common ground with her in her self-inflicted state of frigid isolation, it must have been a time of total wretchedness for this gifted, wayward young woman. But the summer of 1904, when she finally achieved the age of eighteen, did arrive at last, and Jo was able to leave school.

'JO WON'T STAY AT HOME FOR LONG.'

This was the combined opinion of Marjory, Agatha and Edward. Since her abortive attempt at escape, their eldest sister had been a constant shadow over the family home, particularly in the holidays. Whatever was going to happen when she came home for good?

'I don't think she's changed her mind at all.' Marjory and Agatha were hitting a tennis ball against the stable wall. 'I know she still wants to go on the stage, and I think she will, whatever Mama and Uncle Evie say.'

Marjory was the only one now who had any real contact with the older girl. Adults and children alike, it was she to whom they turned for help with Jo. The whole family knew that Marjory was of the opinion that Jo would go her own way, despite fervent advice to the contrary. All of them tried to push the uncomfortable suspicion to the backs of their minds, tried to pretend that, despite everything, all was reasonably well. But the atmosphere was tense, and it came almost as a relief when, a few weeks after Joe had walked out of the school gates for the last time, the storm finally broke.

At the end of dinner, as chair legs started to scrape on the dining-room's wooden floor, Jo hurried to the door and stood with her back against it.

'I've got something to say.' Her voice was tense, her hands clenched by her sides.

There was a pause, a moment of total silence, an interruption in the flow of time. Six pairs of lungs suspended their pumping; six hearts accelerated.

Then just seven simple momentous words.

'I shall be leaving home tomorrow morning.'

Annie was the first to collect herself.

'What on earth ...?'

Aunt B and Uncle Evie spoke together.

'What do you mean, child?'

'Where do you intend to go?'

'Don't be such an idiot!' snapped Agatha.

Fortunately for him, the muttered 'golly, wish I could' from Edward was buried in the general hubbub, for everyone was speaking at once.

Marjory, pushing her chair right over in her haste, rushed to her sister and threw her arms around her. But Josephine pushed her roughly aside.

'No-one will be surprised to hear that I've had no change of heart about going on the stage. I didn't want you all to know about the letters I've been getting about jobs, so I made an arrangement with the post-office and they've been keeping them for me. A few days ago, I heard I'd been offered a small part with a repertory company in York. It's not much, but it's a start. They say that they can easily find me cheap lodgings, so I see no point in hanging around waiting. Legally, I suppose you can try and stop me. But you'll fail. I've made up my mind, and whatever you do I shall keep running away until I succeed. If you really want to lose touch altogether, that's the way to go about it. My way, I'll write from time to time.'

Her face suddenly crumpled, and tears came.

'I'm sorry I've been such a disappointment – I'm just not like the rest of you,' And she fled from the room.

21

AND THEN THERE WERE THREE. Though this new loss affected each of them differently, nothing was ever quite the same again

Agatha had been jealous of her eldest sister, of her own relegation as she saw it to an inferior school, perhaps of a disproportionate share of their father's affection. In fact, she did not like Josephine very much.

Edward found her all right. He didn't really have much to do with her. After all, with only ten years behind him, his sister wasn't far short of double his age. On the whole he was sorry she'd gone.

Marjory was the most complex of the three. Her initial reaction was one of despair for her sister, but she could find no-one who would explain exactly what was so disastrous about 'going on the stage.' After all, was the school not going the very next term to see *A Midsummer Night's Dream*, presumably performed on exactly the same sort of stage that Jo was heading for. There was clearly more to this than met the eye, and in the end it was Aunt B who came closest to a feasible explanation.

'You see, dear, there's acting and acting. Shakespeare's all very fine and good, but there's some that is quite the opposite. There's Music Hall, where the men drink beer and they all make jokes that are, well, impolite, to put it mildly. Then in some theatres they actually have dancing ...'

'But what's wrong with that, Auntie? At school we get taught about ballet in our form music lessons, with famous composers writing the tunes. They're not bad men, surely?'

'No, of course not, dear. But there's much worse kinds of dancing, or so I've heard, where the ladies all get in rows and kick up their legs high in the air...'

The two women, young and old, lapsed into silence as they contemplated this heinous possibility. Why, if you kicked up your legs, your bloomers showed. Marjory knew this from personal experience. And to do it in public, along with a whole line of other girls and in front of an audience, too – well, that was almost past imagining. She just could not begin to believe that Josephine, her own sister, would do such a thing.

She felt at last that she was beginning to get nearer the truth. But a suspicion lingered that there was more, and that it had something to do with men. Now Aunt B was not married. She did not have a man of her own, unless you meant her brother, and Marjory had a shrewd suspicion that in this particular respect Uncle Evie didn't really count. So how was she to find out more?

The only person who was married and that she should have been able to talk to was, of course, her mother. Somehow, though, this seemed impossibly difficult; impossible, that is, until she woke one morning and knew that she was dying. True, the acquaintance at school who had been struck down with consumption had coughed up the blood and hers was coming from the other end, but she was certain that it all came to the same thing. She was destined for an early demise, and she was scared out of her wits.

'Mama, mama! There's something awful happening!'

It was early in the morning, and she had rushed screaming to her mother's bedroom.

Annie, half asleep, had thrown back the covers and leapt out of bed.

'Whatever's the matter?' Were there burglars? Was the house on fire?

'I think I'm dying, Mama.' The terrified girl showed her mother the crimson stains on her nightdress. To her utter disgust, after a single glance her mother actually laughed. And, at first, 'you silly goose!' was all she said.

Then came the comfort, the surprise, and finally some sort of explanation.

'Surely you know what happens to you when you reach your age? Josephine must have told you, or one of your friends at school.' But Josephine had not told her; since coming to live here, each had had her own room, and Jo was not one to encourage confidences. At school, certainly, there had been whispers among her friends. But Marjorie was small for her age and, as some of them became positively buxom, she remained stubbornly flat-chested. She thought she had heard the strange word 'monthlies,' but she was shy and afraid to ask.

So now it was her mother who told her that every month from now on this awful thing would happen to her, and would go on for several days. That often it would be painful, and that it was all Eve's fault for eating that apple in the Garden of Eden. That the point of it all was to have the blood ready and waiting for making her children when the time came. That, in a nutshell, it was all perfectly normal and she must not fret.

Not fret? How could anyone not fret? Doomed for the rest of her life to nearly bleed to death every single month, and to have tummy-ache as well. She had no intention of having children anyway for years and years, so there was absolutely no point in her wretched body making such long-term plans. Anyway, one thing she did know was that you had to be married before you could have children.

'So, Mama, what part will my husband play in all this?'

That really stopped Mama in her tracks. She hummed and hah-ed and went pink in the face.

'I really don't think this is the right time to go into all that, dear,' she said. 'You've had a shock and are probably feeling a little unwell, so I think you should go back to bed for a while.'

But Marjory was not to be put off so easily.

'I really do need to know, though.' Poking demurely at her navel through the cloth of her sinned-against nightdress, she said:

'Of course I know this is where babies come out; that's why it's called a tummy-button, because you can do it up again afterwards. What I don't see is how they get inside there in the first place, and what the man has got to do with it. Does he have to kiss you first or something, and that makes a baby? Did Papa have to kiss you before I grew inside you?'

Now Mama seemed to be getting really cross.

'That's quite enough questions, young lady. I don't want to hear another word. Go to your room at once, and I shall send Agatha to tell you when you can come down.'

And with that poor Marjory had to be content.

THE NEXT TWO YEARS AT SCHOOL were the best she had known. Fond as she was deep down of her older sister, there was no doubt that Josephine's presence had overwhelmed her. She had lived in a state of constant apprehension, never knowing quite what would happen next. Now, at last, she could relax and for the first time let her own particular personality develop. She thrived as never before. The choir and the Wild Flower Society took up most of her spare time; nearly every Sunday afternoon found her wandering round the fields and woods near the school, collecting specimens of wild flowers to take back to her science teacher for identification. This was a passion that would last her whole life. She was skilled, too, with the pencil and brush, and would spend hours making meticulous botanical drawings of her finds. So gifted was she that in later life she applied to act as assistant to Edward Wilson, the doctor-naturalist who died with Scott on his last Antarctic expedition, but without success. How different her life might have been.

'What,' asked her form-mistress as the last few terms of school approached, 'what are your plans for the future? Miss Hill tells me that you have made great strides with your German this term. Does that influence your thinking? You should be capable of obtaining a place at Cambridge University, where of course you could continue your studies. And it is so near your home that you would still be able to see a lot of your family. How does that appeal to you?'

Marjory loved her German. She knew that to study at such an ancient and historic university would be an amazing opportunity. But somehow her whole being rebelled against the idea. Shocked, she found that she no longer wanted to see a lot of her family. Beyond anything else, she needed to get away, to be her own person at last. Her childhood had not been a happy one, and the time had come for it to end. She would not go to Cambridge. She would go somewhere far, far away, and in the gentlest possible terms she told her family so.

IT WAS DEAR AUNT B who had come to the rescue yet again. She wrote and, a few days later, received a reply.

The very next day, Marjory was summoned to the rectory drawing-room. This, with its dark red velvet curtains and chair covers patterned with stiff sprays of foliage and flowers as foreign to nature as the room itself, was rarely used, and Marjory's stomach performed one of its more spectacular somersaults. She searched her memory; which of her heinous crimes had led to this? It must, she supposed, be that Cambridge business.

But she need not have worried. The three important adults in her life, assembled around the unlit fireplace with its china dogs and fire-screen embroidered with Ely Cathedral, smiled kindly at her as she crept round the half-open door and came to a halt just inside.

'Come along in,' said her aunt, patting the ornate and overblown rose on the seat next to her. Beatrice turned to her brother.

'We have some exciting news for you,' he said. 'Your Aunt Beatrice has written to a friend in Weimar, in Germany, who has agreed to have you to live with her and her husband while you attend finishing-school. In return for your board and lodging, you will teach English to their little daughter. You are to go as soon as arrangements can be made, as you will need time to settle in before the new school year starts in September.'

Evie, standing with his arm draped elegantly over the edge of the mantelpiece, his long legs in their clerical black crossed, smiled down at his pretty niece. Her mother and aunt watched her face. All three caught a glimpse of – what? Surely not anger? Surely excitement, surprise, astonishment even, but not the rebellion to which they had become so accustomed in the face of her sister Josephine? But to all three, just for a moment, it had been obvious. It lasted only a second, but there was no doubt that it had been there.

How dare they? Marjory's immediate reaction to this news surprised even herself. What right had they to decide her future without consulting her first? How much longer did she have to put up with being pushed around, by her sister, her teachers, her uncle and aunt, even her beloved mother? Although even at that moment she was aware that this was indeed a fabulous opportunity, she was no longer a child and suddenly she had a better understanding of Josephine and her passion to be free.

PART FIVE

22

Cambridge 1895

I'M HERE! I'M ACTUALLY HERE! It's hard to believe, but it's true, true, true!

The uniformed man in the porter's lodge had raised his cap to Charlie.

'Good morning, Sir. Welcome to Clare. May I have your name?' Glancing at the long list of undergraduates in his hand, he went on ...

'You're very fortunate, Sir, if I may say so. You've been allotted one of the best sets of rooms in the whole college. If you would just leave your luggage over there with the other young gentlemen's, I will point you on your way. '

THE NEXT EVENING, Charlie sat at the table in his new rooms and wrote a letter.

Dear Matt.

I've had the most extraordinary, wonderful, amazing day. Of course there was all the business of getting out at Cambridge station, heaving my trunk out of the luggage van and finding a cab. The trouble was that there were so many other fellows doing the same thing, and not nearly enough porters, or cabs. Anyway, eventually I got to Clare. Walking through those imposing iron gates for the first time was an incredible experience, I can tell you.

I dumped my belongings and walked the few steps into the town. I'd pictured it all for so long, but now that I was actually here I was completely overwhelmed. How on earth had I, Char, just an ordinary fellow, come to be even the tiniest part of all this? Almost without my knowing it, I turned in through the great open gates of Kings College and into its chapel. For some reason I looked down at my feet, and thought of all those thousands – millions, probably – of other pairs of shoes that had trodden this same path over so many centuries; sandals, fancy boots with pointed toes, long boots, soldiers' boots, slippers, boots with buckles, ladies' dainty shoes, and probably bare feet as well. And then I was inside. I'd expected sudden darkness after the glare in the great court, but as I went through the door it seemed as if the whole vast building was flooded with a light and majesty beyond anything I'd ever experienced. The stained glass windows glowed with a glorious brightness that drenched every surface, patterns of red and blue and amber that seemed to fill the actual air with joyfulness. But it was a fearful joy, fighting with the power of the crashing cords hurled out by the great organ, a tumult that made even me hold my breath, musical philistine that I am. The glorious harmonies bounced back from the soaring arches high above my head and resounded through the vast building in a sublime and mighty dissonance.

I was completely transfixed. More than anything, I wanted to fall on my knees then and there, just inside the doorway. But I'm much too inhibited to make a public spectacle of myself so I did the next best thing – got myself into one of the tidy rows of seats, and used a hassock, like everybody else.

But I couldn't pray, not with words. My whole being seemed to reach out to the Power that overwhelmed that place, and myself within it; it was a moment out of time that I know I shall never forget and that will never really fade for as long as I live.

You will think I've lost my reason, writing like this. Perhaps for the moment I have gone a little mad. I wish you were here, and could share it all with me.

Your friend
Charlie.

The organ had suddenly stopped, and at the same moment a cloud must have come over the sun for the brightness faded. The great door banged, and someone scraped a chair over the stone floor in a painful screech. Charlie sat up on his seat, and at almost the same moment the newcomer plonked himself down beside him.

'Didn't I see you in Clare this morning?' The loud whisper seemed to echo round the empty building, and Charlie turned to look at his companion. He recognised one of the other freshmen whom he'd met at the porter's lodge. He didn't really want to talk, but it would have been churlish not to reply, and he held out his hand.

'Yes,' he said, 'I'm Garrad.'

'And I'm Fortescue, Forty for short.' And they smiled at each other as they rose to their feet and left the chapel together.

'FORTESCUE, WHY DON'T YOU COME and have a cup of tea with me in my rooms this afternoon? Say about half past four?'

Charlie couldn't believe his luck. Not only was he one of the minority allotted accommodation actually in college, but his rooms were indeed accepted as being amongst the very best. He was longing to share his pleasure with someone, and who better than his new friend? The two young men met at the foot of Charlie's staircase, and the proud resident gestured to his companion to lead the way up an elegant wooden flight of steps ascending towards the attics. This was the first of three straight flights, each with its small landing supporting a wooden coal-bin half full of coal. 'Probably where my scuttle gets filled,' thought Charlie as they passed the third.

'Fork right here,' he said as the fourth flight of stairs divided into two, and after a few more steps they came to an open door leading into a sparsely furnished sitting-room. The open fire was laid but not lit; a square table and four upright chairs, a desk with bookshelves, and two easy chairs completed the furnishings.

'Is that you, Sir?' came a cheery voice from the communicating room, as its owner poked his greying head round the door. 'Kettle's on – it shouldn't be a minute. I thought you could do with a hand today, Sir, as you've only just arrived. But normally it'll be up to you to get your own tea.'

'Fortescue, meet Sidney – he's my gyp.' And Fortescue nodded wisely. Though not one of the lucky ones living 'in,' already he had learned that the college servants were called gyps and that each staircase had one allotted to the needs of its residents.

'Shall I cut the cake, Sir, or would you rather do that yourself?'

Charlie was rather in awe of this source of all knowledge; there seemed nothing about Clare that Sidney didn't know, and he most certainly was not used to issuing orders to any sort of servant. His sisters saw to all that sort of thing at home.

'Oh, er – do whatever you think best, Sidney.' Smiling to himself, Sidney did just that. Half the cake, brought from home and wrapped in a pullover to prevent damage in the young man's flimsy suitcase, disappeared into two enormous slices.

Sidney and the tin hip-bath between them occupied most of the gyp-room but the two boys fought their way past the obstacles and through the final doorway. This was Charlie's bedroom. A narrow bed with a small table beside it, a chair, a chest of drawers, a wooden washstand complete with white china jug and bowl, and a cheap wardrobe took up all the available space. An unlit oil-lamp and a candle in its saucer-shaped candlestick stood on the table, and Charlie had already added his Bible, an elderly copy of *David Copperfield*, and a framed photograph.

Fortescue picked up the picture.

'Is that your sister?' he asked.

'No, my mother, a year or two before she died. I was eight then.'

Fortescue didn't know what to say.

'You'll be wondering when you takes your bath, Sir,' said Sidney, catching his foot on the tin tub as he brought the tea things into the sitting-room. It was the last thing Charlie was wondering, but he let it pass.

'The young gentlemen usually has it when they've played games. I lights the fire, and brings the bath in here in front of it. Then I gets a can of hot water from the kitchen, right across the other side of the court. Do you play much in the way of games, Sir?' He looked meaningfully at Charlie, who had no hesitation whatever in reassuring him on that point. From that moment another new friendship was forged.

'You're lucky to arrive in such good weather, Sir.' Sidney was clearly in a mood for conversation, as he leant up against the windowsill and crossed his arms.

'It's been raining something shocking. It don't half pour down them slates.' He looked out of the window, across the square court with its perfectly mown grass, at the row of dormer windows opposite, evidently a mirror image of those on their own side.

'These attic rooms gets ever so cold in the winter. That little fireplace don't do much for your bedroom, Sir. Many's the time I've heard banging – and swearing, if you'll excuse my language – when the water in the washbasin's frozen that thick you can't hardly break it.

'Well, this won't do. Mustn't keep chatting here. Oh, I nearly forgot, the most important thing of all. You'll be wanting to visit Lady Clare, Sir.'

Charlie supposed that this Lady Clare must be some sort of descendant of the one who had founded the college, over five hundred years ago if his memory served him right.

'Will I? Is it the thing to do? Where would I find her?'

'I'd show you myself, Sir, but it's a tidy step and I'm getting late. Lady Clare's the name the young gentlemen's given to the earth-closets. Of course they're right down by the river – got to empty somewhere, haven't they? You'll find them all right – just follow your nose as you might say.'

And with that Sidney banged his way down the stairs. Garrad and Fortescue looked at each other and burst out laughing. But Charlie made a silent resolution; in return for the minimum number of baths, Sidney would have to keep his mouth shut, or he, Charlie, would never get any work done.

23

'WHAT ON EARTH'S ETHNOGRAPHY? And whoever would want to go to a lecture on 'The Psychology of the Dung Beetle, Its Passions and Procreation?' Oh, but this one might be fun, Garrad ...'

But Garrad wasn't really listening. Like Fortescue, he was mesmerised by the variety of societies, clubs, lectures, events and activities, imaginable and unimaginable, that was on display on the Clare common-room notice-board. He was pressingly invited to play ping-pong and rugby football, to 'Stand Up for the Lord' with the Christian Union, to attend a course of lectures on the Black Arts, to learn to paint, play the Serpent, skate, meditate; the opportunities were endless and bewildering. He really would like to join the chess club – oh, and look at that notice about 'Bicycling for Beginners.' These new-fangled machines looked splendid, much more manageable than the old penny-farthings.

After all, I should have plenty of spare time. I don't actually have to go to any of my lectures – bit of a change from school. I could spend the whole term finding out about Ancient Egypt or the habits of the tsetse-fly for all anybody cared. Really rather a responsibility, having to make my own decisions. Better not to rush into anything, I suppose. I would like to row, though – but I am supposed to be here to work, so I mustn't get carried away.

In the end, he wrote again to Matt. He had a lot of commonsense, did Matt. He would give good advice.

The answer, a surprising one, wasn't long in coming.

Dear Charlie

Isn't the whole point of your being there to learn your job? If it was me, I'd start off by working hard and see where that gets me. Then I'd find out how much time I had to spare ...'

Dear Matt

Of course you're right, as usual. It would have been fun to do some of these things, but maybe later on, as you say.

And so Charlie made his decision. He would work hard. He would try and win a scholarship on his first year's exams, to help his father with the fees. He would try and get a really good degree. In his heart of hearts, he knew that this was right. He was, after all, a true scholar and would like above all things to learn and understand.

⚜

AT THE BEGINNING, he discussed these things with Fortescue. A few days after that first tea party in Charlie's rooms, Fortescue returned hospitality in his 'diggings', lodgings in a small street nearby. In answer to Charlie's ring on the doorbell, he was shown into a dark sitting-room by a very tall, thin landlady, her hair pulled severely back from her bony, freckled forehead into a copper coloured bun. Charlie's immediate reaction was one of pity for his friend, but the smile that almost bisected that long, thin face was one of such warmth that he instantly rejected his first impression.

'Here's your friend, Mr Fortescue. Please go in. My young gentleman's expecting you.'

The digs were much as Charlie expected, and not so very different from his own family's drawing-room. Everything was rather dark, from the heavy maroon curtains to the carpet, patterned in browns and greens, with sturdy polished mahogany furniture in between. An occasional table covered in a sombre green cloth ornamented with tassels proudly upheld a dusty aspidistra crying out for fresh air and freedom. The bright coal fire burning in the grate would have been wonderfully welcoming had it not been such a warm day. As it was, the heat was stifling and Fortescue laughed as Charlie stripped off jacket and waistcoat.

'Sorry about the temperature, but Mrs Jennings is such a kind landlady – she insisted that you must be homesick and a fire would cheer you up no end.'

Over a plump brown pot of tea and delicious scones made especially for the occasion by Mrs Jennings, the two boys got down to discussing progress so far.

'Seems to me, Garrad, that you're taking life a bit too seriously.' Fortescue lounged in an easy chair, pulled as far from the fire as possible, as he sipped his tea.

'My people, you see, aren't expecting too much of me. Anyway, taking the English tripos is a bit of a cinch. Hardly any lectures, lots of novels to read, and plenty of time for sport. My pater's keen on all sorts of games – he was a cricket blue here, you know, played for his county and all that. Don't somehow think I shall spend too much time swotting.'

The cracks in their unlikely friendship were to widen rapidly and irreparably, but for the moment they were glued together by the need for some stability in this unfamiliar world. It was Fortescue who took the lead, Fortescue who insisted on visiting the best stationer in town to purchase 'visiting cards' engraved with each one's name and college address, Fortescue who led Charlie into the tobacconist to buy for himself a hundred Turkish cigarettes.

'Excuse me, but you've left your cigarettes behind.' Charlie picked up the packet and held it out to the customer just leaving the shop as they arrived.

'My dear fellow, we don't carry our own stuff. Jim here' – he indicated the proprietor behind the counter – 'sends his boy. I've only a couple of smokes left in my rooms, Jim – you'll be quick about it, won't you?' And he swept through the door, black undergraduate gown ballooning out behind him.

It was Fortescue's turn to make his purchase.

'Where would you like them delivered, Sir?' The young man extracted from his waistcoat pocket one of the brand new visiting cards and handed it over with a flourish.

'You next, Garrad. How many do you want?'

The nearest Charlie had ever got to smoking was watching his father enjoy a pipe. From early childhood he had been fascinated by the ritual; the scraping out of the bowl, the unscrewing of the tin lid with a bearded sailor's portrait on it, the careful extraction of just the right amount of tobacco, the tamping down, the scrap of paper carefully folded into a spill, the lengthy ignition process and finally the expression on his father's face as he took the first satisfying puff. He had tried it once, and didn't much care for it. But he was one of the 'men' now, (they had quickly discovered that the undergraduates were referred to as the men) so perhaps this was the time to start. He looked at the row upon row of pipes of every sort of shape, made from every kind of wood, at all the different kinds of tobacco (where was the one with the sailor on the tin?) and decided it was all too difficult. He would come back, alone, when Fortescue was not there to laugh at him.

'I don't smoke,' was all he said. He hoped that he misinterpreted the look his friend gave him.

At the beginning, they called for each other to go to dinner in Hall.

'May I have your name, Sir?' The buttery-clerk stood in the doorway. It took him just three nights to master the names of all the new students; thereafter 'Fortescue' and 'Garrad' and the rest were checked off on his list from memory with perfect accuracy. Eating in Hall was compulsory and woe betide you if, without valid excuse, no tick could be made against your name.

They took their seats at one of the vast oak tables.

'Soup or fish, Sir?' and then, 'beef or mutton?'

This remained the invariable formula throughout the whole of Charlie's time at Clare.

He was used to waiting to be served; after all, there were twelve children in his own family and carving was a slow business. But to his amazement on that first night, the words were scarcely out of his mouth before a huge plateful of meat was placed in front of him.

'Those fellows ought to be surgeons!' he remarked to Fortescue as he watched the senior gyps attacking the great joints at the nearby carving table with such dexterity that a cheer went up from the nearest diners.

To the unsophisticated boy it was all so grand, but his critical freshman's eye missed nothing as he looked around the room.

What a shame – suppose they've really tried, but they have overdone it a bit. Bit of a mess, really, mixing the new with the old. I suppose you've got to move with the times and make life more comfortable, but this wonderful old room must have looked much better when it was left alone.

Modern furniture standing against the walls alternated with battered antiques, their corners spoiled and surfaces scuffed. Dusty curtains spoilt the line of the windows. Certainly the sooty clusters of gas-lights that nestled like colonies of bats on the ceiling did allow them to see what they were eating, but surely candles would have given a kinder light, would have provided more contrast, would have accentuated the elegant starkness of the ancient design.

Charlie picked up his pudding spoon from the polished table, gleaming in the light of the despised lamps. It weighed heavy in his hand, and, turning it over, he looked at the row of tiny hallmarks on the handle. His sister Mary had taught him the little he knew about silver. There was the lion, next to it the letter 'h' in old-fashioned script, and then the tiny engraving of Queen Victoria facing left.

'What' said Fortescue, watching him, 'is so interesting about an old spoon?'

'Oh, I'm just curious. It's amazing what you can tell from these little marks. See that 'h'? If I remember aright, that means that it was minted in the early seventies, just a few years before we were born. The Queen would have been middle-aged then, of course. There's her portrait.'

He turned the spoon back and saw on the handle in bold letters the initials JD, presumably those of the donor, and the college crest.

'What about mine?' said his friend, handing it to him.

'And mine?'

'And mine?'

And before he knew it spoons and forks were coming at him from all directions, until the pudding was served and all implements rapidly reclaimed for their proper purpose.

In the midst of the hustle and bustle, the cries for 'more beer' in the silver tankard by each place, the hurrying footsteps of the uniformed college servants, the dull roar of male voices, Charlie tried to make out the figures portrayed in the paintings on the walls. Notable alumni, no doubt, but many were so dirty from years of exposure that it was impossible to distinguish them.

'Look, over there on the mantelpiece, that must be Lady Clare.'

Fortescue was pointing down the room at a female bust, flanked on either side by a buxom wooden wench frozen for ever in the act of placing a wreath upon her mistress's stony brow. Beneath the central figure's disconcertingly watchful gaze stood the top table, and for those first few nights Charlie's eyes were as busy as his digestive juices as he tried to make out who was who and what was what.

One day I will sit at that table.

He instantly chided himself for such gross impertinence.

Time alone would show. For the moment he was more than content to be there at all.

IT WAS IN HIS SECOND TERM that the entertaining started in earnest. The first person to invite him to a breakfast party was Fortescue. Clearly, no cost was spared and the redoubtable Mrs Jennings had done 'her gentleman' proud. The spotless white cloth that covered the mahogany table could hardly be seen for the array of different dishes upon it, and even the aspidistra was looking more cheerful. Mrs J. herself was in attendance, filling the ever-empty tankards with an endless supply of beer, and it was a very merry group of students that finally broke up and went their several ways.

Within a few days Charlie found one of those engraved visiting cards slipped under his door, commanding his presence at a different breakfast party with a different host. It seemed churlish to refuse; in any case, why should he?

It would be fun, and he was always hungry. So along he went, and before he knew it he had got himself caught up in a whirl of socialising with a group of young men whose parents had clearly set them no financial limits. It was inevitable that at some point he, Charlie, would have to return their hospitality. But how? He had no money to spare; any that he managed to save from his meagre allowance went on all-important books and he was too proud to write home and ask for more.

There was only one answer. Dinner in Hall was compulsory six days a week, but undergraduates were expected to provide their own meal on the seventh. On that night he would tighten his belt, which already went almost twice round his skinny waist, and go to bed hungry. Over several weeks he would surely save enough to entertain his friends.

Garrad's breakfasts were never lavish, but the chosen few who attended them began to realise the privations suffered by their friend on their behalf and respected him for it. All was well.

24

Bures, England 1897

'HOW'S IT GOING THEN?

Both young men had spoken together and, awkward in each other's company after a gap of a few months, laughed self-consciously. Perched side-by-side on two of the empty milk churns that stood outside the Bures cowshed, Charlie and Matt looked at one another and laughed again, this time in pure pleasure. Their meetings had been few and far between over the last eighteen months, but the bond had not faded and they were truly glad to have some time to spend together.

'You first,' said Charlie.

'Well, I've nothing new to tell you really. Your father's bought a couple more heifers, and I'm sure you knew about the bull goring old Mrs Perkins' dog nearly to death ...'

And then out poured the village gossip, news of the births, marriages and deaths of the folk that Charlie had been brought up alongside and that were so familiar to him. He found himself going back in time, back to the familiar old life, school holidays when home had been so vital to the preservation of his sanity. How different it was now. All this was still important to him, of course, but at a distance. He had discovered a new life, one that was better than he had ever dreamt possible. He had moved on.

'Here am I blathering on when you've got so many more interesting things to talk about. Now it's your turn. You did tell me a bit about it when you were last home, but there must be lots more things now. How's that posh friend of yours, the one with a number instead of a name?'

'Er, who on earth ...? Oh, you mean old Forty, real name Fortescue! I don't really see much of him now. We're very different, you know. His people are enormously wealthy, and you know – well – how things are here. Father doesn't approve of splashing money about. It was difficult at first, but I have got a bit more now since ...' and he stopped.

'Since what?'

'Well, you see, I sort of got this scholarship, which has helped the finances. I don't know where to start – there's so much to say ...'

Fanny, looking down from her bedroom window, watched the tops of their heads bobbing up and down as the two boys talked and laughed together. It must be lovely to be such friends, she thought, and gave a gentle sigh.

CHARLIE HAD COME HOME to discuss his future with his father.

'So what do you think I should do? My supervisor thinks that sitting for Part One of my degree after just two years, instead of the usual three, would be perfectly safe – he even seems to think I might get a First. Then, you see, I could try for this other scholarship which is open to anyone planning to go into the Church. It's given by Jesus College and would mean me taking the second part of my degree from there. If I got it, that is – the scholarship, I mean.'

Garrad senior smiled. He wanted to give his clever son's hand a reassuring pat, but, unheard by even his sharp ears, Charlie had moved a little, and the outstretched hand faltered and came back to roost on his own knee.

'You know best, Char. If that's what your supervisors suggest, I'm sure you should go ahead and take the plunge. I know how much you love Clare, but it seems to me a wonderful opportunity to experience a new college as well, with fresh minds to broaden the knowledge you already have.'

And so the decision was taken. The talk meandered on, but was cut short by the gong for midday dinner and the older man took his son's arm as they set out for the dining-room. Charlie's time at home was short and, as with Matt, there was much to catch up with. Dinners grew cold on plates as the returning hero tried to help the family understand his new life. The questions were endless, but Char didn't mind. There was nothing he enjoyed more than talking about Cambridge, and it was only Violet's impatience over 'clearing' so that she could get on with the washing-up ('after all, Cook, it is supposed to be my half day, Mr Charlie or no Mr Charlie' – Violet's ringlets had flattened and faded somewhat over the years, but, alas, not so her temper) that stemmed the flow. It was sister Fanny in particular whose interest never flagged. Somehow she made Charlie think of his mother. They both possessed that rare gift of listening, of wanting to understand.

The time came to sit the scholarship at Jesus College in the company of a crowd of other aspiring clergymen. It was not long before Charlie was sent for by his supervisor.

'Congratulations, Garrad. Provided you achieve a satisfactory result in Part One of your degree in a few weeks' time, the scholarship is yours. Well done.'

The spur to success was there. Now it was up to him.

The university Examination Hall was filled with the sound of scratching pens as row upon row, column upon column, of undergraduates from every Cambridge college sat Part One of the Theological Tripos.

Then came the wait, the endless summer wait for the postman. The time passed, but all too slowly. Most of the family were there for most of the time, but, frankly, Charlie was bored. They still went for picnics on the river in their rowing boat, they still played tennis and croquet, he still helped Matt with the milking, but somehow the old pursuits seemed to have lost much of their charm.

It was when Bob, the next brother up in the family sequence, came back at the end of his last term at the Leeds Clergy Training School that everything happened at once.

Bessie, self-appointed lookout, waylaid the postman at the gate that wet, grey day. She stood for some time in the shelter of the porch, earnestly studying the letters he gave her, and then ran into the house as fast as her little legs would carry her.

'Char, where are you?' Bessie was a special favourite. At thirteen, her stature and mind were those of a much younger child, but she was always cheerful and they loved her for it. Her tiny shoes, put out for cleaning, looked fairylike sandwiched between the great boots belonging to the boys on either side of her in age. So, when her brother heard her shrill voice calling him, he made special haste.

'Is this it? Is this the one you want?' Bessie held out an envelope of heavy white vellum. She had presented him with several letters over the last few weeks, hoping to make him happy. None had. But this one did look different, and when Charlie took it from her and turned it over he was almost apprehensive of what he would see. Sure enough, there it was; the Clare College crest embossed on the flap. His heart seemed to miss a beat and he held his breath as he tore it open.

'What does it say, Char, what does it say?' The little girl was jumping up and down with excitement. Why didn't he speak? At last, he did.

'Yes, Bessie, you've done well,' and the child clapped her small hands. 'This certainly is the one. And do you know what it says? It says I've got a First Class in Part One of my degree!'

Bootalet, Burma, 1897

The day his father drowned, Pyau knew he wouldn't go to school any more. It had all started so normally. After their morning rice, Father had set off to the river to fish. It was only three miles or so, and he was always back before dusk. This time he didn't come. Pyau went with a group of men from the village to look for him, but there was no moon and they had to give up. Next morning, they found him, held fast in a cluster of lotuses half a mile downstream. There were tangled roots wound round his legs, and he must have been pulled under and drowned. It was strange, for he was a good swimmer, accustomed to the river and the plants and animals that lived in it. Pyau's mother said he'd had a bad attack of shivering the night before – perhaps he had the fever, malaria they called it nowadays, and it had weakened him. They would never know for sure.

Now Pyau was the man of the family and he must stay at home. At least he had been at school long enough to learn to read and write.

25

HOW CAN YOU DESCRIBE THE SCREAM of a human animal at bay, in mortal terror of its life? No words, no thoughts even, can penetrate the depths of that dark place; but, once you have heard it, it will stay with you for ever.

That's how it was that night. We'd gone home to Bures for a holiday, Bob and I. For Bob, it was to be a short one, just a few days snatched from the smoke and grime of Liverpool. He'd just finished his training for the priesthood and was about to start work.

'My goodness, Char, you're lucky. I'd give a lot to be you – still a couple of weeks of freedom ahead and then back to the best university in the world. Though I don't know – it's actually incredibly exciting to be starting my first job. Mr James – that's the vicar I'll be working for – seems a really nice fellow. He's never had a curate before, and I think he'll probably give me a lot of the routine stuff to do – he's said a bit about his plans for the sailors' club down by the docks, which is really what he's keenest on.'

I told Bob I was bored, and we joked about me going back with him, up north, as he put it.

'Maybe I could come and stay with you for a week or two?'

'Of course you can – come up and keep me company for a bit.'

But I knew really that I must stay with Father and the family. They loved it when my brothers and I came home – they had such an unbelievably dull life, and it gave them something to think about.

And then came the letter from Clare, to say that I'd got a First and so could take up the scholarship at Jesus, and suddenly something snapped and I changed my mind. Why shouldn't I go with Bob? He was family too, wasn't he? and anyway, I needed a bit of experience.

I said as much to Bob.

'Of course you do. There's one thing certain – we don't see much of life from here. If you're going to be a parson in the real world, you need to find out what the real world is about. No doubt Cambridge is wonderful, and you're covering yourself with glory. But it's like living in a bubble, a beautiful rainbow-coloured soap-bubble, and you can't keep floating about for ever. Anyway, bubbles burst.'

So the goodbyes were said, tears mopped up, wet hankies waved, and we were on our way.

'Look, Ma! There's two men with Father James!'
We could see, and hear, the little girl as she pointed down the street. The three of us, the vicar, Bob and I, were on our way to the sailors' club that Bob had told me about, the place that his new vicar, Mr James, was so interested in.
'Shhush dear – they might 'ear yer.'
'But Ma, why've two of 'em got black dresses on an' the other one ain't?'
'I don't know, do I? Any rate, they ain't dresses – they're 'assicks or summat, wot they wears in church. They ain't 'alf alike, them two young 'uns. Brothers, p'raps? Off t'club, I've no doubt.'
The club secretary, a heavily built man in a seaman's jersey and grubby white trousers, greeted us at the door.
'Bill, I'd like you to meet the two Mr Garrads, Robert and Charles. I'm delighted to say that Robert is to be my curate, and will take over most of the visiting here. Of course, I shall still come and see you all from time to time, but my poor old leg is playing up a bit, and I need to take things a bit easier these days.'
And we all shook hands. There were a lot more hands to shake too, calloused hands from years of hauling on wet ropes; brown ones, yellow ones, hands that were black on the back and pink when you got a glimpse of their palms. We could smell foreign cooking and hear talk in unfamiliar languages; we were greeted with big smiles of welcome – and a few suspicious glares, too. There were tall men and short men, young ones and not so young, all well built and with outdoor faces. Some wore smart uniforms, but most were dressed in a motley assortment of well-worn jerseys and patched trousers.
'Good to see you again, Father,'
'Thanks ever so much, for what you did for my wife, Mr James ...'
And then, from the vicar:
'I do hope the baby's better, Will.'
'Oh, and Fred, did you ever hear from that young lady of yours?'

And so it went on. The old priest seemed to know almost all of them by name; not only that, but he remembered and shared their joys and their sorrows. Poor Bob; he told me later that his heart failed him. How could he ever hope to rise to such giddy Christian heights?

At last,

'Come on, boys, it's time to go.'

Mr James hauled his watch out of his cassock pocket by its chain. 'My goodness, we are late. It's after ten o'clock. As there are three of us I think we're safe enough to take a short cut, but I certainly wouldn't advise doing this on your own.'

He evidently knew the area well, and led us through a maze of small, dark streets. You could see that the uneven cobbles made walking very painful for his rheumaticky leg. There weren't many people about; two or three men stumbled past, singing, and swearing, at the tops of their voices. I learnt some new words that day, I can tell you. There were a few couples with their arms round each other, and one which Mr James hurried us past – I don't think he thought we were old enough to look! Pairs of disembodied green eyes shone out at us from sinister pitch dark alleys, and a couple of moth-eaten mongrels trotted past, intent on some vital private mission.

We took a left turn into yet another street. At first it seemed much like the others, except for a few red lanterns here and there – and then I saw them, a shadowy figure in almost every dark doorway, all of them women. It was ridiculously childish of me, but I remember whispering to Bob:

'Are they really what I think they are?'

No doubt his scornful reply was more than well-deserved, but I'd never seen a prostitute before, you see, and I suppose all those sermons I'd heard on the Evils of The Flesh came rushing back and I was, frankly, terrified. I must have thought that one of them might inveigle me into her den and I'd be done for. I stayed close to Bob, but Mr James just ploughed on – he didn't even seem to notice.

' 'Ullo dearies! Come on in! It's getting ever so cold out 'ere.'

Of course the voice took us by surprise and all three of us turned towards her. I suppose the other two's dog-collars must have caught the street-light – anyway, the girl gave a little start.

'Ooh, ever s' sorry,' *she said.* 'Didn't see as 'ow you was reverends,' *and she backed away into the darkness.*

It was then that we heard the scream. We stopped dead in our tracks, I remember, and then came the men's voices, loud and angry, and another terrible rasping, rending screech. Normally, I'd have turned tail and fled. But my awful temper got the better of me and I was so angry that nothing in the world could have stopped me, for it had been a woman's scream. I was off like a whirlwind and heard myself yelling

'Come on!'

And old Mr James shouting

'Wait!'

But I couldn't wait, and good old Bob was right behind me as we rounded the next bend at full gallop. For once, I didn't fall over my own feet.

I shall never forget what we saw.

For a split second, there in front of us on the edge of that sordid road was a living tableau, a scene from a sacred painting, frozen in time. In the glowing circle of light from the street-lamp stood two men, their bowed heads close, the arm of the taller one raised as if in blessing. Beneath them, her hands held up in prayer, knelt a woman, her blue dress bunched up round her, her fair hair catching and condensing the dim light into an untidy halo. Just for a split-second; then reality. Down came the raised arm in a vicious blow. The girl's clutching hands slid down the lamp-post and she subsided on to the road and lay perfectly still, a pathetic heap of dirty blue. If I hadn't known better, I'd have thought she was just a pile of old rags.

We must have taken them completely by surprise, two black-clad avenging angels springing out of the darkness into the light.

'Stop that!' *I think I yelled. And then both of us were in there, fists flailing. I was angrier than I've ever been. I picked out the man who'd delivered the blow. By a miracle, I caught his jaw and he staggered back, hitting his head on the lamp-post and breaking the beer bottle in his pocket on the pavement as he fell. The ground was slippery, and I must have had time to look down, for I remember the frothy brown liquid bubbling out of his pocket to join the blood and vomit under our feet.*

'Look out!' *It was Bob's voice. As I turned, I saw the light flashing on the jagged bottle in the second man's hand as he lifted his arm to strike. I wasn't quite quick enough and felt a sharp pain in my arm; it seemed at the time of absolutely no consequence. And then, abruptly out of the darkness behind us, sprang a third black apparition, and suddenly Bob's opponent had had enough. Dragging his injured friend to his feet, the two of them made off at a drunken canter, leaving their victim lying still and silent on the foul pavement. Old Mr James had arrived just in time.*

'Have they killed her?' *he asked.*

26

I WONDER WHAT MATT WILL MAKE of the letter I'm going to write him.

At the end of that extraordinary day an absolute typhoon of emotions was whirling round in my mind and I felt I had to talk to somebody or my brain would explode. Bob was the obvious one but, although he's my brother, we've never been really close. Sister Fanny would be the best, but she's far away and, anyway, it wouldn't be fair to burden a woman with all the things I saw and went through.

So I've decided to write to dear old Matt – he's so good at understanding, and yet he's such a practical chap, full of good advice. I've already sketched out the bit about the fight to put him in the picture, but it's what happened next, and what I've found out from it all about Mr James and the way his mind works, that really confuses me. So I'm going to write all that part down in detail to Matt, partly to ask for his help but just as much to help me sort it out in my own mind.

...SO YOU SEE, MATT, I am in a complete muddle. All the values that I've been brought up with have been turned on their head. It turned out that the poor girl – she wasn't dead, by the way, just stunned, and with lots of cuts and bruises – was one of the local prostitutes. Well, you know as well as I do what our Bures vicar would have had to say – or anyway, to think – about that. That she deserved every bit of what she got, that she was completely beyond the pale, etc. etc. But as soon as we'd picked her up and taken her into her poky room, it turned out that there were two children living there as well, her little brother and sister. Their father had been a docker and they'd always been poor, but they'd had a decent roof over their heads and more or less enough to eat. Then one day the chain on a dockside crane had snapped and the huge packing-case it was hoisting had fallen on top of him and crushed him to death. Their mother had carried on as best she could for a bit, but she'd had a cough for ages and it turned into consumption and she died, too. That left the three children on their own, Lizzie, the eldest, the one who'd just been attacked, Joseph and little Amy. Lizzie was just fourteen when they were orphaned. They were desperate to stay together, and they'd heard awful things about the nearest orphanage, so brave Lizzie took herself off on to the streets to earn enough money to keep the three of them. She hated every second of what she did but she hadn't ever been in real physical danger until that night. We never heard exactly what it was all about – some jealousy for her favours between the two men, I think.

The most amazing part of it all was Mr James. He actually knew Lizzie by name.

'and she comes to my church sometimes,' he said! Can you imagine the reaction if a 'woman of the streets' came to St. Mary's in Bures? He was just utterly full of concern for her and Joseph and Amy. There was no preaching, no blame – just immense love.

It was me that got the preaching, when I asked him about it the next day.

'Charles,' he said. 'I used to think exactly like you do, that black is black and white is white, that there is right and wrong and nothing in between. But when you've worked in a parish like mine for as long as I have, all those ideas are knocked out of you. Lizzie is probably more saintly than you or I will ever be.' He pulled a battered copy of the New Testament out of his pocket, and thumbed through it for a minute. Then he said

'Go home and read St. John's gospel, chapter seven. The story you need to remind yourself of starts at verse thirty-six.'

So I did. It's the bit about the woman who 'lived a sinful life in that town.' One day, while Jesus was at a dinner party with an important friend, she went in and washed Jesus's feet with her tears and wiped them with her hair. Then she soothed them by rubbing in a whole alabaster jar-full of perfume. Jesus's host said to himself

'If this man were a prophet, he would know who is touching him and what kind of woman she is – that she is a sinner.'

Jesus read his thoughts. He pointed out that his host had done nothing for his physical comfort when he had arrived, whereas she, a poor stranger, had done everything.

'Therefore, I tell you, her many sins have been forgiven for she loved much. But he who has forgiven little loves little.'

Then Jesus said to the woman

'Your sins are forgiven. Go in peace.'

I can't help thinking that that woman could easily have been Lizzie.

I don't agree with Mr James that Lizzie is more saintly than he is. Yesterday was a real eye-opener for me. I watched him at the sailors' club, where he greeted every lonely man as though he was the one person in the world he wanted to see. I saw his reaction to the fight, ready to throw himself into the fray in spite of his grey hair and gammy leg. I watched him in Lizzie's house, so squalid that most people wouldn't even have gone in through the door, let alone turn the whole atmosphere around with his love and spiritual comfort. There is no doubt now in my mind. I will do my utmost to follow in his footsteps. To do that I must first train for the priesthood. First stop Cambridge and a theological degree. Second stop, clergy training school – perhaps even the one up here in Leeds that Bob went to. Third stop – who knows?

Thank you, Matt, for taking the trouble to read all this. Hope you're well, and that your life is a little more predictable than mine. How are the cows?

Ever your affectionate friend
Charlie.

27

JUST FOR A MOMENT, it was an ordinary day. The chaffinch's repetitious song woke Fanny at dawn as it always did; there must, she thought, be a nest in the climber that threatened entry through the open window of the two girls' bedroom.

Then, suddenly, she remembered. Today! It was today he was coming! She leapt out of bed with such vigour that the bird flew off in surprise.

'Don't go! Come back!' How handsome he was with his pink breast, endlessly declaring his love at the top of his voice for his dull little mate. She wished he hadn't flown away.

'Who? What? Who's gone?' Katie sat up in bed, her long plait hanging over the shoulder of her flannel nightgown.

'Only the silly old chaffinch, dear. But it's who's coming that matters – both of them, today, today, today!' Fanny capered round the bedroom, bare feet in a mad dance round and round on the worn carpet.

CHAR'S LETTER HOME from Liverpool a year ago had caused a considerable stir at Brook House. He had taken the plunge; that weird experience on the streets of Liverpool had left no shred of doubt in his mind, and he had registered at the Leeds Clergy Training School. In his letter he asked if he might bring two of his new fellow students back with him for part of the Easter vacation. Both lived in East Anglia, but for personal and family reasons neither were welcome at home for the first few days of the holiday.

The discussion at the dinner table had gone on for several days. The immediate reaction of sister Mary had been a firm 'no.' She had five younger sisters and was far too busy, she said, with household chores to find time to chaperone them with two strange young men in the house. Admittedly, the two youngest girls would not pose a problem; neither the poor simpleton Daisy, nor Bessie, so late in reaching maturity, were likely to get up to trouble. And Edith, next in line to Mary herself, was too old to worry about – after all, she was already thirty. But what about the other two? It would be Easter time; there would be parties and, if the weather was good, boating on the river. How was she supposed to cope? Didn't she have enough to see to without such added complications?

'Mary,' her father had finally said. 'All four of my older daughters are sensible girls. What sort of trouble are you anticipating? Men are not monsters, you know. These two are friends of Char's, and as such I am sure would be thoroughly trustworthy even if I had twice as many beautiful daughters. Let the boys come and enjoy themselves as part of the family. After all, they have nowhere else to go.'

Poor, overworked Mary had simply looked at him and left the room.

Right from the start, Mary had been worried. After three short days, it seemed to her that Mr Adams was paying too much attention to Fanny and that her younger sister Katharine was enjoying the company of Mr Thomas rather more than was seemly. But their visit came to an end, goodbyes were said, and she breathed a sigh of relief.

No more was heard of them, and Mary forgot her anxieties as others moved in to take their place. And then Char wrote again.

Dear Father

I shall be home soon for the summer vac., or rather part of it, as I must do some studying up here for some of the time. I'm sure you will remember Adams and Thomas, the two friends I brought to Brook House at Easter. Well, they have hardly stopped talking about you all ever since, and I was wondering if it is too much to ask if we can do the same again for a few days this summer? It was such fun for all of us, and I don't think they disturbed you too much, did they?

Let me know what you think.

Dear Char.

By all means. I think all of us enjoyed their company, though I saw very little of them.

Father.

And so they came. The first visit at the beginning of the holiday only lasted two days, but they were charming and helpful, and even Mary warmed to them. There was not a great deal that they could do to help on the farm. Haymaking was over, and it was too early for harvest, but, as townsmen and each the only child of their respective families, they found the appeal of their new friends' farming life deceptively romantic. Could they come back for a little while in September to help bring in the corn, before they returned to the dust and dirt of Liverpool?

So back they came. Pitchforks were put in their unaccustomed hands, and blisters commiserated with at the end of their long days in the fields. They worked hard, improved quickly and found that the evenings in the company of this great big, happy family touched something in them that they had not known existed. It was heady stuff.

Mary had been lulled into a sense of security, so that when the two letters, one from each, arrived for her father just before Christmas, she assumed that they simply bore more thanks and Christmas wishes. Even when her father took them to his study and then sent for her almost at once, no alarm bells rang.

'Mary,' he said, 'I have received letters from Charlie's friends ...'

Mary nodded.

'... and they have asked that they may visit again.' He tried to assess her reaction, but none came.

'More importantly, each has asked that he may have a private interview with me.'

It was bitterly cold outside, and had the silence not been absolute, the old man could have sworn that the window had been thrown wide open. In his mind's eye he could imagine his daughter's frozen face, the face that he had never seen except through his fingertips. He could imagine the feel of the muscles round her mouth suddenly taut, the puckered texture of her young brow. For long seconds, he could not even hear her breathe, and the silence ill prepared him for the bitter outburst that came next.

'So we both know what that means, Father. Didn't I tell you how it would be? Those two young men, who we know almost nothing about really, are going to ask you if they can marry Fanny and Katie. And, knowing you, you're going to say "yes" without any thought for the effect it will have on the rest of us – or for our future happiness.'

'Mary, think of your mother. Think what she would have said, what she would have wanted for all her daughters. We often talked when you were small about the future, and laughed about the little boys then who would grow up to be your suitors.' He put out his hand to touch her, but felt her pull away.

'I lie awake often thinking how desperately hard it is on you older ones, tied to us all here because of your mother's death. But now it does seem as if these two of your sisters may have a chance of a fuller life. Mind you, we don't actually know what they're going to say – it could be anything, you know. And we don't know for sure what Fanny and Katie's feelings are. So let's just wait and see, shall we?'

Her breathing was loud and harsh now, but no more words came. Then he heard her footsteps going to the door and the particular sound of that particular doorknob as it turned in its socket, and of the door closing behind her.

THE TWO YOUNG MEN arrived together. From the outset, things were different. Instead of the normal cheerful chatter, the visitors seemed unusually stiff and polite, and at the first opportunity Charlie took them off on their own 'to see what the cornfields you vanquished look like in the frost.' When they came back, flushed and excited, it was tea-time; and after tea came the first of the two summonses.

FANNY WAS TO REMEMBER the next two days for the rest of her life. On the first had come the attainment of the impossible; Father's 'yes' to Norman's request for her hand in marriage, her own 'yes' to Norman's impassioned plea. It seemed that everything she had ever dreamed of was to come true and her joy was all the greater for sharing it with Katie, whose own rite of passage had been equally straightforward.

They lay awake a long time that night. The two slept in the same bedroom, and in the darkness and with the rest of the family in their own rooms, the confidences flowed.

It was Fanny who plucked up courage to open the conversation.

'I wonder what it's really like being married. I know it will be delightful, of course, but I can't quite imagine it, the two of you all on your own without the rest of the family.'

'I know I shouldn't say such wicked things, but I think it will be wonderful. It's all right for the boys – they can escape, like Bob and Char going into the Church. But can you imagine what it would be like spending the rest of our lives in Bures? With nothing to do except be gracious and give away our old clothes? Poor Mary – just fancy being thirty-one! She's already turning into one of those bad-tempered old maids like the Fentons in Mount Bures. Anyway,

Mr Thomas – dearest Joseph – is so handsome and I'm sure I do love him so!'

'But Katie, what do you think actually happens when you're married? I know you kiss each other. That will be nice. But how do you have babies? There must surely be something else ...' and the discussion went on far into the night. In her heart of hearts, Fanny knew that, for a cow, it had to do with being mounted by the bull; she had watched him do it, several times with different cows, when he'd almost climbed right on top of them. But then what happened? In any case, the idea that this could possibly have anything to do with humans was so grotesque that she couldn't bring herself to speak about it, even to her sister.

THINKING ABOUT HER engagement afterwards, she told herself that it had all been too easy. Real life was not like that. That kind of joy was only for the story-books; there was no living happily ever after. For, on the second of those two days, a very different encounter had taken place. She and Katie had been sent for by brother John.

'Mary has asked me to speak to you both. She overheard you talking to each other last evening and realises that you both have great uncertainties about marriage. It is far too serious a step to take unless you are absolutely sure, so she and I have decided that we must withdraw permission. Father is an old man now and does not always know what is best. So you, Fanny, will not marry Mr Adams, and you, Katie, will not marry Mr Thomas. You will not see them again and, after writing to them to tell them that the engagements are broken off, you will not communicate with them ever again by any means. We will brook no argument and there is no possibility that Mary and I will change our minds.'

A poor sleeper, the old blind farmer was always the last to go to bed. As he walked the length of the upstairs corridor that night, he paused longer than usual outside every one of the seven bedroom doors. He liked to spend a moment thinking in turn about each of his children, picturing them all in his mind as they lay sleeping in the old house. That night he had deep sorrow in his heart. He had not been able to deflect John and Mary from their bitter and, to him, unaccountable decision. But he was old and no longer understood the ways of the modern world. How could he say that he was right and they were wrong? Oh, if only Isabel had been here ...

The sobs coming from the room shared by Fanny and Katie were pitiful to hear, but he did not go in. What could he say? He was just finishing his nightly round when his sharp blind man's hearing picked up a sound from Mary's room. He turned back and listened at her door. Her crying was quieter than her sisters' but it held a quality of despair that clutched at his throat. Why was she weeping? Was it for her own lost opportunities? Or in sorrow at her harsh decision, in pity for her bereaved sisters? He did not know and could not understand. He turned away, taking refuge in his own private darkness. There was nothing he could do.

In the morning, the letters were written and posted. Char went back to college and the house was silent.

Fanny would dream about her Norman until the day she died, nearly sixty years later. That day, so long ago, had changed her life for ever.

28

'EXCUSE ME, BUT PLEASE CAN YOU COME QUICKLY?'

Charlie was panting so hard that the policeman could scarcely understand him. In the dim light of the streetlamp, its gas flame spitting and flickering in the pouring rain, the constable could just make out a very young Reverend, his distressed face cut off abruptly at the neck by a shiny new dog-collar. Pointing back the way he had come, Charlie went on:

'There's a man back there lying in the gutter. I think he might be dead. I wouldn't have seen him, except I tripped over him.' Charlie brushed fruitlessly at his muddy trouser-legs.

He pulled the other by the arm, and then, as they ran together, he continued:

'There, by that letterbox. I took particular note, as I thought I might not find him again.'

But Charlie need not have worried. A loud snort from the corpse as they approached had him nearly jumping out of his skin.

'Bless your heart, Father, he's only had a drop too much to drink. If we were to pick up every one of them sailors and bring them in, we'd have to build a station the size of a warehouse!'

It had taken Charlie just fifteen months to be transformed from a young man like any other into a Man of God, and he was finding the responsibilities that came with the job of curate startlingly demanding. Mothers trailing shamefaced pregnant daughters came to his Liverpool church, seeking his counsel and his prayers. Funerals seemed to him to be the commonest church service. Many of the old buildings near the docks were still in existence, and hygiene was poor. An endless line of tiny coffins stretching away into the distance became a recurring nightmare, and when he awoke, his face wet with sweat and tears, the concerted wailing of the bereaved mothers still sounded in his ears.

There was huge contrast between the rich and poor. Wealthy woollen merchants drove their fine carriages up and down the wide main streets while, just a few yards away, hidden behind the splendid facades of rich men's houses, alleyways yielded a crop of poverty-stricken families struggling for survival.

It was hard, very hard, but Charlie was learning a positive schoolful of lessons that were in the end to stand him in excellent stead. Often he wished himself back at Cambridge, back where he knew he belonged, but it seemed that avenue was closed to him now and he must seek his spiritual fortune elsewhere. Bob's ethereal soap bubble had wafted away and disappeared in the black clouds of reality. Suspended between two extremes, its future was in the balance and only time would reveal its fate.

THE FIRST TELEPHONE twanged its way into the world in 1875, the year before Charlie was born. But the machine matured much more slowly than the man, so for years to come letters were to remain the main means of communication. It was another white vellum envelope embossed with the Clare College crest that once again threatened to turn the young priest's world inside out.

This time it was given to him by his landlady.

'I thought I'd better bring this straight up to you, it looks that urgent,' she said, as she arrived at the top of the stairs, puffing slightly, and tapping discreetly on Charlie's half-open door.

But he was not expecting anything of importance.

'Thank you, Mrs C, but I'm already late for the Church Council meeting, so it will have to wait.' He propped it on his mantelpiece, went down the stairs and disappeared out of the front door, closing it carefully behind him.

Mrs Carter smiled as she went into his room.

'Such a nice young man – always so thoughtful, and that tidy, too,' she said to herself as she glanced round at his neat desk, books and papers in symmetrical piles, two pairs of shoes, one black and the other brown, gleaming as they lay side by side under the dressing-table. She took the letter off the mantelpiece and looked at it again. He should have taken time to open this, she thought; her bones, always reliable, told her that the contents would mean a great deal to her conscientious lodger. But now she would just have to wait until he came back. She hoped the meeting would be a short one.

She heard him come in at last and go slowly up the stairs. When his door closed she opened her own, and stood in the dark little hallway, waiting for – what?

She didn't have long to wonder. The upstairs door flew open, and she had only just time to get back into her own room ('well, I never wanted him to think I was spying on him, did I?') before his black-clad figure exploded down the staircase, waving the letter.

'Mrs C, Mrs C, Clare have awarded me a fellowship!'

Mrs C presumed from his excitement that a fellowship was a rare and wonderful thing and did her best to look suitably impressed. She failed.

Charlie took pity on her evident puzzlement and did his best to explain.

'You see, every Cambridge college has a Master in charge, but really it's run by a group of graduates called fellows. They're the college officers, if you like. There are usually about a dozen of them and unless one dies or retires they can't appoint a new one. It's their job to make sure the college runs smoothly and to supervise the undergraduates; see that they're doing some work, and fill in the gaps in what they're learning. You live free in college, and get a decent salary. And you have time to read and think and research – oh, it's all just too good to be true!'

Mrs Carter couldn't wait to tell Mr Carter all about it when he got back from the pub.

'And do you know, he got me round the middle, apron an' all, and gave me a great big squeeze! I just couldn't believe it, him so shy and quiet! An' all it was was this fellowship, whatever that may be. He did try to explain – said it was to do with schoolmasters and chaps called aggravates or summat, but it didn't sound much to me. Just seems to make it easier to go back to that Cambridge he's always on about, and do some teaching or summat. I don't think the vicar'll be that pleased about it.'

'AUCTORITATE MIHI COMMISSA, admitto te in socium huius Collegii.'

The Reverend Charles Edward Garrad knelt at the feet of the Master, upheld hands enclosed between those of his liege lord.

This must surely be another dream, but of the day and not of the night. He, Charlie, was entering the holy of holies; he was joining the elite band of fellows of Clare College, Cambridge.

'By the authority given to me, I admit you to the society of this College.'

So the bubble had not burst after all. The black clouds had released their hold. The sun had come out. And he, Charlie, had achieved his ultimate goal. Ahead of him lay the perfect career, a scholar amongst scholars, a haven from the hell on earth of Liverpool, the perfect means of achieving his academic ambitions.

'IT'S A SHAME,' said Charlie to his next-door neighbour at dinner that night, 'it really is a great shame that even when things go really well there still seem to be difficulties.'

He was sitting for the very first time in his life at Clare College's coveted Top Table, the same table that, as a freshman, had seemed so impossibly out of his reach five years before.

'Why? What's bothering you?'

'Well, for a start, you have to be a curate for three years before you're a fully fledged priest, and I've only just finished one. So I can't leave to take up my fellowship before 1902. I suppose that must be all right with the college – they surely realise that I'm tied for two more years.'

'Yes, it's fine. We discussed just that at the last fellows' meeting, and we all agreed it was best to grab hold of you now while there's a vacancy rather than wait until another one turns up. It might be a very long time before that happens, and everyone wanted to make sure of you while the going was good.'

Charlie blushed.

'In actual fact, in some ways I'm quite glad to be staying in the parish a little longer. I'm really only just beginning to get to know the ropes and to be useful. And then there's the Seamen's Retreat ...'

'Which is?'

'Oh, it's a sort of club for sailors coming in and out of the port. I go and talk to them – we play games and so on, and I'm slowly getting to know how to reach them.'

'Do you mean you try and convert them?'

'Well no, not as such. But we talk, and they tell me about their religion – they come from all over the world – and then I tell them about mine. It's quite fascinating how often our views are the same, coming from completely opposite directions. Of course, I don't expect them instantly to fall on their knees and cry "baptize me, Father," but a few times they have seemed really interested. And then, the next time I visit, they've vanished, recalled to their ship. Frustrating, really, but perhaps they'll find another Christian priest to talk to in some far-flung place. So, by and large, I'm happy to stay on for a while. Anyway, knowing that I have all this to look forward to will make all the difference.'

And the talk turned to the circumstances of this, to Charlie, miraculous turn of events. It seemed that a few months earlier one of the fellows who was well into his nineties had died in his sleep, leaving a vacancy in that elite band of scholars. Meetings had been called and discussions held by the remaining fourteen members. The task before them was to choose 'a young graduate with such outstanding academic promise and acceptable personality that to secure him as a colleague would be a significant gain, irrespective of his academic field.' Names were proposed and seconded, but the final vote was unanimous. Garrad was their man.

WELL-HEELED AND DOWN-AT-HEEL ALIKE, Charlie's parishioners welcomed him back to Liverpool. The news of the honour bestowed upon their curate had been given out at church, and the rumour quickly spread that he was not coming back, that he had abandoned them for this obscure new glory. So when, the following Sunday, he processed in with the choir looking the same as ever, the reaction was considerable. Plumes on bonnets waved as Godfearing Liverpudlians exchanged meaningful glances, nodding at one another in approval and relief. They liked the young man. He wasn't easy to get to know, didn't talk much, and his sermons were a bit stiff, ('a bit above my head, if you know what I mean,' and the listener certainly did) but clearly his heart was in the right place. He did look ever so young though, but none the worse for that, they supposed.

He went to see the vicar and told him that he would definitely be leaving after two more years.

At the end of that time, the vicar begged him to stay on. He was doing such good work, he said, and 'I'm not so well, you know and, frankly, my heart quails at the thought of losing you. Stay just a little longer, do, please, just until I can get the right man to succeed you.'

Torn between his duty to the parish and his duty to Clare, Charlie simply did not know what to do. But the decision was made for him. A retired naval padre was looking for a post on land where he could at long last live with his wife and family. He was perfect for a position in a port where so many were connected with the sea and, to everyone's satisfaction, the problem was resolved.

Charlie was free.

29

Cambridge 1902

'MR GARRAD, YOU'RE BACK, SIR! I heard you was coming. I'm ever so pleased that I'll be looking after you again, Sir. I've been promoted, see, since you was gone an' me and a couple of the others takes care of the fellows now. Congratulations, Sir. I was ever so glad to hear the news. But you've been a long time coming.'

Sidney had spotted Charlie from the kitchen door as he walked across the hallowed grass of the Clare court for the first time, a privilege reserved for fellows only. It was four years since he had left Cambridge and few of his friends were left; he was truly pleased to see his old servant from undergraduate days.

So Charlie had to fill in the intervening years until even Sidney's curiosity was satisfied. They walked as they talked, and soon found themselves mounting the stairs to the Combination Room on the first floor, through an archway inscribed with the date 1688.

'I works in here now, you see, Sir, so I can show you what's what.'

Even Sidney evidently was a little in awe of the atmosphere of the place, for his voice had sunk to an unlikely whisper.

This was the fellows' common room, where they lunched, discussed, gossiped and generally relaxed. Charlie had never been inside it before. He saw a long, beautifully proportioned room, its dark oak panelling crowned by a magnificent gilded cornice. He saw for the first time the inside of the great windows, their heavy crimson curtains reaching from the ceiling to the red patterned carpet that covered the floor. Sidney, aware of his eyes on the carpet, whispered:

'That rug, Sir, comes all the way from Persia – made out there to order specially to fit this room. The villagers who wove it hadn't never had an order for as big a one as this before, and they do say they still talks about it there now.'

Down the middle stood a long mahogany dining-table, its gleaming surface reflecting both the ceiling and years of elbow-grease. A row of huge, heavy mahogany chairs stood guard on either side, and above it hung a monstrous bronze oil lamp nearly five feet across, each of its six mock-ivy-entwined arms supporting a curvaceous lampshade of white glass.

'You should see that when it's lit, Sir – it's ever so bright.'

Privately, Charlie thought it hideous, and that it spoilt the room.

'Is it a gas lamp?' he asked.

'Oh no. It runs on the colza oil they gets from a kind of turnip, swede-turnip I think they calls it. My wife's cousin has a farm on the fens, and he grows fields and fields of the stuff. After they've extracted the oil, they makes cattle cake out of what's left'.

Charlie was fascinated. He wondered whether his father knew about this. He would ask him in his next letter home.

Two elderly gentlemen, the taller one immaculate in a tail-coat, the other dressed in a crumpled suit and food-spotted tie, its knot creeping towards the hair sprouting from his left ear, stood with their backs to the fireplace. The blue and white chequered pattern of the glazed tiles surrounding the grate gleamed in the afternoon sun, but the fire itself had not been lit. Spring was technically here; money must not be wasted.

'Damn cold in here, Sidney. Can't you put a match to this thing?' Spying Charlie's clerical collar, the speaker quickly added:

'Oh dear. So sorry, my dear chap. Careless of me.'

Charlie introduced himself as the new fellow.

'Welcome, welcome,' and they both shook him by the hand. 'We knew you by repute, of course – otherwise wouldn't have voted for you. But it's nice that you've honoured us with your presence at last.'

This was not the best of starts, and Charlie began to stutter an explanation for his delay in taking up the position; how he had only been a year into his curacy when the offer arrived and ...

'No matter, no matter. You're here now, and the college hasn't fallen down without you. But some extra supervision for the theology undergraduates will be greatly appreciated by the faculty, I have no doubt.'

Sidney was left to prepare the Combination Room for afternoon tea, and the three fellows went down the stairs and out into the court once more.

'Are your rooms to your liking?'

'Are you pleased to be back?'

'What have you been up to all this time? After all, it's several years since you were appointed, and it's usual ...'

'How do you intend to spend your spare time?'

'Do you have an interest in a particular aspect of theology, anything that you wish to research?'

The questions were fired at him without mercy, the two older men interrupting each other in their interrogation. But Charlie didn't mind. He was back. That was all that mattered.

The three scholars crossed the bridge over the Cam, and Charlie caught his breath. In all his years at Cambridge he never tired of this annual miracle; the blooming of the daffodils along the Backs. As far as the eye could see in either direction spread a profusion of nodding yellow flowers; it was as if the brightness of that beautiful spring afternoon had crystallized out into a glorious flurry of gold. He turned to look at the backs of the mellow college buildings, their magnificent architecture displayed to perfection. In the foreground punters glided past behind the daffodils, their feet and the boats they stood on hidden from view below the banks of the river. Could anything be more beautiful?

At first his sense of discord was barely perceptible. The sun continued to shine, the invisible boats to glide past, the daffodils to bloom.

So what's wrong? Yes, that's it; the punters look so – well – so arrogant, so irritatingly self-confident. The way they swing those poles, so faultless, so proud, so superior, the rhythm so perfect. It's as though the river has soaked up all the introspective atmosphere of this ancient university and is passing it on to everything that touches it.

He stopped dead in his tracks. Without warning, a sudden image of Merseyside, with its noise, chaos and grinding poverty, unwanted and uninvited, had intruded on his dream and pushed it aside. The familiar stench of Liverpool's great river filled his nostrils, its filthy scum almost choking him. He shivered.

'Ghost walking over your grave?'

His companions were looking at him, eyebrows raised.

Charlie pulled himself back to the present and managed a laugh.

'I don't believe in them,' he said. 'Not the sort you're thinking of. But yes, you could say that.'

The moment had passed almost as soon as it had come, but it had left its mark, a mark that was to prove indelible.

The trio continued their tour, crossing the road to reach the fellows' garden, where Charlie would be able to sit and read and think in the summer months ahead.

'Time for tea, I think,' The tall don turned to the short one, who nodded in agreement.

'Are you coming back with us for one of Sydney's excellent collations?'

'No, I don't think so, thank you. I've got a bit more settling in to do.' Charlie left them in the direction of his rooms. The joy had gone from his day.

'Bit of a rum fellow, that.' The two dons nodded in agreement as together they paced back to tea. But they liked him all the same.

TWO YEARS PASSED, two years of the study of erudite texts and manuscripts in one of the world's greatest libraries, of lectures given and received, of efforts, in the main successful, to keep his temper with students who seemed to him almost totally without brain. He ate with his fellow dons, lived in his comfortable rooms, walked by the Cam. While he was out one day, someone delivered a letter by hand. He opened it, and read the short half-page of typing.

> Dear Mr Garrad
>
> The Council of the Cambridge Clergy Training School is searching for a suitable candidate to assist our new Principal in his work. If you should be interested in applying for the non-resident position of Vice Principal, we suggest that you come to the college at 10am on Friday next, the 10th April, when you will meet the Revd H.J.C. Knight and matters can be discussed. Kindly inform us as soon as possible of your acceptance or otherwise of this invitation.
>
> Yours faithfully
>
> W.G. Hammond, Secretary.

Within fifteen minutes, the reply was written. It was an appointment that would suit Charlie perfectly, and would give him the opportunity to work with young would-be priests, with whom he would clearly have a great deal in common. Of course, he must leave time for his other tasks, but yes, thank you, he would be at the meeting on Friday. His gyp was summoned, and the letter delivered before dark. The school was a five-minute walk away from Clare.

Charlie went to bed a happy man, the ghost stalking the graveyard forgotten; for the time being.

Bootalet Burma 1902

Pyau unharnessed the buffalo and sent him off with a slap on the rump into their field. Five whole years since their father had died – the time had gone so quickly! Mother was still faster and better at rice-planting than either of her sons, but she was so proud of them. They'd done well with the farm – the buffalo was surely proof of that.

The stranger's arrival altered everything. He just appeared one day, saying he'd been living with a group of white men in Mandalay and that they'd turned his world upside-down. At first, the brothers thought they were just the senile ramblings of an old man, but somehow they had to listen to him – they didn't seem able to help themselves. He kept on and on talking about this Jesus Christ he'd been told about and how He was the son of God and that Buddha was only a kind of stepping-stone and never said he was God anyway, and how everyone had got to be Christians and then they'd be really happy and not worry about evil spirits any more and they'd all go to a sort of Nirvana called Heaven when they died.

The more he talked, the more excited and curious – and confused – they became.

At last, they decided that they must go to Mandalay and find out for themselves. They sold the precious bullock to pay for their travel, with enough over to support their mother until their return, and set out on their adventure. They had never been further than the nearest village – there and back between the sun's rising and its arrival at the summit of the sky – and now they would be far, far away for countless days and nights. But this, somehow, was something they had to do. The old man had lit a fire inside them which would not be extinguished.

30

Cambridge 1904–1905

IT SHOULD HAVE BEEN PERFECT.

It had been, at first. The girls at home at Brook House had pounced on his regular weekly letters and read them aloud to each other:

Clare College,
Cambridge
16th October 1904

Dear everyone

You can't imagine how happy I am here. It is all I have ever wanted, and I keep having to pinch myself to make sure I'm not dreaming. Some of you have visited me and know how comfortable my rooms are, and there's plenty to keep me busy supervising undergraduates in theology – most of them are from Clare, but I am visiting supervisor to a few other colleges as well, including Newnham, which is one of the two colleges for women. I spend a lot of time at the Clergy Training School, of course. They have given me a big airy office where I do my share of teaching, but also have to sort out quite a lot of the administration, which I actually enjoy.

The clergy students are an interesting bunch. Most of them have come straight from one or other of the Cambridge colleges, though we do have several 'outsiders,' too. They do seem very young and inexperienced, and I can't help wondering sometimes whether they wouldn't be better off having a change, as I did in Leeds and Liverpool. I am very grateful to Bob for that. There are a few from overseas, too. They are more difficult to get to know, of course, partly because of the language problem, but I think we're making progress. I hope so.

How are you all?

As time went on, there was not such a rush for the postman. The letters were still written, read and answered, but they arrived at increasing intervals and had clearly been penned from a sense of duty rather than enthusiasm.

'We can't really expect anything else,' the sisters would say to one another.

'Char must be well and happy, otherwise he'd tell us. He's working so hard – we can't expect him to write much.'

His letters, still in their neatly-opened envelopes dated on the outside in Fanny's spidery hand, were filed in shoe-boxes, one for each year. '1904' held its full quotient, but the 1905 box was slow in filling. Sometimes several weeks went by without a letter bearing the familiar Cambridge post-mark.

How am I going to tell the family? I haven't even mentioned Miss Turner – Gertrude – to them. I should have told them about her when I first took her on as one of my students at Newnham. But I had no idea then that things would turn out like this. I thought she was just a very clever girl, and that that was why I enjoyed teaching her so much. And then we found gradually that we had so much in common, that she'd had just as rotten a time at school as I had, and for the same reasons.

And then, when she poured it all out the other day when we were watching the punting, I felt so terribly sorry for her. I think the girls at her school were really cruel to her, not just spiteful, and all because she's no good at ball-games. It's hard to believe what children can do to each other. Of course, she's done really well in spite of it all, and she's certainly got spunk. Women undergraduates are pretty few and far between and she'll get a good grade in her finals, though, of course, women aren't entitled to a degree.

Anyway, I do admire her tremendously. I have to admit that it would be nice if she did something a bit different to her hair and perhaps even splashed out and bought a new skirt – I think she's worn the same one for the whole three years. But, after all, none of that really matters, and I'm plucking up courage to ask her to marry me when we go out to tea at the Copper Kettle next week. I'm pretty certain she'll say yes.

I wonder if I should say something now to Father and the others? No, I think as I've left it so long it's probably better to wait and present them with a fait accompli. If there is one, that is, but I'm almost certain she'll say yes.

THE DATE AT THE COPPER KETTLE CAME – and went, with nothing to show for it but a couple of embarrassed young people, both rather red in the face.

Thank goodness I waited, and didn't tell them at home what was in my mind. I had completely misunderstood Miss Turner – she was absolutely flabbergasted when I asked her to marry me. She was obviously seeing me as a Father figure, in more ways than one; after all, I am nearly ten years older than she is, though I didn't even think about that. She evidently had no idea at all about my feelings for her.

So now I must forget about it all if I can, and just get on with my job. I am actually very surprised at myself – I thought I should be completely devastated, but somehow I'm not. How odd.

AND SO THE REGULAR correspondence started up again and the '05 shoe-box began to fill more quickly. Not a single member of the family at Bures ever heard even a whisper of the affair that never was.

Or that almost never was, for it did have an effect, on Charlie at least. It unsettled him.

What an ungrateful fellow I am. I thought I'd got everything I wanted, but recently there seems to be something missing. Perhaps I was fonder of Gertrude than I thought – after I'd recovered from being turned down flat. I wonder what's happening to her now?

Anyway, I've still got all my students to look after – I think that's really one of the best bits of the job, apart of course from my research. I do like the contact with the overseas ones – something else that old Mr James in Liverpool taught me, I suppose, with his interest in the sailors' club.

Shortly after the exit of Gertrude, who fortunately had finished her three years at the university soon after the fiasco and had departed his life for ever, two young Indians had arrived at the college. Both had degrees from Calcutta University and had come to England to train as priests before going back to work in their own villages. Their English was excellent, and Charlie found himself increasingly drawn to their company. The more they told him about their homes, about the sort of lives their families led, about the problems between Hindus and Buddhists and the lack of Christian teaching, the more fascinated he became.

The pair of them came up to him after class one day. They did not beat about the bush and their words knocked the breath out of his body.

'Father Garrad, will you come back to India to work with us when we finish our course here?'

Speechless, he simply looked at them.

'We need you so much. You are such a good teacher – we do not have teachers like you at home. That is why we came here to learn how to tell people about Jesus. Please come!'

They looked at me with those great big brown eyes, so beseeching. But how can I? I have everything I've always wanted here. I don't want to leave it all – how CAN I? It really doesn't seem fair. I had my struggles with deciding to train for the priesthood in the first place, but with God's help I overcame those and took the path that seemed to have been laid out for me. Now I'm doing all I can to train other young priests, and what we're achieving between us does seem to be appreciated here. Surely to goodness that's enough? There's the family, too. Is it right just to up sticks and go? After all, I may never come back. A lot of missionaries fall ill and never get home again. Father's getting old – surely I shouldn't leave him?

And so the mental argument went on, and on, and on. Night after night, his conscience literally gave him hell.

The Hound of Heaven, still not satisfied, was on his scent again.

CHARLIE DECIDED IF THERE was anyone who could help him in this predicament it would be Mr James, Bob's old vicar in Liverpool. They had kept in touch, and over the years he had found a wonderful mentor in the wise old priest. It was almost the end of term, and Charlie wrote to him.

Dear Mr James.

I'm afraid I need your help yet again. Briefly, two of my students, young graduates from Calcutta University, have approached me with a view to my going back to India with them when they finish their course, to work as a missionary. Such a thing had never entered my head, but my conscience is giving me a bad time over it, and I would value your opinion, as always. They would like to come with me on my visit to you, partly to see a little more of England. We would stay in a guest house, of course.

It would be lovely to see you again anyway. Tell us when we can come.

Yrs affectionately

Charles Garrad.

The answer arrived by return.

'Come as soon as you can, all three of you. I am always here.'

TWO DAYS LATER, the four men were sitting in Mr James's study in Liverpool. By the end of the week, three of them were on their way south again, the decision taken. The two young Indians would finish their course and go back home alone. When he had given due notice to the Clergy Training School and to Clare, Charlie would apply to the Society for the Propagation of the Gospel, or SPG, for training as a missionary and would go wherever they sent him. It would not be up to him to choose.

With this, the Indian priests, though saddened that they might not be the lucky ones, had to be content.

Bootalet, Burma 1905

Of course, the first visit Pyau and his brother made to Mandalay was the strangest. The noise took a bit of getting used to, and the crowds, and as for the markets, why they simply could not believe their eyes! So much of everything – clothes, pots and pans, even jewellery. Some of the things were so strange that they couldn't begin to guess what they were for.

They managed to find the place where the old man from home had lived and it was all exactly as he had described. They talked to the white men – Fathers, they seemed to be called, though there weren't any white children about as far as they could see – and learnt more and more about this Jesus. And the more they learnt, the more they wanted to learn. So the time slipped by until, suddenly, the thought of Mother alone at home, trying to run the farm just with the help of neighbours, made them realise that they must go back.

The Fathers gave them money for their train fair and a bit extra, so that when they had put things to rights at home and had got the rice planted, they could come back. If they really meant to become proper Christians, there had to be a special ceremony called Confirmation which only the Fathers could do. The two brothers wanted this, more than anything else in the world.

BOOK TWO

BURMA

31

I HAD TO WHISTLE CLEMENTINE.

How this made the family laugh. For all his brilliance, there was one part of Charlie's brain that simply did not function; he was tone deaf. Musical appreciation was beyond him. So, when his letter arrived from Port Said, explaining the deck-sports that were arranged to keep passengers amused, the irony of this particular activity was not lost on his avid readers.

'Poor Char.' Little Bessie was helping Katie to polish the silver. 'Fancy him having to whistle, and to a lady, too!'

Poring over the thin sheet of paper, closely written in their brother's tiny hand, they had finally managed to decipher the whole page:

> Today we had a whistling game. Your partner had to stand one end of the deck and you the other. The starter told you the name of a tune. You had to rush down to your partner, whistle it to her until she guessed what it was, and then rush back. I had to whistle Clementine.

Whether he and the unknown lady came top or bottom was not revealed.

THE VERY FIRST LETTER had come from Birkenhead, the port from which the SS *Casanova* was due to sail on October 18th 1906. The train journey there, marred by an unexpected absence of dining-car and therefore lunch, was made up for by a slap-up tea at The Bear's Paw on Merseyside. To Charlie's delight, a number of his old parishioners from St Jude's had come to see him off, and the Bures family learnt in due course that it had been 'quite a party.' The ship was new and smelt of paint. There were three of them sharing a cabin; one was 'not at all an exciting looking man, but I hope we shall get on all right. He is a great traveller and I believe a public singer.' They had christened him 'the Turk,' as he claimed to have lived for some years in Constantinople; Fanny was disappointed to learn by letter that he did not wear a turban. The other was a fellow parson by the name of Edmonds, also travelling to Burma and destined to become a close friend. Poor Edmonds; he evidently found his prearranged position at table that evening next to a young lady an extreme embarrassment. 'He blushed badly several times,' reports the relentless Charlie.

Darkness fell that first night, but there was none of the expected bustle of departure. Instead of the anticipated sound of the ship's engines came the mournful hoot of fog-horns conversing across the unseen water, some loud, some eerily soft, as the invisible ships signalled their positions to each other in the blackness.

'I'm going up on deck,' Charlie told his new friend. 'Coming?'

Arriving at the top of the companionway ladder for the very first time, the fresh air on their cheeks was the only indication to the two young men that they had reached their goal. Their eyes were useless. The fog was so dense that even the deck-rails were hidden from sight. It was a ghostly silent world, totally cut off from any sort of reality, a fitting start for a venture itself so unknown as to be almost unimaginable. The English shipbuilding town, just a few hundred feet away, was as invisible as if they had already completed their journey. The absolute stillness was thrown into relief by the moaning fog-horns, and for a moment both of them were totally disorientated, visitors to an alien planet.

But all of a sudden they nearly jumped out of their respective skins as their own ship hooted its warning to the world. The noise was overwhelming and they scuttled for the ladder and the cheerful, warm light of the passenger quarters.

By next morning the fog had lifted and the sun shone. Alas, the tide was out and there was insufficient depth of water for the ship to cross the bar. But, as the tide came in, so once more did the fog and it was not until their second morning that they were awoken by the sound of the ship's engines starting up.

Charlie leapt out of his bunk and shook his friend awake. Even the Turk slithered out of bed.

'Come on Edmonds! I want to see us leave!'

He threw on his clothes and, leaving the cabin, found the whole world deckward bent. Cabin doors were flying open and half-dressed men and women pulled on jerseys and jackets as they ran for the companionway and up into the sun.

The pilot had evidently come on board while they slept and quickly set to work to steer the ship across the bar and out of the mouth of the Mersey. The passengers lining the deck-rail watched engrossed as, his task at last safely accomplished, he climbed from their own deck down a rope ladder into the waiting rowing boat that was to return him to dry land. In Charlie's mind, that last chorus of 'goodbyes' called across the ever widening expanse of water between them severed their last links with England. Surely now they were finally on their way.

The next days passed without major incident. Sometimes the sea was smooth as a millpond, sometimes so rough that there were few takers for the excellent evening meal. In his diary, Charlie wrote of 'a parade of the crew after afternoon tea. A hundred and twenty of them, all black. Such a sight! Some in slippers, some in bare feet, most of them wearing skull-caps and all very dirty. These I suppose will be the sort of people that I shall be working among.'

He quickly made a second friend, Mr McAlastair, a fellow missionary returning from furlough. In the entry in his diary of Saturday 1st December he wrote:

'He helps me with my Burmese, which I am trying to learn while I sit on deck in the sunshine. This business about it being a tonal language makes it terribly difficult for me, without a note of music in my body. There seem to be three main tones – high, low, and (would you believe?) creaky! I think I shall be extremely good at that one – perhaps that will make up for the other two. McAlastair explained why the letters are all rounded, almost without any straight lines at all. It is because they used palm leaves as the traditional writing material. Straight lines would have torn the leaves, he says, though I don't quite see why.'

The Anchor Shipping Line did its very best to entertain the eighty or so passengers travelling aboard their brand-new ship. A wide variety of games was laid on in an attempt to suit all tastes. For the young and active, there were sporting events, much like those Charlie was familiar with from the village fete at home.

He was tempted by the potato race, always one of his favourites, where competitors race to pick up a row of potatoes one at a time and throw them into a bucket. Charlie astonished himself by being the first to collect all six, but to his great chagrin was deprived of his prize by a lady who, because of the intrinsic weakness of her sex, was required to gather up only five. He was ashamed at his own disappointment.

Diary, Sunday 2nd December.

'Six days out. The sea is very rough and I am feeling rather ill. Half-way through last night's concert some of the ladies collapsed and had to be carried to their cabins. Great waves were dashing over the sides of the ship. It was a glorious sight; I sat up late watching it.

'This evening there is a lot of lightning about. I can't help thinking of the family all peacefully in Church at home, and us being tossed about here, off Algiers. There was to have been a service this morning, but there was no-one to go to it, and no-one to take it. I always feel so ill directly I get into the dining saloon. There is a wooden frame round each place at table to prevent the things rolling off. The very sight of this upsets me. Another nasty sight is to see little balls of butter floating about in the milk. I had never though of waves being used to churn cream into butter. Sea-power would be no bad thing in the dairy at Brook House, if only we could harness it! We haven't done nearly so many miles the last two days, owing to the bad weather – 276 and 246.'

That day it had become apparent at once that the previous day's race was out of the question. The potatoes rolled everywhere, one tripping up a passenger so comprehensively that he sprained his ankle and had to be supported to the ship's doctor.

32

DIARY, THURSDAY 6TH DECEMBER.

'At last we have a nice day, beautifully warm and the sea quite calm – I put on my white boots for the first time. The Turk now calls himself Mr Jones, but his profession remains a mystery. He told us this morning that he wants to stay in various towns in Burma without the people knowing what he's there for. Could he be a spy?

'I have had some talk with the lady who sits next to Edmonds at breakfast, who turns out to be a hospital matron. She is not at all exciting.

'We are due to arrive at Port Said tomorrow. Only an eight hour stop, though, and I believe it is unlikely that we shall be able to land.'

HE WAS RIGHT, but even so the pause at the head of the Suez Canal held a great deal of interest for an inexperienced traveller. The ship was besieged by small boats from the land, some coming so close that their masts tapped against the side of the steamer. One of the *Casanova's* passengers leant down and grabbed the top of the tallest and was nearly responsible for its capsize, and a great deal of shouting and fist-shaking ensued. But tempers calmed and no real harm was done, and soon the ship was under steam once more.

The Suez Canal was an excitement, but Charlie dragged his friend Edmonds off the deck down into the bowels of the ship.

'Come on – come and look at this. It won't take long,'

He had asked one of the ship's officers some questions about the cut between the Mediterranean and the Red Sea, and had been directed to a small passenger lounge that had seemed rather dull and uninteresting. But on the wall was a big map, and the two young men could trace the dotted-in courses of the various canals that had been dug over the millennia between the River Nile and the Red Sea.

'Can you believe this?' he said, pointing to a small paragraph printed below the map.

'It says, "There is an inscription on the temple at Karnak which suggests that one such canal existed right back in the second century BC. And that our new channel incorporates the original one for much of its length." Isn't that incredible? Especially when you think that this modern one was only opened a few years before I was born.' He did a quick calculation. 'Just seven, in fact.'

And so back on deck, to see as much as they could of the shorelines before darkness overtook them. It was extraordinary to be in such a big ship, yet so close to the land on either side that they could actually watch the activities of people, almost as if they were travelling in a tram at home through a busy street. A man drove a donkey in a big hat, its ears sticking out through special ear-holes; a gang of gawky adolescents threw stones into the water; a group of children ran along the shore trying to keep pace with the ship, their shrill voices clearly audible even above the thrum of the engines.

And so on through the Red Sea, with awnings up over the deck and electric fans working at full speed. 'Tin things like coal scuttles with an open back are put into the portholes to catch any air there may be outside.' At times there seemed to be no air to catch, not even the faintest breeze. At others, a strong wind blew the waves into a rainbow-coloured spray, creating magical patterns and colours. By day, when it was calm, shoals of flying fish surrounded the ship a little distance away, so small that they looked like dragon-flies skimming the water. By night, as Charlie strolled round the deck in the cool of the evening, he would pause to watch the sharp bows sear the sea into a shining phosphorescence, sending bright white daggers of cold fire along the ship's sides.

Between the day and the night came the astonishing spectacle of the setting sun. Each evening almost the entire company of passengers would line the western deck-rail to watch; those who were late missed the performance, for it all happened in the twinkling of an eye. The gigantic ball of fire approached the horizon faster and faster, slipping ever more quickly down the smooth slope of the sky until, in a final blaze of glory, it disappeared, snuffed out behind the crimson hills. The sea itself seemed changed to blood, its surface shining with a brilliance that for a moment almost hurt the eye. Then suddenly red turned to steely grey, the colour washed away by the cold waves in the fading light. It was a sight none of them would ever forget.

Real blood became rather more of an issue when the SS *Casanova* was roughly halfway down the Red Sea.

'The Captain says that a shark's been following the ship for a couple of days. He told me at lunch to-day, but says that it's nothing to worry about, and that it's a long way off.'

This report from one of the superior passengers seated at the Captain's table in the dining-room spread like wildfire. This time it was the stern rail that was crowded with people, as passengers screwed up their eyes against the glare in an attempt to see the giant fish.

But the sea behind the ship was empty and soon more pressing pursuits called; a snooze in a deckchair, or a game of deck-quoits. Charlie, though, was not so easily distracted. He settled himself down in the shade of one of the lifeboats, his Burmese grammar on his knee, and awaited events.

'Shark ahoy!'

His excited shout awoke the sleepers, and there was a rush for the rail as a sharp knife-point, tiny at first but growing rapidly in size, cut through their wake and careered towards them. Suddenly it was alongside, only a few yards away, and now it was easy to see the huge dorsal fin incising the water with a purposeful precision that was frightening to watch. The shiny black body humped up through the sea just a few yards from the ship, and there was a gasp as the onlookers instinctively stepped back from the rail, almost falling over one another in their alarm.

Charlie found Edmonds at his elbow.

'Suggest you don't choose this moment to jump overboard,' said his friend. 'Though, of course, it would give people something to write home about. "Promising young missionary converted – into shark-food." Not a bad newspaper headline, that. How about it?'

But Charlie was not amused. It wasn't even a very good joke.

SOON THE RED SEA was left behind and, with no more excitements and no shoreline to watch, the passengers settled once more into the routine of ship-board life. The crew worked hard to keep them amused and the physical games seemed to get more and more daring as they approached Bombay. Charlie hesitated over entering for the obstacle race; it looked very challenging, but he scolded himself for being a coward and took his place in the queue of competitors. It was tempting, too, for the temperature was rising daily and this competition involved a wetting.

That morning, he had watched the preparations made by the crew. The end of a huge piece of sailcloth had been slung over a high spar, and secured there with very nautical knots. The other end was tied to a lower beam, the belly of the sail bulging down between the two, producing a sort of lopsided trough which the men filled with sea-water. Finally, long ropes were flung up and over the high spar and down the other side, and were made fast at either end. It was all highly intriguing.

He had asked the young officer in charge whether this was some life-saving drill in case of capsize. The man had laughed.

'Oh no, Sir. This is part of the obstacle race.'

'So what would I have to do if I entered?'

'Well, Sir, first you jump in the water in the sail. Then you grab hold of this rope, and you climb up it hand over hand. Once you reach the spar' – he looked up, shading his eyes with his hand – 'you climb over it and slide down the rope on the other side to the deck. Then you run to the winning-post, and there you are!'

Charlie had an uncomfortable feeling that he wouldn't in fact be anywhere except splashing helplessly about in the ingeniously designed swimming pool. But that in itself was a tempting thought, so he had signed on and here he was.

The starting-pistol popped. Climbing through the initial series of four suspended lifebelts was relatively easy, and Charlie maintained his position. But next came the real challenge.

Getting into the sailcloth bath wasn't difficult. Half sitting, half standing in the salty water, he grabbed the thick, heavy rope and started to haul himself up. Right hand, left hand, both feet; right hand, left hand, feet; right hand, left hand – on and on and on. The sweat, salty as the sea-water, was pouring down his face and into his eyes, blinding him. But he was not going to be defeated; he would get to the top even if he perished in the attempt. Suddenly the rope tightened over the beam and he was looking down the other side, down at the deck far below. Scrambling over the spar, he let himself down backwards, the rope running through his hands so fast that only its wetness saved them from skinning. A short distance from the bottom he let go, landed on his feet, and ran for the end of the deck as if Neptune and his trident were on his tail.

He had got there first! The applause was surprisingly sweet music to his ears.

He celebrated his win with a proper bathe in the sailcloth pool. There was just room to swim a few strokes; a welcome relief from the ever-increasing temperature.

Diary, 12th December.

'A couple of nights ago when I couldn't sleep for the heat, I managed to get myself out of my bunk to go and look at the Southern Cross. One of the crew told me that at this stage in the journey you can see it, but only at about four in the morning. I thought you could only see it from the southern hemisphere, but I suppose we are not so very far north of the equator now. Anyway, it was rather disappointing. I was glad I didn't have to find my way by it, as sailors are supposed to be able to do without any trouble at all. At least the trip made me go back to sleep.'

Diary, 18th December.

'We are all getting rather mad as the end of the voyage gets nearer and nearer. Ladies and gentlemen are very friendly to say the least of it. There are three couples on board with daughters of marriageable age. We had a most successful dance last night, with very select programmes and supper ices etc. As there are so few gentlemen, married ladies were not supposed to dance; they had to play Bridge in the Music Room!

'I have been very proper throughout. Someone warned me to Beware of the Mothers, but there has been no need.'

On December 19th the *Casanova* lay at anchor off Bombay. They had arrived at last. The passengers' luggage was spread out on the lower deck, ready for unloading in the morning. Charlie and his two companions spent one last night closeted together in their little cabin; whether they slept or not is not on record. The last sentence of his journal of the voyage reflects perfectly his attitude, his way of managing.

'There is always an end to everything.' And ends lead on to new beginnings.

33

A WALL OF HUMID HEAT, of humanity, of clamour hit them with an almost physical blow when they disembarked from the motor launch that brought them ashore. Sea breezes had kept off the worst of the heat until now, and Charlie had never experienced anything like this. Hot steamy bodies seemed to encompass them on every side. The noise was overwhelming.

'Very good gharrie, Sahib!'

'Where you want to go?'

'Very cheap!'

Charlie had expected that there would be someone to meet him from the SPG office, where he had been told to report before catching the Calcutta train and then the boat across the Bay of Bengal to his final destination, Rangoon. But there was no sign of anyone; in any case, how could they possibly find each other in the midst of all this chaos?

A hundred raggedly-dressed Indians jostled them, each one of them clamouring for their custom; choose me, choose me, choose me. With no-one to meet him, there was no help for it. Choose he must.

It was the smile that did it. It was the most glorious smile Charlie had ever seen, lighting up its owner's face as the young man laughed with a gaiety that even in this utter turmoil was infectious. Charlie couldn't help but smile back, and before he knew it he had been led by this dark, handsome boy to a small carriage, drawn by a pair of the thinnest horses he had ever set eyes on. Their heads were scarcely visible for the swarms of flies buzzing round them, and a sudden picture of the glossy, placid Suffolk Punches in his father's farm flashed before his eyes, and homesickness struck its first gut-wrenching blow.

But this was no time for the luxury of emotion, and he was in the act of climbing into the rickety vehicle when he suddenly remembered the very first lesson he had been taught. Jumping out again, he pulled a few annas out of his pocket, together with the address of his destination carefully written in the Hindustani script.

'Sixteen of those little fellows go to a rupee, and four of them will take you to most places in Bombay,' he had been told by an experienced fellow passenger on board ship. 'Always be sure to settle a price for your journey before you start.'

So 'how much?' he said, pointing first to the address and then to the money.

The driver looked at the scrap of paper. The message Charlie received back from the simultaneously nodding head and shrugging shoulders seemed somewhat mixed. Of course – the boy wouldn't be able to read. Charlie had learnt the words off by heart, and for the very first time in real earnest he tried his tongue round the strange syllables and was rewarded with a positive barrage of Hindustani. His delight at his success quickly changed to despair as he realised that he could understand nothing, not one single word.

By this time the surrounding throng of gharrie-drivers was becoming uncomfortably dense. Charlie's self-appointed guide snatched the paper from him and it was rapidly passed round the group, getting grubbier with every hand that held it. Once again the noise level was rising as a fierce argument got under way. Arms were extending north, south, east and west and all points between. Clearly no-one had any idea where it was that he wanted to go.

'I take the Sahib.'

An older man, better dressed than most, was standing at Charlie's elbow, holding his horses by their bright red bridles.

'I know the Fathers at your office. They are good men.' He beamed at Charlie. 'I am Christian. I take you cheap!'

And with that recommendation, what could the new Christian Father do but accept?

The driver was as good as his word, and after the statutory four annas had exchanged hands, and the short journey had been accomplished, Charlie signed on at the office. Profuse apologies were made for the failure to meet him, and he soon found himself on his way back to the dock, this time in an official SPG vehicle, to pick up his luggage. The street was broad but unpaved, with wonderful trees casting a welcome shade on either side. Their wide-spreading branches were covered with an exquisite display of large white, waxy flowers, but Charlie was even more struck by their perfume, so delicate and yet so well able to disguise all that lay beneath its more than welcome presence.

'We don't have those at home,' he said to his new driver. 'They're wonderful!'

'We call them Frangipani.' The man smiled at him. 'All the Fathers like them.'

THERE WAS ENDLESS PAPERWORK to be seen to at Bombay's Victoria station, the setting-off point for Calcutta. Every piece of luggage had to be weighed and then sorted, the heavy trunk to go to the luggage van, the lighter bags into his carriage. Forms had to be filled out for each one in triplicate, one for Charlie, one for the guard, one for the luggage officer. Then each item had to be meticulously labelled. There was almost no common language, and the heat in the stuffy station premises was intense.

But, at last, it was done, and only one thing remained. Charlie's diary summed it up nicely:

'Lastly I had to march on to the platform followed by a whole army of coolies, each carrying one piece of luggage, a case, a topee (just purchased), a Gladstone bag, two carrying a cabin-trunk, a box of books, etc etc. Then all had to have a tip. It was a business! Of course I travelled first-class.'

'EXCUSE ME, do you mind if I take the two lower bunks?'

Charlie's travelling companion in their cabin was an elderly man with a marked limp.

'I have this tiresome gammy leg, so I can't really manage a top one. I'm afraid, though, that it'll be hotter up there.'

They were fortunate that the two of them had the four-berth cabin to themselves. Charlie spent much of the journey lying prone on his high perch and looking across the wide landscape at his first view of India. It was bare sandy country that they passed through, mile upon mile upon empty mile of it. The brilliant green of paddy fields or a small patch of wheat or sugarcane were a sure sign that they were nearing a village, a little palm hut settlement with tiny dots of people going about their business that made him long to be able to get out and explore. A couple of times, quite close to the train, he saw a pair of buffaloes dragging a wooden plough through the inhospitable earth, the farmer guiding it from behind. Once, far from people, he spied a herd of elephants, babies following their mothers as the group moved to a new feeding ground.

Every now and again the light in the compartment would change and dim as the railway line penetrated a patch of jungle, inquisitive monkeys peering at the train from the safety of massive trees and occasional flashes of bright reds and greens through the branches as birds fled from the noise of the engine. On the edge of a small town was a train of camels, each animal laden with some unrecognisable burden.

At night, they lay down in their clothes; no bedding was provided. There was a lavatory of sorts, without soap or towel. But the train stopped several times each day for the passengers to get out and buy a meal at the station and all in all Charlie found it a pleasant enough journey. With every mile he was getting nearer and nearer to his final destination and to the life that was to be so different from anything he had done before.

34

THE CAMEL HAD HIM by the collar and was shaking him, surprisingly gently at first but with ever increasing vigour. The huge stained teeth were perilously close to his ear but, try as he would, Charlie could not open his eyes to see what it was that was causing the beast to behave so strangely. With a gigantic effort he tore the lids apart. The camel had inexplicably vanished, its place taken by a human hand lying beside him on the pillow that was improvised from his own rolled-up jacket. As he watched, mesmerised, the fingers came to life and grabbed his collar again, almost pulling him off his bunk.

'Wake up, can't you? Wake up, wake up, wake up!'

He recognised the voice of his travelling companion, and rolling to the edge of his perch saw that the hand was attached to that gentleman's arm and that the face next to it was very red indeed.

'Thank God for that! I began to think you had died of apoplexy in this damnable train. Oh sorry, Padre – shouldn't use such language to a man of the cloth. But how you can have been so fast asleep is beyond my understanding. Better get a move on. We've arrived.'

Only then did Charlie realise that the train had stopped. The noise coming through the window was indescribable; unfamiliar language shouted at full pitch, animals squealing, hens clucking, beggars whining, babies crying, trolley wheels screaming and the occasional snatch of the clipped accents of a British traveller like himself. Yes, they had most certainly arrived at Calcutta, and it was time to collect himself and his possessions and to embark on the last leg of his journey.

Jumping down on to the platform with his immediate belongings, he had no idea what to do next. He knew that his objective was the port where he hoped to find the steamship that would carry him at last to his final destination, but how on earth he would get there was quite another matter. A throng of beggars had instantly detached themselves from the crowd and were pressing up against him; ancient hands with claws for nails were thrust at him, scrawny babies whimpered under his nose, amputated brown stumps waved in his face. He felt his gorge rise and began to panic; to calm himself, he stood for a moment to his full height and allowed his gaze to wander. He was of average height for a European, but most of the sleek dark heads around him reached only to his shoulder, and through the empty air above them he spied a uniformed British army officer standing at the platform exit. Salvation was in sight. Their eyes met, and Charlie, with a surge of relief, indicated that he would come across to meet him. But it was not so easy.

'Backsheesh! Backsheesh!'

The cordon of miserable humanity around him grew ever tighter, and Charlie was pulling a fistful of change from his pocket in a desperate attempt to buy them off when suddenly they scattered.

'You shouldn't give them anything, Padre. You'll only encourage them. I know it seems terribly cruel, but they are professionals, and most of 'em don't actually need the money. They saw how green you are and laid it on extra thick.'

The young lieutenant grinned at Charlie.

'Got bags in the luggage van, have you? I'll give you a hand. I've just been seeing a chum off on another platform and thought I'd look in here to see if anyone I knew was getting off the Bombay train. You never know.'

In experienced hands it was all so easy, and before long Charlie found himself installed in a hotel nearby, to await his ship to Rangoon.

The next day, Lieutenant Robinson called for him as promised, and helped him stack his bags and baggage in the army vehicle at his disposal.

'May I introduce you to a fellow-traveller, who'll be coming on the boat with you? Sir, this is Mr Garrad, a padre coming out to Burma for the first time. Mr Garrad, this is Colonel Johnson, a long-term member of our garrison here. You're in luck,' he said, turning to Charlie. 'The Colonel is an old hand – been here for ages. He's about to pay one of his regular visits to the garrison in Rangoon, and as I say he's travelling on your boat. There's nothing much he doesn't know about this Godforsaken part of the world – begging your pardon. I'm sure he won't mind if you ask him a few things. That right, Sir?'

'I should be only too pleased to help you out, Padre, if I can.' The voice was gentle, matched by the smile on the veteran soldier's weather-beaten face.

'Godforsaken' – the word had sent cold shivers down the missionary's spine. But the Colonel – did he think that too? Charlie had taken an instant liking to the older man, and relief at the chance of long discussions to come with someone of his calibre took a great weight from his shoulders.

CHARLIE AND THE COLONEL sat opposite one another at their little table in the ship's dining-room. They had just finished eating an excellent meal of chicken curry and rice, and the older man had been highly amused by the number of glasses of water the newcomer had been forced to drink. This curry was decidedly hotter than any he had eaten before, and Charlie felt his face reddening as the spices took hold.

'You'll get used to it. Always eat plenty of rice with it – cools it down. Better to do that than to drink water. You should be safe enough on board this ship – the staff on this line are well trained – but water can be lethal, you know. Carries enteric, jaundice, all sorts of nasty things. Must always be well boiled. Not many of us get away without catching something pretty unpleasant.'

The porthole by their table faced west, and at that very moment the sun was once again laying on a startling performance. As they had put down their spoons, the huge fiery disc had been well above the horizon. By the time the colonel had delivered his homily on the dangers of water, only a giant crimson nail-paring was visible, and now suddenly all the light had gone from the sky and it was dark.

'This is something else I'll have to get used to. At home, dusk lasts for ages. But of course you know that.'

The colonel smiled.

'Don't worry. Everything will seem impossibly strange at first, but it's surprising how quickly you accommodate.'

THE NEXT DAY they sat together on deck in the shade of a sailcloth awning. Each man had a book on his knee, but neither seemed inclined to open it.

'How long have you been out here, Sir?'

'Far too long, really, but I love it. I first came out as a young subaltern, way back in '78. There was a king of Burma in those days, King Thibaw Min, but we soon put paid to that. He and his wife and two daughters lived in their palace in Mandalay – a vast place, enormously rich, protected by a great stockade, all of it in the middle of the Mandalay fort.' He paused, lost in thought. The ship's engines throbbed. Sailors called to one another in a foreign tongue. Somebody dropped a bucket.

After a few minutes, Charlie broke the silence.

'You just said that you put paid to the king, Sir. What exactly did you mean?'

'Ah yes, I'm sorry – I was just thinking about that poor royal family, and what we did to them. As an officer of the crown, I suppose I shouldn't harbour such thoughts, but after all your mind's your own, isn't it?

'You see, England had been chipping away at Burma for ages. It all started back in 1824, long before my time. That was when our army chiselled off bits of Burma and added them to our Indian empire. Then we got greedier – we began to realise what a rich country Burma was. And we needed to secure our supply route through it to Singapore. So nearly thirty years later, in 1852 I think it was, we had a second war. This time we captured the southern end of Burma, including Rangoon, and the Burmese moved their capital out of our reach. First of all they moved to a place called Amarapura. A few years later there was a change of plan – because of some Buddhist prophecy or other they shifted the whole thing to Mandalay. That was in 1857. Finally there was yet a third war, and that's where I come in.

'I'd been out here just a few months when the king died. That one's name was Mindon Min, the one who'd moved the capital to Mandalay and who built the great fort with the palace inside it – I suppose he'd guessed we were likely to try and capture more of the country at some point. When he died, his son Thibaw took over. I don't know too much about it really – it was all highly political – but I do know he wasn't popular with the British. There was talk that the new king was in cahoots with the French – we evidently weren't the only ones who realised what a prize Burma would be. So, a few years after this new king Thibaw had come to the throne, the British powers-that-be decided to act.

'That was in 1885 and although it's all so long ago my memory of it is very clear. I was a captain by that time, probably a few years younger than you are now. One morning, my battalion was ordered to form up on the parade ground, and we were told that we were to board ships, a company to each, and sail north from Rangoon up the great Irrawaddy river until we got almost to Mandalay. We were to disembark there and march on the city, capture the great fort, and take the royal family prisoner.

'And that is exactly what we did. It all went like clockwork. We mopped up quite a few small Burmese garrisons on our way north – shelled 'em from the ships, y'see. The toughest battle was at Minhla, our last port of call, but we had the latest weapons and the Burmese hadn't really got a chance. Literally thousands of us poured out of the hundreds of ships we moored off Minhla – must have been a terrifying sight. Then our huge army was on the march, most of 'em Indian Sepoys – apart from our regiment, of course. It was only a few days before the Burmese army threw in the sponge – there hadn't even been time to get a message to King Thibaw to tell him his army was done for.

We had won the war.'

There was silence for a moment. Then Charlie asked:

'But King Thibaw and his family. What happened to them? You said you did something to them. If you don't mind my asking, what was it that you did?'

'That's the sad part. We had to turn them out of the palace, lock stock and barrel, with hardly any warning. They were to be sent into exile in India travelling in bullock-carts – wretchedly uncomfortable. I was in charge of some of the troops who marched alongside them on their way to the port – we were half expecting trouble from crowds along the way, but in the event nothing happened. At the port, we shooed 'em on to the ship that was to take them to India, and that was the end of that. In India, they were taken to a place called Ratanagiri, and there they are still, I gather – nobody hears anything about them any more.'

There were so many questions that Charlie would have liked to ask. Did his companion have a chance to talk to the royal party? How old were the children? Were they in huge distress? Couldn't something better have been done for them? But the colonel had retreated into a world of his own, and Charlie knew better than to disturb him. Tomorrow, perhaps, he would have a chance to find out more.

After a few minutes, the older man rose wearily to his feet.

'I think I'll turn in,' he said. 'Got a bit of a headache. Sorry – I seem to have done all the talking today. Tomorrow you must tell me about yourself. I've come across a couple of the missionaries in Rangoon – excellent fellows, but my word they're up against it. They'll be pleased to have a new recruit, I'm sure. Anyway, goodnight – I'll see you at chota hazri.'

Charlie tried, unsuccessfully, to look wise, and once more the colonel had to help him out.

'It's a sort of snack to keep you going until breakfast time.'

'Goodnight, Sir. I hope you'll feel better in the morning.'

But he was too late. The colonel had already left.

35

THE YOUNG INDIAN BOY came up to Charlie as he sat at breakfast and, bowing low, presented him with a folded piece of paper. The message inside was written in a hand so shaky that it was hardly decipherable. It read:

> Dear Padre. I am so sorry but I shall not after all be able to join you for chota hazri. I am unwell and shall stay in my cabin.
> R.G. Johnson

Of course, this was a disappointment; there was so much more that Charlie wanted to discuss. But he had already grown fond of his companion of yesterday, and his uppermost feeling was one of concern. Burning his tongue on the remains of his cup of tea, still as hot as when the boy had poured it fifteen minutes ago, he made his way to the colonel's cabin and knocked gently on the door. No answer. He called out softly:

'Are you all right, Sir?' When he heard nothing, he repeated it more loudly. Still nothing. Hoping that no passer-by would misinterpret his action, he put his ear to the keyhole and heard a curious persistent rattling sound. 'Like carpet tacks jingling on a tin tray,' he thought. Puzzled, he turned the handle and, pushing open the door a few inches, looked inside. It seemed that the whole tiny cabin had come alive. Despite the calm seas around them, everything in it was shaking. Papers were trembling and sliding to the floor, and loose change danced in a metal ashtray on the table next the bed. The colonel lay stretched at full length on his bunk. His face was ashen. With his right hand he hung on for dear life to the table beside him, desperately trying to hold himself still against the violent rigor that convulsed him. Despite the heat, blankets were piled on top of him in a great heap and began their own descent to the floor just as Charlie reached the bedside.

'S-s-s-sorry, old b-b-boy. B-beastly b-bout m-m-malaria. T-t-taken qu-quinine – have to wait till it w-w-works. So c-c-cold!'

Charlie picked up the blankets and held them on top of the shivering man. He had heard about malaria, of course, but never in his life had he seen anything like this. The heat in that tiny airless cabin was suffocating and the sweat poured off him, dripping from the end of his nose on to the dry, ice-cold skin of the convulsing man. How could any living thing feel chilled in such conditions? Perhaps the colonel was going to die, now, right in front of him. For a brief moment, he panicked. He knew there was unlikely to be a doctor on board such a small ship. In any case, he couldn't leave him. What on earth should he do?

'On earth.' No, that was wrong. He sent up an arrow prayer and instantly his sanity returned. After all, he had read about malaria. He knew from his medical book that, though at the moment the colonel's temperature was hurtling skywards, it was likely to take an equally sudden downward dive. And so, for a while, it would go on, until the medicine had had time to take effect. Once the quinine had clocked in, the extraordinary mechanism that is the human body would settle comfortably back, its balance restored, and all would be well. Until the next time.

Sure enough, even as these thoughts were going through his mind, the shaking lessened.

'That was nasty,' said the colonel as he kicked off the blankets. 'Feel as weak as a kitten. All that shivering makes you ache all over, too. Pass me that glass of water, would you? Devilish hot in here, isn't it?'

FOR THE NEXT TWO DAYS, Charlie sat alone at his table in the ship's dining room. He was deeply concerned for his new friend. He had gone back to his medical encyclopædia and knew that, although the colonel appeared almost normal on the day following his frightening attack, another paroxysm was due forty-eight hours from the first. Would they have landed in Rangoon in time? Somehow he had little faith in the quinine tablets the colonel had shown him. Despite the latter's reassurances, he couldn't believe that a couple of little pills could cope with the immensity of that awful disease.

'YOU SEE? I TOLD YOU SO!' The colonel leant a little on the younger man's arm as they slowly sidled across the narrow gangplank from ship to shore. 'I do feel a bit shaky and I shall go to my quarters as soon as we get to barracks, but the bark of that tree those South American fellows discovered way back has been my saviour many times. Wonderful stuff, quinine. Never travel without it, and I advise you to do the same, my dear chap. What a good man you are. Come and call.'

And with that, he was whisked away by a group of tall smartly-uniformed young officers who had come to meet him. As he waved in reply to the soldier's salute, Charlie's thoughts turned to the first-aid box so lovingly and thoughtfully packed by his sisters before he left England. Iodine, bandages, aspirin – the list had been endless. Certainly, the directive from SPG had insisted on quinine tablets too, but Charlie had put them in almost with a shrug. Malaria was just a word; he'd swat the mosquitoes and show them who was master. But now he knew differently. It had been a good object lesson.

The crowd on the quay whirled about him. Short, brown-skinned men, naked to the waist and with loincloths tucked between their legs, staggered under the immense weight of the tin trunks they were unloading from the ship's hold. Several other military figures towered above the porters; elegant British ladies, sweating profusely under fancy hats, their parasols knocked from side to front and back again by the struggling mass of people, were escorted by solar-topeed gentlemen, trying in vain to protect them. The beggars were there in force. A pock-marked face was thrust into his own, so close that the man's foul breath seemed to clot in his own nostrils. Despite himself, Charlie took a step back, treading on the bare foot of a small, almost naked girl, who set up a howl so loud that even in the midst of the din heads of all colours and sizes turned to look in his direction.

Perhaps this was a blessing in disguise, for within a few moments he heard his name from behind him.

'Garrad! That must be you!'

Turning quickly, relief surged through every atom of Charlie's being. There at last stood a figure with whom he was utterly familiar, an English clergyman, dressed in the way that English clergymen should be, in a long cassock. Admittedly, the cassock was white, not black, but after all this was the tropics.

36

IT DID NOT TAKE THEM LONG to reach the headquarters of the SPG mission. Charlie had expected to find his first impressions of Rangoon, the very last lap of his long journey, to be even more riveting than the rest. But once ensconced in the carriage, his tin trunk on the roof and his new friend at his side, he suddenly felt very tired. His eyes followed the passing scenes as he gazed through the window, but the fresh sights and sounds made little impact. There had been so much that was new and impossibly strange that it seemed as though there was no room for more. And after all, there would be plenty of time. This was not just a holiday, a short adventure into the unknown. There were years ahead of him, an aeon of time in which to develop, to change himself into somebody better, stronger, quite different, someone who would not panic in the face of illness as he had done a couple of days earlier, or of all the other difficulties that would come his way. For the first time, but by no means the last, the piercing thought ran right through him with painful intensity.

What had he done?

WHAT HAD HE DONE?

This thought would return to him often as he lay sleepless through the long, hot Rangoon nights. It buzzed round and round his tired mind in tune with the insistent whining of the insects that smelt his blood through the flimsy life-saving mosquito net. But then, in the cool of the pre-dawn, he would fall asleep at last and, waking refreshed after even those few hours of rest, the excitement and challenge of each new day would strike anew.

Nothing was familiar. Everything was new and strange. At the beginning, not a single hour went by without some adventure, some surprise, however small. But fight against it as he would, homesickness became his constant companion. He was, after all, a countryman to the core, the mud still clinging to the roots so mercilessly torn from the fields of his beloved Suffolk. The north-country city where he had held his curacy was the furthest he had ever been from home. But he was a young man, at the peak of his powers and full of the spirit of adventure, and even the Rangoon streets, despite their differences, would not have presented too great a challenge were it not for one thing. He had nothing constructive to do.

Without a job to engage his energies, the weight of homesickness crouching on his chest grew heavier by the day until he felt he could bear it no longer. Commonsense told him that once he had something familiar to hang on to, work that he understood, all would be well. He knew that those in charge had the best of intentions, that the vacuum created around him had been put there for a purpose, to enable him to suck in the strange sights and sounds and smells that pounded him on every side, until he began to understand. He knew that after this probationary period was over there were plans afoot for his future, plans for the work that he longed to do amongst the people of this strange land. But waiting, just waiting; no, this was not his way.

AT FIRST, HE THOUGHT it was just the homesickness. But as each day went by the nausea grew until one morning he could not even face his first cup of tea.

'Good morning. Sleep well?'

Moncrieff, his companion in the mission-house, sat down opposite him at the breakfast table. The sun glaring in through the open window shone in Charlie's eyes as he turned to reply, but before he had time to answer, Moncrieff, his voice shrill, rushed on:

'Oh I say, what rotten luck! Have you looked in the mirror this morning? Your eyes are bright yellow. I'm terribly sorry old chap, but the chances are that you've got jaundice.'

As it turned out, that was to be just the beginning. But Charlie knew full well that he, like every other newcomer, was unlikely to survive without picking up some tropical complaint. He took his medical book to bed with him, and between his bouts of vomiting and to the mesmeric tune of the fan that revolved above him, he learnt about the germ that had wormed its wily way into his liver. For several days, his only companion was the boy squatting on his bedroom floor whose task it was to keep the fan revolving, and Charlie wondered at his patience. Half awake, he watched him. The regular bulge of the slender muscles in his forearms; the movement of the rope; the turn of the fan; one, two, three;

boy, rope, fan; sleep if you can; boy, rope, fan; one, two, three ... On more than one occasion, a visitor bringing drinks or companionship found both of them fast asleep, and tiptoed out again.

Charlie was an object of sympathy, of course, but not of great consternation. After all, nearly every new arrival suffered jaundice, and he would be well again in a few weeks at most, and immune against the wretched thing thereafter. Besides, he had not yet been given any real responsibilities, so work did not present a problem. At first, the illness took its usual course. The sickness gradually stopped and the bright yellow of his skin faded to a pallid tan. He left his bed and attempted to rejoin his Burmese language classes, but he was simply unable to get going. His limbs felt weak and his usual boundless energy had deserted him, had trickled like sawdust from the toes of the lifeless doll that seemed to have taken over his body. His head ached, his stomach hurt, and a troublesome cough interrupted his sleep.

'Come on, Garrad. What's up?' Moncrieff had found him drooping over his Burmese homework one day, and suddenly lost patience. 'Time you pulled yourself together. Everybody feels a bit feeble after jaundice, but you're better now and you really do need to get on with things. We all have to pull our weight here.'

Poor Charlie; there was nothing he would have liked better, but he didn't have much weight to pull. By nature he was as thin as a rake and now, since his illness, he 'looked edge-on like a cardboard cut-out,' as Moncrieff was to say later. But try as he would, he simply felt too ill to do anything, and as his friend looked at him again, he felt ashamed of his outburst.

'Do you think it is just that you're missing home, or is there something else, I wonder?'

And Charlie had to admit that he thought there must be something else, something physical that was interfering with his recovery.

37

It had taken just one glass of unboiled water. The innocent-looking drink that had turned him bright yellow must have concealed more than its fair share of poison for, within a matter of days, Charlie was admitted to hospital as an emergency with typhoid fever on top of the hepatitis. By this time, complications had set in and he was a very sick man indeed. With no antibiotics to get at the source of the trouble, it can only have been the excellent nursing he received that pulled him through.

As soon as he was well enough, Matron paid him an extra visit. As she bustled up to his bedside Charlie could see that she was bursting with important news.

'Oh Mr Garrad, have you any clean pyjamas? I've just had a message that the Bishop of Rangoon is coming to see you. He'll be here in less than half an hour.' Charlie's heart sank. He could almost feel it plummeting down through the thin mattress and lurking just beneath the 'springs.' There surely could be only one reason for the great man's visit. He was coming in person to break the bad news. He, Charlie, was to be sent ignominiously home before he had achieved anything at all. He was to be invalided out of the service.

What a hullabaloo in the ward. Brooms were brandished, bowls of half-eaten rice snatched away, and Burmese visitors, crowded cross-legged on to their relatives' beds, shooed outside. Curtains were drawn round Charlie's own corner of the ward. Had a throne been available, it would surely have been dusted down and placed strategically by his bed. As it was, a chair would have to do.

The preparations were completed in the nick of time. It was in exactly half an hour that a tall, purple-clad figure strode through the door, pectoral cross swinging, a sheaf of papers in his hand. With Matron dancing attendance, he advanced on Charlie's bed, sat himself down and spread out the papers on the sheet over the stick-like invalid legs.

'Well, Garrad. I'm afraid you've had a really bad time. I must say you do look pretty thin, but the twinkle's back in those brown eyes of yours. I wonder, is it too soon to discuss your future?'

Charlie smiled sadly and shook his head. After all, what was there to discuss?

'Excellent. Then I won't beat about the bush. You've probably heard rumours already, but now it's time to get down to things.'

He glanced down at the papers in front of him. What, Charlie wondered, could be written there? Why would the Bishop concern himself with the mundane details of his return home?

So certain was Charlie of the outcome that it took him a moment to concentrate on what the Bishop was saying and he missed his first words.

'... the Winchester Mission. I've got details of it noted down here which I'll leave with you, but I'll tell you briefly about it now – I don't want to tire you. The Mission is the brainchild of the wealthy Diocese of Winchester, thought up thirty years ago to start a link between themselves and Burma. Their plan is to establish the Winchester Brotherhood, which would set up a training ground for native Christian priests and also a medical mission. The Brotherhood would consist of a small group of unmarried Anglican clergymen, who must be graduates of Oxford or Cambridge. And that's where you come in. We thought it would be an ideal posting for you. There is one man there already, Edmonds by name – oh but of course you travelled out with him. He says he would be delighted to have you with him, and, between the pair of you, you could get the Brotherhood off the ground. How does that proposition strike you? Not till you're fit again, of course. Are there things you would like to ask?'

For a moment, the young man was speechless. Had he really heard aright? The typhoid had affected his hearing, but for the worse, not the better. Had it turned his brain as well? With a mighty effort, he opened his mouth and the words came out with a squeak.

'It sounds too good to be true.'

Against all the odds he was being sent not back but forward, to be part of an innovative project that would suit him to perfection. Even in his weak state, he felt shivers of excitement at the thought of the challenge ahead. To set up something entirely new – why, that was beyond anything he could have hoped for.

But the Bishop was waiting for him to go on.

'I have only one question, Sir – My Lord. When can I start?'

To his dismay, the Bishop shook his head.

'My dear fellow,' he said, 'have you seen yourself in the looking-glass?'

Of course the invalid had looked at his chin every day, when he shaved. He had got used to the haggard lines, to the extra folds of skin that had increasingly baffled the razor as the flesh beneath shrank away. He had got used to the fact that each day there were more hairs caught in his hairbrush, that the lush growth had thinned almost to nothing.

But the Bishop had not seen him since he had become ill, and was secretly shocked. He turned to the matron, standing quietly at his side.

'Have you such a thing as a full-length glass?' he asked, and she led them to her own office.

'Take off your pyjama top,' commanded the holy man. Puzzled, Charlie complied.

'Now, have a good look.'

The three of them gazed at the image of a young man who had shrunk into an old one almost overnight. The spectacle was not a reassuring one.

'I spoke to your doctors before I came to see you, and all agreed that it was unnecessary for you to go home. Seeing you today, I can't for the life of me see why. But if that's their opinion, and you are so keen to stay, I will concur. But on one condition only; that you go for a prolonged convalescence. I have a friend, a young doctor I met on my last furlough, who is working in a small town in the Himalayas, near Darjeeling. He has a spare room which he told me would make a wonderful resting-place for tired missionaries. I shall telegraph him at once.'

At once. There may well be no translation into Burmese for that very Western phrase. It appeared that Dr O'Neill was away on tour, working in outlying villages, and his native staff at his home were unable to say what answer the Sahib would give. So once again poor Charlie found himself back in the Rangoon Mission House, waiting impatiently for the promised holiday. Resolutely, he decided to use the time to learn more about his future destination, but try as he would he could not concentrate. It did seem that the typhoid, not content with removing a quarter of his flesh, half his hearing and three-quarters of his hair, had softened his brain as well. Too tired to think, he abandoned the tome on his knee and allowed his mind to wander.

Mandalay. To convert the heathen, he told himself sternly; this is why I am here. He tried it on his tongue again; Mandalay. It was a name that spelled romance and, for once, he allowed his imagination free rein, the release of a suppressed sensibility that finally would take him by the scruff of his neck and turn him upside down. But all that was to come much later. For now, though, surely no harm could come from savouring a name to dream about, that conjured up a past of all-powerful kings and queens, of glittering gold and glowing jewels, of pomp and circumstance, of wealth beyond imagining.

Until the British came.

Charlie had been a small boy at prep school when the British army drove out the last king and queen of Burma for ever; his mother had died just the year before. But he had been too young still to read the newspapers so, until he had met the colonel on the boat from Calcutta, everything he knew about his new home and the war that had ended in its loss to the British had come from his reading.

A WEEK OR SO AFTER his discharge from hospital came a knock at the door.

'You have a visitor, Sahib.'

It was the last person he expected. His old friend, the colonel from the Calcutta boat, was paying another visit to the Rangoon barracks, and word of Charlie's long-drawn-out illness had reached him.

'My dear fellow, what's all this I hear? Goodness me, I hardly recognise you. You must have lost a couple of stone, what?'

And the older man sat down beside him. Over cups of weak tea constantly refilled by the attentive houseboy, Charlie explained his predicament. '... so you see, although I'm longing to find out more, I simply don't seem to be able to concentrate.'

The colonel sat and thought in silence. Then:

'I think I just might be able to help you,' he said. 'There's an old man living here in Rangoon with an amazing collection of stories.' His voice lowered. 'He's Eurasian, you know, poor fellow. Not that that seems to bother him, though it does some people. He's a great favourite, in fact, particularly with the children, and there's often a small crowd in front of his house. He sits on the balcony and talks to anyone who wants to listen. And there are plenty who do, for he's a wonderful raconteur. A lot of his tales are just that, based on myth and legend, but not exactly historical. But I believe he does have a phenomenal memory and there's probably lots of history squirreled away in that clever head of his. Speaks perfect English, too – father came from Norwich or somewhere – your part of the world, anyway. Tell you what, if you like, I'll try and get hold of him and ask him to come and see you. He'd be thrilled to bits.'

The colonel was as good as his word, and just a day or two later anyone looking in through the open window from the busy street would have seen the two of them deep in conversation. The tall, pale young man in formal jacket and trousers, dark balding head bowed in concentration, and the old man at his side, white whiskers wagging in the flood of words that flowed between his last two fangs, lips and gums stained blood-red from betel-nut. Gruesome drips of it stained his loose-fitting shirt and had found their way on to the grubby longyi knotted round his waist. Both were totally intent; even the minor collision that provoked a major row outside did nothing to disturb them.

'Yes,' said the old man, 'I was fifteen when Rangoon fell to you British. Everything went to pieces then and I couldn't get a job, so I set out to seek my fortune. I worked my passage on a boat going up the Irrawaddy and got off where Mandalay is now. It wasn't there, then – didn't exist, you see.'

'How do you mean, it didn't exist? There must surely have been something – a village, at least. After all, that was only about fifty years ago.'

'No, there was nothing. Just a big, flat plain at the bottom of a hill, what they call Mandalay Hill now. You see, the king who was on our throne then, King Mindon Min, was a devout Buddhist and took his duties very seriously. He and his astrologers put their heads together and decided that the exact moment had come to fulfil a prophecy made by Buddha over two thousand years ago. The Lord Buddha had predicted that on the 2,400th anniversary of the founding of Buddhism a Holy City would be built right there, at the foot of that hill. So our king set about doing just that. Which was lucky for me, because they needed every man-jack they could get hold of. The idea was to dismantle Amarapura, where the royal palace was ...'

'Why was the royal palace there?'

The old man looked pityingly at him.

'Well, it was the capital, wasn't it?'

'Not Rangoon?'

'Not since your friends captured it years before.'

Then Charlie remembered the colonel's words on the boat from Calcutta, how the Burmese had had to move their capital to this town called Amarapura when Rangoon fell into British hands. He'd said something about a prophecy, too – that must have been what his visitor had been telling him about.

'As I was saying, the whole city of Amarapura was dismantled and loaded on to elephants and transported to where Mandalay is now. That was in 1857. So they needed hundreds of men to unload the elephants and build it up again. People came by bullock-cart and river from up and down the country to help; that's how I've got to know so many stories. So many different people, so many different places ...'

But Charlie was no longer listening, his thoughts on the enormity of the task ahead. This town, Mandalay, where he, Charlie, was to set up what amounted to a centre for Christianity, just fifty years before had been purpose-built for the worship of Buddha. His heart failed him. Humanly speaking, it was impossible. But, if this was what God wanted of him, then he must try. Of course he must try.

He dragged himself back to the moment. It was important to make the most of his unusual companion while he still had him at his side.

'And the king, Mindon Min. Can you tell me a bit more about him?'

'Oh, he was quite a character. My father – he was English, you know – had a job to understand his ways. He had fifty-five wives altogether, including the eight chief ones, and more than a hundred children. Father and Mother used to argue about the rights and wrongs of his goings-on, as Father put it. Mother was a Buddhist and I think she rather admired him for it all. In any case, he did a lot of good – built lots of new roads and factories and things, and generally tried to modernise the country. And, of course, he built the new royal palace in Mandalay, as I said. And he was broadminded, too. He wasn't against Christians – he could see that missionaries had a lot to offer. So he actually built a Christian church near the palace and a school to go with it, and sent several of his sons to study there. I suppose that's the church you'll be working at when you get to Mandalay. He wanted to mend fences with the British, you see. But, at the same time, he did all he could for his own religion – for instance, he organised the Fifth Great Buddhist Synod which was held there.'

All this information was more than a little bewildering and Charlie was finding it difficult to grasp. What a tightrope this extraordinary king had walked. Yet, somehow he had retained his balance perfectly, for, unlike his son and successor, he had an excellent reputation on all sides, with British and Burmese alike.

The visitor was getting up to go. Charlie would have liked to ask more; what, for instance, was so terrible about the next king, Thibaw Min, the one whom the British had sent into exile? From all accounts, he had been notorious. But why? Clearly, though, the story-teller had had enough and that would have to wait.

After all, now there was plenty of time.

38

India 1907

THE TINY FEATHER TICKLED HIS NOSE and made him sneeze. As he slid his feet even further down into the warm softness, one eye flicked open and then closed again. But his unfinished dream had slipped utterly away, and with it a depth of sleep unknown to him since childhood. What was it that had roused him? Of course! That momentary glimpse from a half-shut eye had shown him that the quilt from which the feather was escaping was yellow. His own eiderdown was green. So whose bed was he in? More particularly, why was there an eiderdown at all? Eiderdowns belonged to the cold clime of England, and he was in Burma, being a missionary. Or trying to be, if only he could get started.

And then the remaining mists of sleep vanished, and the yellow quilt landed on the floor as Charlie leapt from the bed, its colour almost blinding now as it reflected the brilliant light. If he had needed any reminding, the wobble in his legs that almost had him falling would have told him the reason for this extraordinary transformation. This was the new beginning, the end of the nightmare of illness; this was not Rangoon but Kurseong, where he would be restored to the health once taken so carelessly for granted.

He was at the window now. It had been late when he had at last arrived the evening before, and exhausted as he was by the long journey he had had no thoughts for his surroundings. Food, drink and bed had been his only considerations. Now, at last, he could gaze to his heart's content. The panorama that lay before him was not entirely a surprise, for yesterday he had travelled through countryside that, to him, was beyond description, so far removed was it from anything he had ever set eyes on before. It was this final leg of his journey from Rangoon that had made him wonder if the typhoid had not done for him after all, and he was on his way to paradise.

The boat and train journey from Rangoon to Shiliguri, the last town on the plain before the entire landscape took a sudden dramatic upward turn, was uneventful. But unloading his bag from the carriage, a wave of exhaustion threatened to drown him, and he sat quickly down on a wooden seat on the platform. Head swimming, the voice seemed to come at him from a far distance.

'Are you all right?'

He looked down at the hand on his forearm. It was a nice hand, soft, small, with clean nails and a very white skin. As the mists cleared, he saw that its owner was a very pretty young lady, her face so close to his own as she stooped over him that a strand of her fair hair tickled his forehead.

'Sorry – I suddenly felt a bit faint. I've not been well, you see, and I'm just on my way up to a place called Kurseong for a bit of convalescence. I believe there's a train ...'

'Oh, what fun!' She was, he noticed on closer examination, a very young lady indeed. 'We'll be travelling companions. My father's a tea-planter and I'm meeting him at the end of the line, at Darjeeling, to go and visit one of his plantations. Your stop's about halfway up. I'm Alice Anderson, by the way,' and he found himself shaking that self-same hand as he told her his own name.

'Have you been here before?' she asked, and, as he shook his head, burst out with:

'Oh you'll love it. It's so beautiful, and such a wonderful trip up into the mountains. It's a pity you're only going as far as Kurseong, but you'll have to take another trip right up to Darjeeling while you're here. Otherwise you won't see Kanchenjunga – you have to go a bit higher on the train for that. Or you could climb Eagle's Crag – then you get a good view of it. And you look down on the plains as well – you feel a bit like God surveying all us ants down here. Oh sorry – I hadn't taken in your dog-collar. Mother always says I do run on so.'

Charlie was not at all sorry; far from it. Already he was in another world, with a companion to match, and for the first time in months his laugh was so full of pure joy that Alice had no choice but to join in.

The little train was waiting for them on the next platform. Above its engine hung an impressive sign: 'The Darjeeling Himalayan Railway.' As Charlie began to read the words out loud, Alice chipped in with

'Nobody actually calls it that. Well, you couldn't really, could you? It's just not grand enough for such a posh name. Everybody calls it what it looks like – the Toy Train. People round here are terribly proud of it. They say it was one of the first in the whole of India.'

As she chattered on, Charlie read the few words of history printed under the title. The notice told him that the railway had opened to the public in 1881; what an amazing feat of engineering, he thought, at such an early date. Turning to look ahead, he felt more than a twinge of apprehension. Dotted ever higher up the steep slope, brilliant flashes of light as the rails caught the sun showed him all too clearly the precarious route they were about to take. But after all, he told himself sternly, if this extraordinary train has lasted twenty-five years it's unlikely to fail on the very next trip,

'Hurry up,' said Alice. 'We're going to miss it if we're not quick,' and she ran to the train, Charlie struggling behind with his suitcase. But the two second-class coaches were both full and the only remaining seats were in the first-class comfort of the leading carriage. At this moment the steam-whistle blew with a sense of purpose that clearly prefaced the challenge of the task ahead, and simultaneously the two forlorn passengers found themselves being pushed into the plush seats behind the little engine.

'Very good, Sahib. No need to pay more,' and the guard waved the train on its way with his bright green flag.

The carriage was open on both sides, and it was difficult to choose which way to look. At first, Charlie felt he could almost have reached out and touched the unfamiliar bushes that walled in the two-foot gauge track. Even by leaning out and craning his neck, he was unable to see the tops of the massive forest trees that encroached so closely on the frail little train as it struggled up the steep gradient. Dark and hidden secrets seemed to lurk just out of reach, and he was glad when the engine burst out into the light of open country.

'I expect some of this belongs to my father,' and Alice waved her hand at the narrow terraces built into the mountainside, looking like steps cut by some prehistoric giant. Each was clothed with tidy rows of hundreds and thousands of bushes.

'Is this tea, then?' asked Charlie, and Alice looked at him with astonishment.

'Of course it's tea – but why should you know? It's just that I thought the whole world knew about Darjeeling and tea. But then, I would – after all, it's how Father makes his living.'

'I'm sorry – there's so much I don't know, about this part of the world, anyway.' And for the first time, Charlie wondered how important all those prizes he had won in Greek and Latin really were. He looked at the colourfully-dressed labourers as they bent over the bushes and realised that he knew nothing,

nothing at all, about things that really mattered. But once again he pulled himself up with a start as he remembered why he was here. 'Christ died for them just as much as He did for me,' he thought, and he looked again. 'Those men, those women, none of them even know that He existed, exists. But I know, and it is to be my privilege to tell them.' Privilege; was it really that? A comfortable job as a theologian back home – now wouldn't that be something he could really do much better ...?

Suddenly, the carriage grew dark. They were back in the jungle again, but this time there were gaps between the dense bushes, giving spectacular glimpses of distant beauty. A waterfall appeared, tumbling over huge rocks that split its splashing torrent into rainbow-coloured spray. Looking backward, far away in the distance, Charlie spied a river meandering across the plains that he had crossed earlier in his journey. The sun caught its surface and it shone silver against the green.

Green of every shade was the background to everything.

'Just look at that!' Alice pointed to a blaze of red.

'What flowers are they?' asked her companion. She wasn't sure; thought they might be Poinsettias.

'And that purple, climbing all over everything?'

'That one I do know; we've got it in our garden. It's Bougainvillea – it grows like a weed, everywhere.' Nice weed, he thought. Dandelions don't quite come up to the mark.

It was a spectacular journey. They stopped in the middle of nowhere, to take on water for the thirsty engine. They stopped again at a sizeable station. The driver jumped down from his miniature cab and conferred at length with a smartly uniformed official, the English letters DHR embroidered in gold on his jacket pocket.

'Oh no!' Alice's wail startled Charlie, and he turned to her questioningly.

'I do believe there must be something wrong with the train, and we'll be held up here for simply ages. There's a big workshop for repairs here, and when they talk like that it usually means there's a problem.'

But her fears were groundless, the green flag was waved and they were on their way.

The gradient grew steeper, the engine puffed harder, the train went more and more slowly. It finally ground to a halt, and once again Charlie looked at his companion.

'It's all right,' she said. 'Sometimes when the train's full they have to turn round here and go up backwards.' She pointed to a little siding that Charlie had not noticed. The engine was uncoupled, disappeared into the siding, and reappeared in reverse. It seemed only a matter of moments before they were off again, this time with the puffing chimney so close to their carriage that wisps of steam often obstructed their view.

'Look!' said Alice, 'there's the Artilleryman!' Charlie, puzzled, gazed around him. Who? Where? Was the man on foot? On a horse? Was he going to shoot them down in their seats?

Alice laughed again and pointed out of the side of the carriage.

'It's only a rock, silly. You see that great big one, there? Well, the story goes that an army chap threw himself off it on purpose and died. And there's Gladstone.'

Surprised at nothing now, Charlie's gaze followed her pointing finger. All he could see was another mighty chunk of stone.

'It's supposed to look like William Gladstone. You know, the one who was prime minister,' she added patiently.

Charlie did know, but he couldn't blame her for treating him as a complete ignoramus. After all, so far he had lived up to that reputation perfectly.

In only a few more minutes, as they rounded a bend, a collection of houses came into view on the hillside.

'That's Kurseong,' said Alice. 'That's where you have to get off. What a shame. I usually have to do this journey alone. It's been lovely to have a companion.' Charlie heartily agreed. He surprised himself by his feelings. He didn't want to say goodbye. He had enjoyed sitting beside her in the little train, her open friendliness, her evident pleasure in his company. What was the matter with him? Perhaps it was that she was so very young, so much in need of his protection. Yes, of course, that was it. An unfamiliar, tender warmth crept over him.

But they were almost there. As they got nearer, the railway approached closer and closer to the road until road and rail were almost touching. With the train puffing slowly along, Charlie could have leant out and bought fruit or knick-knacks from the road-side stalls. Indeed, looking behind him he could see several of the second-class passengers doing just that, the stall-holders keeping pace on foot as bartering took place and purchases were made.

The train stopped. The goodbyes were said. Once again, he shook the soft, small hand with the very clean fingernails. All of a sudden, he felt extremely tired. He hoped against hope there would be someone to meet him. He was not disappointed.

꧃

'MR GARRAD, MR GARRAD! Your brother is here!'

Charlie was sitting in the garden of the little hotel where he took his meals. He had borrowed the proprietor's address stamp, and was just imprinting on to the top of a sheet of writing-paper the legend 'MRS MONK'S GRAND HOTEL, KURSEONG' in purple ink when a junior Monk arrived panting at his knee.

Brother? What could he mean? No doubt a mistake in translation, one of the many, and he thought ruefully of his own lack of language skills.

But the 'Char' in that distinctive, that unbelievably familiar husky voice momentarily turned his stomach upside down as he twisted round to look.

'George! But it can't be you. You're doing clever agricultural things in India!' But, of course, he himself was in India now. So perhaps this was not some extension of the dream he was living in, this cool, glorious utopia of English spring flowers and familiar birds, of calling cuckoos and trickling streams between fern-covered rocks. The familiar handshake, the strong arm around his own thin shoulders, the wonderful reassuring smile, the particular kindred smell; these were not imagined. This was his own dear brother, come to visit him and make sure that he was well again.

What a time they had for the next few days; the walks, the mountain pony rides, the meals together, the gazing on clear mornings at the distant snow-covered peaks. And, above all, the talk, of their own doings, of hospitals, of the dear family at home.

'How did you find me?' asked Char, and could but join in when that great guffaw of laughter scared off the little flock of birds that had gathered round their garden chairs, picking up crumbs from their chupattis.

'I very nearly didn't.' And then came the story of how George had left the address at 'home,' had thought Char was in Darjeeling, had done the round of all ten of the hotels there, had remembered the (wrong) name of the doctor Char was staying with, was put on to the right one, had telegraphed him, had been told the name of the hotel where he ate, and finally, more than forty-eight hours later, had landed up here.

Of course, it was sad when the time came to say goodbye, but nothing could have propelled Charlie more quickly up the ladder to full recovery than that short visit, and now there was to be no sliding back. It had been an unlucky throw that had sent him slithering down and down that particular serpent almost to the bottom of the board, but this was a game of snakes and ladders that he could not, would not, lose. There would undoubtedly be more snakes, but more ladders too. The worst was over, and the best was about to begin.

Bootalet 1907

Such excitement! Two of the Fathers from Mandalay came to visit them! It seemed that one of them was their headman – the other one called him 'Bishop.' He'd been away when Pyau and his brother had been in Mandalay, but he'd heard all about them and wanted to help. The way he talked was spellbinding – they'd never heard anyone tell stories as well as he did. He had the same book as the Fathers, and he'd sit there in the evenings reading bits out of it and then telling the story in his own words so that they could understand. He only stayed for the first quarter of the moon, and then they went with him to catch the boat back to Mandalay – that was the way he wanted to travel. Mark you, it was difficult to see the moon at all, as the rains had come early and the Bishop often had to wade through swollen rivers up to his waist like the rest of them. Pyau's younger brother took his luggage for him, one bag on each end of a pole over his shoulder with plantain leaves over it to keep out the rain. The Bishop didn't believe they would do any good, but they did. They all had to run the last bit as they were late for the boat; it had been a long and difficult day's march.

Pyau himself travelled on the boat with the Bishop, as planned, but his brother went home to run the farm. Secretly, he was rather pleased; two visits to Mandalay were quite enough for him – they'd both been back again once, to be confirmed.

Pyau, though, was different. This time he stayed much longer at the Mission, almost half a year, and learnt as much as he possibly could from the Fathers. The only schooling he'd had was from the monks until he was twelve, when his father had drowned, and he found all the listening and learning and trying to understand very hard work. But he was determined to find out enough to teach his friends and family at home to be Christians, so he stayed until he thought his brain would burst.

At last, exhaustion and homesickness got the better of him. He said goodbye to the Fathers and set off for Bootalet. The parting was not too sad, as he knew that at least some of them would come to visit him. When he got home at last, he could not believe his ears. Everyone, even his mother, called him Saya – Teacher. He had achieved his heart's desire, for surely now they would all listen to what he had to say.

39

BACK IN RANGOON, it took Charlie only a few days to pack up his few belongings and prepare for the journey north to Mandalay.

At last the moment of departure arrived. Once again his bags and boxes were loaded on to the roof of the carriage that would take him to the railway station. Once again, the intricate paraphernalia of travel for the Englishman Abroad had to be gone through – forms signed, provision made for his comfort on the overnight journey to Mandalay that lay ahead. The train left just as the day was coming to its sudden end. It was his first venture on a Burmese train and he was surprised to find it so comfortable. The long seats were at right-angles to the window, so there was plenty of room to stretch out at full length. True, there were problems. It was not a smooth ride and, as the words on the page of his book jigged up and down before his eyes, he began to feel the old familiar sensation of nausea creeping up on him once again. The book was quickly banished, but he was not yet ready for sleep. In any case, the blind that took the place of glass in the window had a noisy habit of unrolling itself and jerking him awake, and finally he left it down, despite the increased airlessness.

However, sleep did come at last, and for the next few hours he dozed fitfully. He was woken by the increasingly familiar screech of brakes as they stopped at yet another wayside station, and in his next letter home Charlie tried to paint a picture of the ensuing pantomime:

'Wayside station, early morning, 4.30 am. Descent of Englishman from second-class carriage. No sign of life anywhere.

'5.00am. The local teashop is beginning to appear, and the Englishman is much interested, has in fact been waiting half an hour. A slate-coloured individual has appeared, his face blank as a schoolboy's slate. He wears but one garment. His mouth is wide open and stays always wide open, except when preparing to spit. His teeth immaculately white and completely perfect. He goes to the booking office and from a cupboard there produces the whole outfit. Urn, tins for water, glasses, cups, food, everything comes from the cupboard without sign of haste or expression of any kind, the mouth always remaining open except for the purpose of spitting. Never are two things carried at the same time, and never is there any concern for those who are waiting. After what seems like hours and after much patience on the part of the Englishman, the tea shop produces a cup of tea.'

The journey of 386 miles was billed to take eighteen hours. The reason had not been hard to find.

Fully awake after such a major event, and with the sun now well up in the sky and the blind rolled as securely as he could manage, Charlie set to work in his corner seat to see as much as possible of the countryside around his future home. The gilt spires of pagodas became more and more numerous as they got nearer to Mandalay, and where rail approached road he could see increasing numbers of monks in their cinnamon robes, some in groups, some single, most with an attendant boy carrying a begging-bowl. He remembered back to his hour with the story-teller, and how he had been told that Mandalay had been built for the sole purpose of the worship of Buddha, and once again a sense of his own total inadequacy overwhelmed him. But he had been spared death in his recent illness; he had been spared an ignominious return home, the fate of several of his predecessors too ill to remain in such a hostile climate; there must be a purpose for his presence here. Resolutely, he determined to find it and to fulfil it, whatever it might be.

He was rapidly learning that it was the unlikely that was likely, to expect the unexpected. The transformation of his world from one of quiet, ordered scholarship to the apparent disorder of this astonishing country and people was total. A simultaneous surge of excitement and of wordless prayer erupted from so deep within him that he found himself on his feet. 'I will lift up mine eyes unto the hills, from whence cometh my help. My help cometh even from the Lord, who hath made Heaven and earth.' Had he not just gazed up at those snow-covered hills, at that reflection of Heaven on the earth?

The message came through, strong and clear.

'MY DEAR FELLOW, WELCOME AT LAST!'

So the Bishop had been right when he made his hospital visit all those months ago; Edmonds, his fellow-passenger on SS *Casanova*, really was working here in the Mandalay Mission. It was not that he had doubted the Bishop's word; it was just that things here seemed to change with such bewildering swiftness that you could be sure of nothing.

'It's a bit of a trek to the Mission quarters, I'm afraid, but at least I'll be able to show you some of the sights on the way.'

They drove in a pony cart through street after narrow street of poverty-stricken shacks raised up on stilts. Under the houses and between the stilts were stalls littered higgledy-piggledy, selling a motley and often unrecognisable assortment of goods. A girl presided over a flat metal tank, live foot-long fish splashing desperately in their attempts at escape from decapitation by the gruesome bloodstained knife that lay alongside. An older woman squatted over a brazier, a row of steaming pancakes on a wooden board beside her. The appetizing smell of cooking reminded Charlie that it had been some time since his last meal, but the spectacle of a mother holding out her bare-bottomed baby over the running gutter, a pi-dog attending to the same function at her side, instantly smothered his appetite.

'It's a bit of a mess, isn't it? And what a maze,' commented the newcomer. 'Strange how straight the streets run, not a bit like I saw in India.'

'Interesting, that,' replied his companion. 'Seems to be the way these chaps like it. Amarapura, you know, the old capital that they took to bits and moved here piecemeal about half a century ago, was apparently just the same. Built on a grid. I don't know why they like it to be so geometrical – it doesn't seem quite to fit, somehow.' And Charlie could only agree.

Suddenly, the pony cart swerved at the statutory right-angle into a much broader street, bordering a wide, straight stretch of water. Beyond the water was a wall, a wall that stretched straight ahead as far as the eye could see and towered three stories high above the water at its foot. The sun shining directly on to it gave a luminosity to the red-brown colour of its bricks and caught in an almost blinding glare the golden umbrella atop a mighty spire behind it. His companion laughed at Charlie's gasp of astonishment.

'Sorry – I'm afraid I am still terribly green. I've read about the fort and the palace, of course, but I had no idea that it was so – well, spectacular.'

'It is impressive, isn't it? I must say Mindon Min made a pretty good job of it. I should think it was a lot more suited to royalty, though, than to our troops. It's officially called Fort Dufferin, now – it's our military HQ, you know. But most people still just say 'the fort.' Sadly, its bricks are beginning to crumble – it's all put together without mortar, you know. That's the moat, of course – runs in a square on all four sides, with the wall behind it. I drove all round once, just for fun. About a mile a side.'

Their pony trotted past the opening of a bridge over the moat, leading to a gateway through the wall. The gate lay open, and through it, beyond a group of small houses, Charlie caught a glimpse of huge upstanding pillars of teak, the stockade that protected the palace within, with the mighty seven-roofed spire soaring above. One day he would like to explore it.

'No such luck, I'm afraid. You would have to get very special permission from the military powers-that-be. Strictly for army personnel only.'

The palace was behind them now.

'Here we are at last, at our own personal moat. Not quite up to the same standard, I'm afraid!'

They were crossing a smelly canal. Charlie thought he spied four stiff legs pointing skywards from the floating corpse of some animal so grossly swollen as to be unrecognizable. The sole of an old sandal kept it company, floating in a scum of debris. Safely over the rickety bridge, the wheels splashed through puddles of water, which from both smell and appearance were closely related to the contents of the canal.

'Not too savoury, is it? Don't worry – the rainy season is over now, bar a few showers, and all this will soon dry up. But the drainage is a problem. This land lies very low, and it's something we intend to tackle very soon.'

Charlie wasn't really listening. Faced with his new home, a few puddles did not loom large on his list of priorities. The overwhelming impression was a sombre one. Huge, unfamiliar trees with massive trunks overshadowed a group of buildings. There certainly seemed no shortage of space. He counted five sizeable houses as well as a solidly-built wooden church, and behind it all stretched a large patch of level ground with a goal post at each end.

'Impressive, isn't it?' Edmonds was clearly immensely proud of their quarters. 'But let me take you straight to the Clergy-house. I gather you've been really ill since I last saw you – not that I need to be told – you're half the thickness you were on the boat. You must be exhausted. The train's not bad, but it is a long way from Rangoon.'

Surrounded by a group of excited boys, each vying with the other to carry Charlie's luggage, they approached a large wooden house, its front half hidden by a covered veranda. The upper floor was supported by wooden pillars, creating the impression of a series of archways, and an upstairs ornamental balustrade ran the whole length of the building. The two men walked in through the nearest arch; the boys put down their burdens, ran back a few yards, and then stood watching.

Inside, Charlie could see nothing, nothing at all. Gradually, as his eyes adjusted to the change in light, he saw that they were not yet inside the building, merely under it. The pillars were functional legs, lifting the living quarters seven feet above the ground. He could see watermarks high on the stilts, proving his companion's worries over the low-lying land. A steep wooden staircase took them up into a large room, divided by a central bookcase into eating and sitting areas. On either side were two more good sized chambers. The walls all stopped far short of the immensely high gabled roof, which soared up to a height of twenty feet at its peak; its massive timbers reminded Charlie of an English ancestral home. His first dormitory at Haileybury had been designed on very similar lines, if he remembered aright.

As he lay in bed that first night, gazing upwards into the depths of that great empty space and puzzling over its purpose, the pleasing simplicity of the design dawned on him. Hot air rises; by dint of trapping it far above their heads, the living area should stay relatively cool. He would never have thought of that.

'So this is it. We've given you the last room on that side. I hope it will suit,' Edmonds had said as he led the newcomer to his new quarters.

40

DESPITE HIS EXHAUSTION, sleep eluded Charlie. The architectural method of air conditioning seemed to have failed entirely and the heat was beyond bearing. The constant whine of the mosquitoes trapped with him inside the net drove him almost to madness. Clad in the barest necessity, he leapt about inside his muslin prison, flailing helplessly at his assailants and subsiding exhausted at last on to the crumpled sheet, every inch of his body coated in sweat. But as the heat of the day faded, the currents of air trapped in the roof of the lofty building found their way on to his moist skin and soothed it, the engorged mosquitoes, their hunger satisfied, quietened and gradually peace was restored. Yet still sleep would not come. The full moon crept round the sky and found his window, and suddenly the room was full of light.

It was nothing at first; just a stray mongrel yelping in his sleep. But that was only the beginning. Singly at first and then in duos, trios and quartets, it seemed to Charlie that every dog in the whole of Burma replied to the stray's opening aria in canine chorus and sang its heart out to the moon. What started with the barking of half-domesticated dogs, ragged and discordant, became a weird wolvish overture, the perfect introduction to this country so steeped in mystery.

Forgetting sleep, the young man lay on his back staring through the shrouding net at the moon, the huge cut-out leaves of some strange plant that climbed his window frame black against its whiteness. The howling was at its height and an oddly sweet perfume filled the room. His senses tuned as never before, this was for Charlie a moment of utter realisation. He had imagined he had come to change others. Now, for the first time, he saw that it was he who must change; he must open himself to a transformation that would alter everything. No, not everything. He knew with utter certainty that his Christian faith would survive and grow. But he also knew that in some unknown way it must be reshaped to meet not just the needs of his new countrymen but also of himself.

The invisible conductor lowered his ghostly baton for the last time and as one dog the chorus ceased. Charlie slept.

NEXT MORNING, FANCIES FORGOTTEN, he rose with the sun and set about exploring his new home. He looked forward to an hour or two of his own company, but this was not to be. To a Burman, it is unimaginable that anyone should want to be alone for long and, as he stepped out of the shadows of his house, yesterday's boys materialised as though from nowhere. He managed the Burmese greeting, and was rewarded with laughter and nodding beaming faces; perhaps such company would be welcome after all.

'Good morning, Garrad. I trust you slept well?'

Edmonds, too, was up early, making the most of the coolness before the onslaught of the sun.

'Having a look round? Come on – I'll show you.'

They walked together, always with their group of lively human shadows, along a covered way that led from the Clergy-house to another large wooden building. This was the school, where three classrooms led off a sizeable central room.

'How many boys d'you have?'

'I think it's about a hundred and fifty at the moment, about half of 'em boarders.'

Edmonds opened another door. It seemed impossibly dark after the early morning brightness, but Charlie gained a vague impression of rows of hammocks, slung close together. For a moment his thoughts fled once more to Haileybury. The contrast was startling; but, after all, was there really so much difference? He looked at their young companions, gossiping away to each other in their strange tongue. What were they chattering about? Probably exactly the same things that he and his own friends used to talk about. He wanted to understand, to join in, to crack a silly joke that would make them laugh. But he couldn't, he wasn't ready, and he made himself a solemn promise that he must make more effort with his language studies. Half the trouble was that the Burmans seemed to speak so quietly, and yet other people managed to hear them. A persistent worry niggled at him. Was he going deaf? Certainly the typhoid had affected his hearing at the time, but it had seemed to improve. Perhaps it was getting worse again. Even in the growing heat of the day, the thought struck chill. If he couldn't hear, how would he ever learn to speak? And if he couldn't speak, how could he communicate?

'Come and watch the football!'

Edmonds' loud cheerful voice brought him back to earth. So distracted had he been that he had not noticed the departure of the gang of boys. Now he saw them on the flat patch of ground at the edge of the compound, bunching their dark heads together as they planned their teams, then, like a flock of humming birds, scattering in all directions, tucking their brilliantly-coloured longyis up between their legs as they ran.

'I believe one of the royal princes was very good at football – or perhaps you didn't know that four of King Mindon's sons came to school here for a bit?'

Charlie looked across at the boys, and tried to picture how it must have been twenty years ago. That agile lad dribbling the ball down the pitch could have been Prince Thibaw, exiled now as king by the British to the Indian town of Ratanagiri, and still living there as far as he knew. Perhaps that was one of his brothers, the little one in the bright red longyi – and his mind went back to the history lesson the colonel had given him on his first crossing from Calcutta to Rangoon.

His reverie was cut short.

'A couple of years ago, the municipality dumped several tons of rubbish on us – at our request, I may say. Spread out nice and flat and turfed over, as you see it has made a splendid football pitch. The whole idea is to make this place as much like an English public school as possible.'

Charlie tried to keep a straight face. The idea seemed too ludicrous to take seriously.

'Yes,' he said, 'I did know some of Mindon's sons came here, but I don't really know why. It seems so very unlikely.'

'Well, I think the story went something like this. After King Mindon built Mandalay a missionary called Marks came to live here. John Ebenezer, he was called – got a good ring to it, hasn't it? The two of them, the Christian and the Buddhist, struck up some sort of rapport, and between them decided that Mandalay needed a decent school for local boys. This was very much in the king's line – he'd done a huge amount of good all over Burma, trying to improve the standard of living. So it wasn't surprising that he set about the building of a school and school house. What does seem so odd is that along with the school he built a Christian church. Strange for such an ardent Buddhist, don't you think?

'Perhaps he thought that having missionaries here would make sure the school always had good teachers?'

'Maybe. It certainly does seem to have worked like that, though for a while things didn't go too well in the school. Last year, though, we got a new headmaster from England, a fellow called Ernest Hart, who's improving things no end. Before that, Maung Tun ran the school. He's a wonderful man, but I think he got a bit old for the job. He's still here, working as our interpreter. You're sure to meet him soon.'

'Anyway, you were saying – the king sent some of his sons here. Did it work out? Did they do well?'

'No – I gather they didn't last long, though I believe it was all pretty spectacular to start with. King Mindon had quite a few sons of the right age, but he chose just four to start with. On the chosen, doubtless auspicious, day they turned up at school mounted on four royal elephants, each of them with two – not one, mind you, but two – golden umbrellas held over him. A hundred and sixty uniformed servants followed behind, forty to each prince. And then, when they finally arrived in the classroom, all the other pupils fell flat face down on the floor and wouldn't even look up! But they got it all sorted out in the end.'

'But you said things went wrong. What happened?'

'Well, everything ran smoothly for a couple of years. King Mindon asked John Ebenezer to design the church. It was to be built to a Burmese pattern, "but with such alterations as Dr Marks might require." He'd just seen a picture of the new chapel at St John's College, Cambridge, so he used that as his model. Queen Victoria offered to help pay for it but the king would have none of it ... "Nga min be," he said – "I am a King, I want no assistance in my works of merit." But he did let her donate a beautiful marble font, which you've probably noticed already.'

'And wasn't there some story about a spittoon or something?'

Edmonds laughed. 'You're absolutely right. King Mindon sent our splendid but –er – somewhat sheltered queen a very special present of a spittoon made from solid gold. The only trouble was that he didn't say what it was for, and the queen wrote back and thanked him for the lovely rose bowl!'

'But that surely can't really have offended him – it must have been something much more serious that upset things?'

'Well, two things happened. The king had promised to maintain the church and school as well as building them, and after a while he got a bit lax with his payments. When Dr Marks asked him for the money, needless to say he got rather cross. Things came to a head when the king tried to make the doctor ask Queen Victoria to return Rangoon to Burma and he refused. Mindon tried to turn him out of the country but he wouldn't go and stayed on until his term of office was up, just eighteen months after the church was consecrated. That was in 1875, I think.'

'The year before I was born,' thought Charlie. How odd that all this had been going on and nobody around them at home had known anything about any of it.

'It's all a very odd story, isn't it?'

And the two young Englishmen stood quietly side by side, each perhaps thinking of the tortuous pathway that had led him from a normal English boyhood to the unfathomable ways of an Eastern potentate in a far off land.

41

'ALL THINGS BRIGHT AND BEAUTIFUL, All creatures great and small, All things wise and wonderful, The Lord God made them all.'

The tune of the familiar childhood hymn was unrecognisable, the faces of the congregation all but invisible in the dark little church. This was Charlie's first experience of a service for Christians in the building put up by the Buddhist king. Sitting at the front, he looked along the row of fellow-worshippers. The man next to him was Tamil; he had introduced himself outside, before the service began.

His 'good morning Father' had been the give-away.

'You don't sound Burmese.'

'No, Father, I am from Madras. Major Mathieson brought me with him when he was posted here.'

'Your English is excellent.'

His companion's teeth shone out from the dark face in a wondrous grin of delight at the compliment.

'There are many of us Tamils here working with English masters, so we must learn. The Fathers are very good. They make us our own service in English, because we do not speak Burmese.'

'Do you have family here, or have you had to leave them behind in India?'

'Oh yes, Sir,' and the man wagged his head. 'My sons go to the school.' He looked across at a group of youngsters, neat and tidy in their bright Sunday best.

'I am lucky to come to the church today. They have gone up into the hills for the hot weather, so I am more free.'

'They?'

'Yes Father. The major and his family. They are your friends?'

'No, not yet. I only arrived yesterday.'

The two had walked into the church together, and sat down side by side.

AND SO BEGAN CHARLIE'S introduction to the intricacies of the new Winchester Brotherhood and its life and work in the Mission. Each night, waiting for the sleep that would not come, he would count off on his sweaty fingers the projects entrusted to the little group of missionaries. There was the church, busy on Sundays and weekdays alike with alternate services in Burmese and in English for the Tamils. He was worried about the church. It looked so solid, but when he had knocked against a corner pillar by mistake the other day it had made a curiously hollow sound. Putting his ear to it and tapping it again, he had been more than alarmed to hear the crunch of a thousand jaws. Even the toughest of timbers were not proof against termites, and he made a mental note to examine it more closely soon.

But there were so many other things besides. The school; the good education of native children was vital to the future of the country. The constant search for funding. Plans for a much-needed children's hospital – and how would they find the staff? The training of Catechists, young Burmans who would spread out into the villages to preach and teach. Updating of the Brotherhood's own premises, wooden and thus yet more fodder for the ants. Pastoral care – and so the list went on.

All of this, and more, against a background of the business of mere existence in the heat, of loneliness and homesickness, of mosquito-bites and diarrhoea, of scorpions in your shoes and snakes under your house, of the constant threat of major illness. The challenges seemed endless, Then there were the complications of the Burmese language. It was difficult enough to learn to speak, but at first reading and writing seemed to Charlie well-nigh impossible. The script of squiggles and circles, almost indistinguishable from one another, he found bad enough, but when during his weekly lesson he was faced with his first written page, he was completely flummoxed.

Turning to his teacher, he complained that he had been given a faulty translation exercise.

'Look,' he said, pointing to line after line of indecipherable signs with not a single gap anywhere. 'This must be badly printed. There don't seem to be any spaces between the words.'

'No,' the teacher calmly replied. 'That is how it is written. Right from the beginning, the words of the Buddhist scriptures have been scratched in the monasteries on narrow strips of palm leaf. There was no need then for spaces. The error probably lay originally with ignorant copyists, who, no longer confined by narrow columns, simply copied what they saw in one long line; and the habit has persisted.'

There lay a challenge to suit the most demanding masochist.

But still, lying exhausted on his bed at siesta time, the inside of the walls of the wooden house too hot to touch, Charlie found himself smiling. There was more to do and to cope with than he could ever have imagined, and yet he was happier than he had ever been. And the cream of the work was yet to come. The touring season was almost upon them, the time when each young priest in turn left Mandalay and went out into the villages. Then he would see the real Burma, the rural Burma, and talk with the farmers with whom he knew he would have so much in common. His language problems were lessening with time; all thought of the deafness which could no longer be ignored he resolutely put aside. There was nothing he could do about it anyway.

42

Burma 1908

BOOTALET. EVERYONE SEEMED to be talking about Bootalet.

'... an extraordinary experience, just coming upon it like that, in the middle of nowhere.'

'... so friendly; you'd never guess that we were the first white people they'd ever seen.'

'... such an opportunity.'

On and on and on. Charlie began to dread the very mention of the name.

At last he could stand it no longer.

'Oh for goodness sake, can't anyone talk about anything else? What's so special about the place anyway?' he burst out at supper one night.

Jaws stopped munching in mid-mouthful, spoonfuls of rice dribbled grains back on to plates. Curry ran down stubbly chins. Garrad never said boo to a goose. Whatever had got into him?

After the silence, pandemonium. The chorus of enthusiasm was deafening. Superlatives beat upon poor Charlie's ears until, for the first time, but certainly not the last, he was actually glad to be a little hard of hearing. It was impossible to try to explain, they said, and anyway, why bother? Wasn't he just about to go off on tour in a couple of weeks, lucky fellow. And where was he going? To Bootalet!

After supper, Edmonds came to his room and handed him an envelope.

'Read this,' he said, and left.

The letter was from Charlie's predecessor, who, going home on furlough, had used the time on board ship to write a letter about his touring experiences to his friends back in Burma. Charlie settled down in his rattan chair and began to read.

'I want to tell you about an interesting tour which I have recently made.

Two hundred or so miles north of Mandalay in a little village within reach of the railway live two brothers, who a year or so ago heard about Christianity. They were much impressed, came to Mandalay, and in due course were baptized and confirmed. There I met them, and promised to visit them when time allowed.

Early one morning, having travelled by train all night from Mandalay, Saya George and I arrived at a little wayside station. I sent someone at once to wake up the headman of the village to make arrangements for us to go to Bootalet, where the two brothers live. Presently the headman arrived, and in an hour or two a boat was ready to take us down the river. We drifted with the stream through picturesque jungle scenery, and came in a few hours to a place only a mile or two's scramble through mud and water across paddy fields from Bootalet.

Twenty or thirty mat houses – standing high from the ground on posts – constitute the village of Bootalet. As one walked through the tiny muddy lane (the High Street) the houses were almost hidden by magnificent palm trees and plantains. One of them had been prepared for my reception, a great event, for no European had ever stayed in the village before. I had my lantern and showed the people slides each evening. At first they were afraid of me, but came in increasing numbers as time went on. We also had services in my house, and half-a-dozen men and women asked me to teach them the rudiments of Christianity.

I found that the two brothers who invited me had sold their only buffalo in order to get to Mandalay for their teaching and confirmation, and that each of them owned a little land which they were arranging to let so that they might be free to go about and preach.

The district, in which no Mission work had been done before, consists of a long and fertile valley with about thirty villages in it, approachable both by river and train. It would form a splendid 'parish' for someone to work at. The people are all agricultural and therefore much more hopeful to deal with than the town people or traders. It really looked like a great opening, but there are objections. The distance from Mandalay, and the inaccessibility in the rainy season, is one. Anyone living there would have to live mainly on vegetable curry and rice – an execrable diet. I stayed about a week in the district and the visit was a happy one, but it cannot be repeated until the dry season owing to the amount of water about.'

The rest of the letter held little interest for its reader, and Charlie folded it and put it back in its envelope, grubby and tattered from much handling. Now he understood. Here was truly virgin territory, lived in by simple people untouched by the world. What an opening indeed. Suddenly the Mandalay mission with all its routine chores and daily disciplines took a step backwards in his list of priorities. He would use this opportunity of a visit to the romantic Hidden Valley to the full, and, who knows, perhaps in the famous Bootalet lay the ultimate reason for his being here, in Burma.

He liked vegetable curry.

⤜⤛

THE RAINS PERSISTED late that year and all idea of touring had to be put aside until there could be reasonable guarantee of dry weather. Charlie could scarcely contain his impatience to be off.

'I don't really see why we can't start,' he complained. 'A little bit of rain never hurt anyone, and it does seem to have almost stopped.'

But Edmonds, the old hand of at least a year's experience, would not change his mind.

At last the skies cleared and towards the end of November the expedition set off again for Bootalet, this time with Charlie as the newcomer. On this occasion the journey from the little wayside railway station was made on foot, their luggage in a bullock cart. Pot-holes brimming with rainwater were a constant trap for the unwary and even Charlie, clad in shorts and with his long legs coated with mud from the knees down, had to admit that the path would have been impassable just a few days earlier.

'What on earth are these?'

He had stopped dead in his tracks, neck twisted round and eyes fixed in horror on three slimy black humps protruding from his calf.

'Leaches,' said Edmonds, and actually laughed.

Charlie shuddered. His one thought was to rid himself of them at once, but as his unwilling fingers closed round the fattest, a brown hand came down and gently pushed his own away.

'No, Father,' said the bullock-cart driver. He took the lighted cheroot from between his lips, blew on the end, and touched the three intruders in turn with its glowing ash.

'Now they'll just shrivel up and fall off,' said Edmonds. 'If you pull 'em off they leave their dear little heads behind and you're left with itchy sores for weeks. I discovered that the hard way,' he added bitterly.

Their walk took them through glorious countryside. Charlie, familiar with the dull clusters of bamboo found in some English gardens, was astonished at the great groves of its luxuriant cousins in their natural surroundings; under guidance from their driver, he counted five different kinds shading their path. Then there were the cane forests, like huge copses of giant fern, some towering over them from a height of ninety feet, their leaves unpleasantly prickly to the touch. Edmonds, always hungry, tried to ask the driver how he could get sugar from them. A great deal of sign language, of stomach rubbing and mouth pointing ensued, for the driver was a local man speaking a dialect that the white men found very difficult to understand. At last, small side-branches were cut with the driver's knife, the bark peeled off, and the core handed ceremoniously to the two young men.

'Lollipops growing on trees,' remarked Edmonds as he chewed.

Not just lollipops either, for suddenly their noses were assailed by a strong smell of peardrops. Puzzled, they looked around them and the laughing driver pointed to a great drift of green blossoms. The scent was almost overwhelming and they moved quickly on. There were other flowers, too, wonderful blooms of every size and shape, a rainbow of colours brought to perfection by the recent rains and present sun.

Suddenly the cavalcade stopped and the driver pointed up to the top of a tall tree where they could just see an almost luminous pink shining out against the multitude of different greens. He barked a command and a young boy, no more than ten years old, lost no time in kicking off his sandals and shinning up the straight trunk as easily as he could run. In moments, he was down again with a posy of orchids tucked in his longyi which, under direction, he divided in half and shyly presented to the two foreigners.

After three days' march they eventually arrived at Bootalet and were conducted by the entire village to their accommodation. The only way in which it differed from the rest-houses where they had slept en route was the addition of bamboo matting walls; otherwise, the standard local architecture consisted of a raised wooden floor and thatched roof supported on posts.

Entry was by ladder, not easily climbed in clumsy British boots. Once inside, Charlie felt an urgent need to wash after three days in the jungle. He strode into the screened-off area set aside as their *en suite* bathroom and promptly put his foot through the floor.

Edmonds came to the rescue.

'I did exactly the same thing when we came last year,' he said, and hauled poor Charlie out.

And what did they have to eat? Rice and vegetable curry. But there were biscuits too and sometimes bananas, and everything washed down with copious supplies of tea.

It was a busy time for the two missionaries. They were never alone. The villagers constantly crowded into their little house, the floor now securely mended with bamboo sturdy enough to bear the extra weight of the two giant Englishmen. White men and locals communicated as best they could and, despite the difficulties of the dialect, chatted about many things. The two subjects of absorbing interest to all were farming and religion. Charlie and Edmonds learnt all there was to know about the planting and harvesting of rice, and never did succeed in persuading their listeners that in their own country rice growing was non-existent. Their audience just shook their heads in total disbelief at such an impossibility. Charlie tried, and largely failed, to explain the intricacies of his father's farm at home.

But, of course, the main purpose of their visit was to tell these lovely, simple people about Christianity. It was a huge task. Although they were enthusiastic Buddhists, their knowledge and understanding of their own religion seemed primitive and tinged with fear. Lying on their pallets in their little hut, the two missionaries would talk far into the night. It seemed to them that Buddhism, though good as far as it went, had simply failed to enlighten their new companions. Now it was up to them to take them a giant step further.

Bootalet 1908

One of the two Fathers who came this time was someone they had not met before. His name was Saya Garrad. He was very tall and very pale and very thin. He often raised his hand to his left ear – perhaps, they thought, he did not hear very well. He had a beautiful face, and spoke much less than the Fathers usually did. And there was something else about him that was different. Pyau turned it over in his mind – perhaps Saya Garrad recognised the space around them for what it really was, not empty or hollow but overflowing with things that were beyond him, beyond them all.

These are matters, Pyau thought, that he would like to discuss with Saya Garrad alone, if he got the chance –

43

'SAYA GARRAD! WHERE ARE YOU GOING, so early in the morning?'

Charlie, sleepless, was in process of putting on his boots. Ever since the unfortunate incident of the bathroom he had followed local custom and left them to wait for him at the bottom of the rickety ladder that linked his bedroom with the outside world.

The soft voice behind him made him jump. It was not yet light and he had thought the whole village fast asleep; he had been looking forward to an hour or so on his own as the end of their visit approached. But, as he turned and made out the figure of Saya Pyau in the dimness of approaching dawn, he was glad. Pyau, he felt, could well hold the key to their success in the village, and he had not yet had a chance to talk to him alone.

They walked together along the rough, narrow road. Charlie already knew that it was Pyau who, with his brother, had come to Mandalay a few years ago to learn from the Christian missionaries, and had clearly taken the opportunity to absorb English at the same time. By common consent, on his return to his village he had been awarded the title of Saya, or Teacher. As the days of his short visit went by, Charlie came to realise that here was a man very different from the rest.

It was that brief equatorial moment of transformation from night to day, and suddenly the vegetation around them shone with such brilliance in the early morning light that he caught his breath at the sheer beauty of it. He was a scholar and a pragmatist, but at that instant the world was transfigured into another universe where such things counted for nothing and only the spirit held sway.

Strange questions crowded into his mind but he felt too confused to formulate them and simply looked at Pyau in bewilderment. As he led him down a narrow path that branched off into the jungle, Pyau turned and, laying his hand on Charlie's arm, gave him his gentle smile.

'I think you feel the presence of the Nats, Father. It is easier for me, for this is where I was brought up, where I belong. The spirits of my ancestors are here. This is their home, here in this part of the forest is the soul of our tribe. I come here to communicate with them – I spend many hours in this place.'

The path had suddenly opened out into a clearing, roughly circular and hidden from sight by the ring of gigantic forest trees surrounding it. The undergrowth was trampled, as though by many feet. An overwhelming sense of peace filled the air.

Guilt crept through Charlie's veins. He should be arguing with Pyau, for in Christianity there is no place for ghosts. But he felt helpless, in the grip of something beyond his comprehension.

As if reading his thoughts, Pyau went on ...

'There is so much that we do not understand, that we cannot understand about each other. You in the West pretend you are cold and hard, that you have in your religion no room for other spiritual things. We in the East are brought up amongst the spirits of the trees and rivers, but that does not mean we cannot believe in the Perfect Man. Jesus will sweep away our bad ghosts and demons. After all, did He not send away many evil spirits from the souls of men and women in Galilee?'

'How do we really know what went on in Jesus's mind?' thought Charlie. 'The Bible doesn't tell us. After all, He, too, was a countryman. Could not the two be complementary, co-exist? God made the trees. Why should He not have given them spirits as well as roots and branches?' Charlie looked up at the boughs that arched way up above his head and felt a new sense of awe; the early morning breeze ruffled the multitude of leaves into a kaleidoscope of form and colour so bright that, for a moment, he had to close his eyes.

THE ANT THAT WOKE HIM with its sting was a massive one and escaped his hand by a whisker. He found himself sitting on a log, with his back against another, his trouser-legs wet through with the morning dew. He must have dropped off to sleep, he thought; after all, he had lain awake most of the night. But surely Saya Pyau had been here and they had talked; about spirits, and the souls of his ancestors. Pyau's words ran through his mind again. Charlie had known that the Burman's English was reasonable, but this time it had been perfect. And where was he now? Charlie called his name, but there was no answer; just the haunting cry of some tropical bird hidden high in the canopy.

Had he been asleep and dreaming all the time? Had this place, this Bootalet, bewitched him as it had others?

He walked slowly back the few hundred yards to the village. Several of the local people had emerged from their houses and, squatting on the ground, were enjoying chota hazri. Already, their sandalled feet were red with the dry dust that permanently covered everything. Saya Pyau stood up as he approached and gave him a smile that, to Charlie, held a great deal more than its usual warmth. He looked down at the Burman's legs. His longyi was soaked up to the knees.

CHARLIE HAD PLENTY TO THINK about on the way home. After the long hot trek back to the little railway halt, a swim in the river in water warm enough for a bath was a necessary pleasure, and they had only just time to clamber back into their grubby clothes before the Mandalay train drew up at the platform. Baggage aboard, they settled back into their corner seats.

Perhaps it was the soothing prospect of a long stretch with their thoughts and their books that made the impact of the crash when it came so shocking. It seemed to be the explosion of sound itself that projected the pair of them across the floor and sent their carriage straight into a tree-trunk bordering the track. The clash of squealing brakes, splintering metal, human screams and the desperate bellowing of some stricken animal enveloped their minds in such bewilderment as they lay on the slanting boards that it took them several seconds to pull themselves together and look for a way out. The door on the uppermost side of the carriage was undamaged, and clambering through it they jumped down on to the single track. They were not alone. Passengers, empty-handed or clutching precious bundles, were erupting from carriages thrown higgledy-piggledy this way and that all down the line. One woman struggled to carry a basket of hens one-handed, her other arm hanging useless at her side; a young man held a live piglet in a violent embrace.

'What on earth ...?'

'We must have hit something.' Both men spoke at once.

'I wonder if there are people hurt – or trapped?'

Together they set off at a run. Others were running with them, looking at each carriage in turn as they passed. Miraculously, most were still more or less upright, disgorging their human content; they saw no sign of serious injury. One wagon had been thrown down the embankment but somehow had landed squarely on its four wheels, its occupants leaving through the door as easily as if it had been drawn up at a platform.

In moments they reached the front of the train, and there all was revealed. Lying close beside the track was a large buffalo, its desolate bellowing awful to hear. Blood was pouring from its mouth and nostrils, and both great horns lay separately, severed from their roots by the wheels of the engine. A farmer, presumably its owner, squatted beside it, tears running down his face and joining the blood-stains on his lap as he nursed the huge head. It was clear from the animal's dreadful disfigurement that it was mortally wounded and beyond help. It had been a fine specimen and in the prime of life.

'Come away; there's nothing we can do. That poor farmer – he'll have lost his livelihood. It was probably pulling logs from the river and decided it had had enough for one day.'

They found their damaged carriage, rescued their bags from the tilted rack, and walked back along the line to the railway station.

THAT NIGHT, THEY LAY DOWN on the platform fully dressed, too exhausted to string up their mosquito nets. Tired though they were, sleep for Charlie would not come. It was not the hardness of the station platform; he was after all used to sleeping on the floor. The buffalo's screams grew fainter until finally they ceased altogether and a dreadful quiet took their place. In the distance he could hear weird stirrings in the forest from strange, invisible creatures of the night and he remembered Saya Pyau's words: 'I think you feel the presence of the Nats, Father.' What right had he, Charlie, to the title of Father? What did he know or understand about anything in this alien land? How brash and self-assured he had been before he came; how he had scoffed at the idea of evil spirits. Now, as he lay looking up at the unfamiliar night sky, he felt truly at the mercy of the Devil himself.

'Our Father which art in Heaven
'Hallowed be Thy name
'Thy Kingdom Come
'Thy will be done ...'
Comforted, the young man slept at last.

The mosquitoes feasted well, and the men's faces were covered in itchy bumps when they woke. It was four in the morning. The Burmans must have worked on the line all night by the light of flares, for it was the reassuring puffing of the replacement engine to Mandalay that had them scrambling to their feet and thankfully crawling aboard the train.

But their troubles were not over even now. The Mission gharrie-driver meeting their train was clearly in a state of great excitement. Their feet had barely touched the platform before he was upon them. Grabbing their bags, he burst out with his news.

'Bad fire,' he said. 'Very bad fire. Many, many houses burn.' Dropping the luggage again, he threw his arms up in a dramatic enactment of flames and smoke rising skyward.

Seeing their worried faces, he went on:

'Mission no problem. No fire there. The Fathers all well.'

The smell of smoke hung in the air and, as they drove through the streets, they began to see the extent of the damage. It was horrific. The little wooden houses had clearly gone up like dry tinder for any sap that had once run through their veins had long since submitted to the relentless sun.

'How did it start?'

But their driver didn't know.

'Easily enough, I should think.' Edmonds turned to his friend.

'We very nearly had a fire at the Mission just before you came. One of the servants left a lighted candle in an empty room. Her husband's longyi or something was hanging over the back of a chair next to it, and a puff of wind through the open window – well, there's no glass in the windows, is there, and the shutters were open – must have done the deed. She smelt burning, and went back to find the whole chair alight. Apparently she screamed so loud that everyone came running, and it was put out before the walls caught fire.'

There had been no rain for several weeks, and it could only have taken just one careless mistake to set the city ablaze.

The driver had been right. Already, as they approached their quarter of the town, the damage was lessening, and it seemed that the smelly, muddy stream that they must cross to reach the Mission quarters had been the final barrier to the flames. Everything was just as they had left it, and they were in a more than usually thankful frame of mind as, washed and refreshed, they stood with their friends round the dinner-table for the evening Grace. They were glad to be home safe and sound. But a third of the city had been destroyed in a few short hours.

44

Winchester Mission
Mandalay
July 29th 1911

Dear Father

It is high time that I wrote to you again. I fear I have left too long a gap between letters – my excuse is that the routine work here in Mandalay is often dull and repetitious and so I have little of interest to report. But I have just been on tour again to the village called Bootalet that I told you about a couple of years ago at the time of the terrible fire here, and I thought it might amuse you to hear what your son has been up to.

My visit was delightful. There has not been much rain there yet, and that saved me from the trouble of roads etc that I had expected to have to meet. I hope that they will have rain very soon, for otherwise their paddy will suffer severely.

I went there quite alone, taking with me nothing but a mosquito net, the things necessary for Holy Communion, some biscuits, and some quinine. On my last visit I had left behind me a mattress, a blanket, and a change of clothes. It was 5.15 a.m. when I got out of the train. I ate the last of the food I had taken with me and then waded through a stream (not much over my knees) and had a jolly walk of some three miles through beautiful jungle. Then I came to another big stream, but I knew that there were always boats there, so that did not bother me. Then I called on a Buddhist acquaintance who treated me to tea and bananas, and would have given me rice and curry too if I had not already had breakfast, and then put me on his horse and himself came on foot in case I should lose my way – all without payment of a penny. There was one serious drawback to the horse, which was that he wore a Burmese saddle, and a Burmese saddle is execrable. In the first place, the cords of its stirrups were about a foot too short, and finding that I could not double up my legs as the Burmans do, I had to dispense with the stirrups altogether. That would not have mattered much, as we only went at a walk the whole way, but the result was that I was thrown all the time on to a big projection which forms the front part of a Burmese saddle and it was most uncomfortable. However, by making an excuse of some sharp dips in the ground, rather steep for the horse, I was able to stretch my legs a couple of times and so escape cramp.

My guide was an interesting man. In his house he had told me that I should always be welcome as his guest, and that I could always get rice from him, but that he would not listen to Christianity as he was a Buddhist, and his fathers before him. As we passed some fisherman, he sadly repeated the Buddhist law against taking life. I told him how as Christians we may kill animals for food, but that cruelty to animals, seen often in the Buddhist pagodas, is utterly abhorrent to us. Later he asked me about caste, apparently feeling a little hurt that I had not accepted his rice and curry, and wanted to know if we could eat food cooked by people of other nations. Of course I said yes, and told him how as Christians we believe that all men are brothers, and that God is Father of us all. I explained again that the only reason I had not eaten his food was that I had already eaten, and had no room for more! He seemed relieved, repeated part of what I had said to him and seemed struck by it.

When we got to Bootalet, some of the Christians brought me food and even remembered to boil my drinking-water. They made me as comfortable as a king. Then I had a good snooze and afterwards spent the afternoon visiting friends, Christians and Buddhists, and after sunset I held a service for them.

The next day, with Saya Pyau, I went over to Tha-pan-gine, a village about 5 miles to the east where there are Christians who have complained of ill-treatment by the village headman. I talked to them first, and I do not know whether I was right or not, but I did not think the situation serious. When I called on the headman, it seemed to me enough to point out that the peace of his village required good relations between the Christians and the Buddhists. I suggested that they should be encouraged to work together at the time of the planting of the paddy – a time when many hands are required, and the villagers ordinarily go *en masse* to each man's fields in turn. It was not a difficult case to put, as love is almost as much emphasised in Buddhism teaching as in Christian, and the headman seemed to agree. He said that he thoroughly agreed, and I hear that the same night he instructed the villagers to that effect, and I hope he will be as good as his word.

You would have laughed if you had seen me on the way back to Bootalet. As the path crosses a small stream repeatedly, one has to take one's choice between two courses – either to have wet feet all day, or else to do a good deal of the journey barefoot. I chose the latter course as I had done the last time we were here, but the watery part was longer this time, as it was the dry season when we went before, and I confess the stones were getting very sharp before the end.

The next morning, back at Bootalet, we had Holy Communion, and with one exception, all 18 of the confirmed people of the three local villages came to receive Communion. The one exception was a woman who was obliged (in her husband's absence at the service) to keep watch over their nursery of young paddy ready for planting out, as paddy at that stage is very tempting food, and a couple of oxen would eat the whole of it in an hour if it was not continually watched, and then the material for the year's crop would be gone.

About mid-day I started off on my return on the Bootalet headman's pony. You would have laughed even more if you had seen me leaving, as the pony was restive and with the execrable Burmese saddle, I was helpless and had to submit to the indignity of being led by a halter for about half a mile.

It was a most invigorating visit. The simplicity of the people and their ready hospitality, not to mention the natural beauties of the country, are thoroughly refreshing.

Please give my love to all my brothers and sisters. I am
Your loving son
Char

Bures, England, 1911

Reading Charlie's letters stumps me every time. I haven't had one of my own lately, so when Charlie's Pa spotted me the other day and called out 'Matt, do you want to see Charlie's letter?' of course I jumped at the chance. Isn't he extraordinary? There's me, still cowman along at the farm, and there's him, miles away in foreign parts astride some bony nag in the middle of a jungle teaching all those Heathen to be nice to each other. When I think how we used to go fishing together and all the larks we used to get up to it fair takes my breath away Of course when he went off to College we didn't see so much of each other, but somehow we've still stayed good friends. And now just look at him – and look at me!

He doesn't say in his letter about Mr Will going out to join him, but that's really put the cat among the pigeons at Brook House. He'll be going quite soon, and Violet told me that when she took up Miss Bessie's early cup of tea the other day the poor little lady was in floods of tears, and said as how it was bad enough to lose one brother, but two was just too much. It'll be that exciting for him though – he always did look up to Charlie no end.

45

Mandalay 1918–1920

HE WAS SO LONELY IN HIS DEAFNESS.

Everyone made light of it, but it was abundantly clear to him that they all found the constant need for repetition irritating, though some were better than others at disguising it. He thought of how it would be at home, how the others would tease him when he misheard and turned what he thought they'd said into a joke. In his mind's ear he could hear all their different laughs, Father's roar, George's chuckle, Fanny's infectious giggle, Katie's polite apologetic titter behind her hand as if to be amused out loud was almost a sin.

Brother Will, now, he had a good laugh, but then of course Charlie had reason to remember it a great deal better than the others. After all, it was only a couple of weeks since they had been together in this very Mission house. Will, five years his junior, had astounded Charlie by his decision to leave home and join him at the Winchester Mission in Mandalay. That had been almost a decade ago now, well before the start of the Great War and those four terrible years when the world had gone mad. Will had been a great addition, filling various vacancies caused by furloughs and fevers. He even turned his hand to head-mastering, good practice for the school he was to set up in Myittha, his next posting.

He could have stayed on in Myittha, the small town just a few hours' journey from Mandalay where he was doing such great work for the Mission. But he was still young enough to join the British army as a chaplain and had chosen to go off to Bombay, to the Cumballa military hospital. Since his return, he had rarely talked of his experiences there, but they had had a profound effect on him which Charlie could not share to the full; he could only guess at the gruesomeness of the sights and sounds in that concentration of human inhumanity. But how he envied Will; how he wished he had his hearing and those five precious years that separated them. He told himself that all the work he had done in the Mandalay Mission, all his achievements in its school and in the surrounding countryside, would have collapsed in his absence. The Mission was running on a skeleton staff as it was; the war had seen to that. Under no circumstances could he have left it if anything were to be saved.

Now, in 1919, a year after the end of hostilities, Will was once more ensconced in Myittha, back with the children in the school that he had started, back with his wonderful Burmese colleague who had kept things going there in his absence. Both brothers were busy, and separated by an awkward journey of two hundred miles. They did not keep company as often as each would have liked.

Laughter; thinking about it, Charlie supposed that was one of the things he missed most in this hot, impossible country. Odd – you could feel sorry for yourself on your own, but you couldn't laugh on your own. It didn't seem fair somehow. Steady on – was he going mad? All this introspection was getting him nowhere. But nowhere, he thought, is exactly where I am. I am nowhere that makes any sense. I am stuck out in the back of the furthest beyond, and soon I shall have no point of contact.

I am nowhere.

Fanny's infectious giggle. All that hot night he heard it, that irrepressible bubbling laugh that would burst out at the most inappropriate moments. It soothed him into slumber, and in his dream he heard her voice again:

'Go to sleep now. It'll be all right, you'll see,' and he felt his sister Fanny's little hand stroking his forehead all those years ago, on his first night home from prep school after his mother had died. And what was it that she'd said that other time, on the dreadful day of the funeral? Something like 'we'll be all right and whatever happens, Charlie, you and I will always stand together.'

Of course! That was it! Fanny must come out and join them! Will was here already, so why not make it even more of a family affair? Several of the fellows had their sisters out here, working in various capacities as teachers or nurses or missionaries, or a combination of all three. He knew that she must be bored at home, this gentle sister of theirs who had never been further from their village than the coast of her own beloved county. Though she would never complain, of course.

AND SO, ON 9TH APRIL 1919, any curious person thumbing through Fanny's diary would have come upon the bald statement:

'Heard from Charlie that he would like me to go to Mandalay.' Just that; nothing more.

On the 17th:

'Went to SPG (Society for the Propagation of the Gospel) House to ask about passage to Burma.'

On the 19th

'I cabled to Charlie that I was coming to Burma in October.'

THERE WERE DELAYS, but on 1st January 1920 ...

'Arrived Calcutta at 5pm. Had rather a shock when we saw our quarters. Used Indian bathrooms for the first time. Felt rather horrified at first.'

On the 5th:

'Arrived at Rangoon in the afternoon.'

On the 11th:

I felt in a perfectly new world, and realized for the first time how I had begun a new life.'

What a weed I've been. With Fanny's arrival, everything seems transformed. It's me that's supposed to be the strong one, the manly missionary coping with all the difficulties without turning a hair. And yet, until she dropped everything and came, just because I asked her to, I was sinking fast. Now, with her jolliness and enthusiasm, everything has turned about. Who'd have thought she would make such a difference – but then, who'd have thought of half the things that happen in this weird country?

CHARLIE, PATTERN OF predictability, was being forced into a new philosophy. 'Expect nothing but the unexpected'; who was it that had said this to him? Now his sister's eruption on to the scene seemed to trigger a positive bombardment of surprises.

The first of the new thunderbolts was the letter. It arrived innocently enough with the whole sheaf of monthly post from England. There was something about it, though, that made him pick it out from the pile before all the rest. He was careful about opening it; somehow it seemed important not to tear the letters B.F.B.S. that were printed boldly on the back flap.

He was not surprised to hear from them. With the approval of the British and Foreign Bible Society, he had been working for a long time on a translation into Burmese of the Book of Common Prayer. But on top of this for several years he had from time to time joined a group of local scholars in their attempts at a new translation of the Bible itself – when he had the chance. It was work that he loved, but the war had taken from him so many of his colleagues that it had been difficult enough just to keep the Mission going, let alone attempting anything extra. Perhaps some triviality had upset the Society, comfortably settled so far away in the rarefied air of England.

He turned first to the end of the typewritten sheet – and sat up straighter in his chair. Clearly this was after all no simple correction of punctuation, for it was signed by the president himself.

'Dear Garrad.

I will not beat about the bush. As you are well aware, work has been in progress for some years on a new Burmese Bible under the leadership of William Sherratt, the Wesleyan minister who is our agent in Burma. Indeed, in your few spare moments during the difficult war years you yourself have made some valuable contributions with which we are greatly impressed.

What we have to suggest is this. Now that at last things have settled down after the war, we propose that you concentrate entirely on this extremely important work. Mr Sherratt needs the assistance of a Hebrew Burmese scholar and has particularly requested you. The Bishop of Rangoon has given his permission for you to leave your position with the Winchester Mission for the next four or five years. What do you say?

We greatly look forward to your decision, and hope and pray that it will be in the affirmative.'

Charlie sat stock still, the other letters scattered forgotten and unopened round his feet. This was a proposal so big, so overwhelming, that his brain could scarcely grapple with it.

The prayer book, maybe – that does seem to be possible. But the WHOLE BIBLE? So many facets and factors. The word for word translation could be done, I suppose. The blood-and-thunder stories of the Old Testament – nothing too difficult there. Straightforward happenings. I always enjoyed turning Hebrew into English. Easier than the other way round. But into Burmese?

The New Testament, though – that's quite another kettle of fish. So many interpretations of Jesus's teachings in English, let alone Burmese. Anyway, the two cultures couldn't be more different – the Burmese are much more spiritual in many ways, though I suppose that's a heathen thought. How could it be remotely possible to get the messages across in language they can understand? Certainly have to have at least one Christian Burman in the team. I wonder who?

Charlie found his mind wandering off to tackle the easier problem and had to force it back on track.

But what a challenge! And, if we could pull it off, what an incredible, amazing opportunity to spread the word of God! Just think of it – a Bible, or at least a book of Bible stories, in every home. Steady on, though – half of them can't read. Have to link it to the schools, somehow. Yes, that's it – every child who learns the three Rs gets rewarded with a Burmese Bible to take home ...

And there he was still, hours later, when one of his colleagues came to see why he had not come into supper.

'What's up, Garrad? Are you ill?'

'Me? Ill? Why should I be ill? Never felt better in my whole life!' And he threw the letter heavenwards. Perhaps the Spirit caught it, or perhaps it was just a mundane current of hot air, but somehow it spiralled upwards and came to rest on a beam high above their heads and the next twenty minutes were spent in vigorous attempts to retrieve it. Their wild hilarity was so noisy that, one by one, other young men came to see what was going on, until the whole room was full of boisterous acrobats vying with each other to dislodge this piece of paper that seemed so important to their friend. Defeated, they collapsed on to the floor, and the letter, left peacefully to itself, came fluttering down on to the long, thin shanks that protruded from the legs of Charlie's khaki shorts.

'So what's it all about?'

And Charlie explained.

THE TRAIN JOURNEY FROM Mandalay to Maymyo had been an easy one. The distance was only forty miles, and when things went well only took a couple of hours.

Charlie remembered looking the little town up in the guide book. 'The

British hill station of Maymyo was created in 1896' – *when I was at Cambridge,* he thought. *Even if I'd read about it in the papers, it wouldn't have meant a thing to me. How odd that seems now!* He read on:

'It was called after Colonel May, its first governor, and the name means Maytown. In its early years, it was home to the First Battalion of the Gurkha Rifles, stationed there in a ceremonial capacity, and has been a garrison town ever since. In the Shan hills and over a thousand metres above sea-level, you may enjoy there wonderful scenery and a cool climate, a welcome break from the heat of the Burmese plains ...'

Charlie had suffered yet another bout of malaria. He was run down and exhausted after the extra work imposed by the war years, when several of the staff of the Winchester Brothers had been called away on active service as chaplains or administrators.

'Got to get you out of here for a rest.'

The bluff British army doctor in Mandalay had told him about Mamyo, and he had found himself bundled off once again into the hills. He dozed off on the train and, between snoozes, remembered Alice, his youthful companion on that first convalescent holiday high in the Himalayas. She must be a middle-aged lady by now, and he pictured her at her home in England, a little plump and surrounded by children.

He woke from his dreams to find the train stopped and emptying rapidly. Landing in a hurry on the station platform, he wondered, just for a moment, whether he was still asleep. Was this perhaps Alice's leafy English home town, with flowers cascading from the balconies of its English houses? Or was he back in the Himalayas, and someone would come to him in a moment and lead him to Mrs Monk's Grand Hotel? No, it could be neither of those things. It was cool, yes, and extraordinarily British, but never, anywhere had he seen anything resembling the station taxi service. The horse-drawn carts looked a little like gipsy caravans, but they were were lighter, and brighter, and altogether prettier, and the animals between their shafts were slender ponies, not the scraggy, underfed gipsy nags he knew from home.

So this was Maymyo, and it came to him almost at once that this was where he would like to be when working on his prayer book translation, where he would like to come when he could be spared from his Mandalay duties. As he wandered through the quiet streets, past the beautiful, but not yet finished, Botanical Gardens and the big lake which he was told had been dug by Turkish prisoners-of-war sometime before the end of hostilities in 1918, a couple of years ago, he yearned for the peace of this place. He wouldn't need a grand European-style house; one of those little palm-leaf huts down that rutted earth road would do very nicely.

> Fanny, you simply must come out to Maymyo and see my stylish home. It has an earth floor, beautifully polished by quantities of bare feet, and a leafy roof made from palm fronds, which shelters me from the sun in the hot weather. I rented it from a local business-man and it's where I sleep and work on the prayer-book whenever I get the chance to get away from Mandalay.

And Fanny could think of nothing nicer.

THE LETTER FROM THE British and Foreign Bible Society came just in time before his home leave. Of course, there had been no question of his answer to them. He was overwhelmed, gratified, honoured ...

> Of course I accept. However, there are problems apart from the enormous one of the work itself. I am sure these can be overcome, particularly as I shall be in England very shortly on furlough and so could come and see you in person. I think we need to discuss my secondment, and the delicate subject of finance. My wants are few, and I have already established myself in a small hut. But the roof does leak during the monsoon, and the white ants find my papers a very enjoyable diet, so I am afraid I shall need something in the way of a salary ...

Fanny's diary for 21st May 1920 noted:

'It was very hot. We all went to the railway station. Char's train started and took him off for England. I felt as if I had been boiled and washed out.'

Of course Fanny was sad to see him go. But he would return and things would doubtless go on much as before. The war years were behind them, Char would be well rested by his furlough, and their life would lapse back into the regular rhythm of earlier days.

Or so they thought.

Bures, England, 1918

I was in the yard feeding our hens when I heard Annie calling. 'Matt, where are you? There's a letter for you with a Burma post-mark!' None of us have had any news from Charlie for ages – it's the war, I suppose. Anyway, the chickens had to wait while I had a read. He's all right, thank God, and Mr Will's all right too, though it seems he had a hard time of it in that military hospital in India. But Charlie seemed mostly interested in what was going on here. I'd told him in a letter how the Armistice came just in time to stop his Godson Charles volunteering for the army. And I'd told him about our poor daughter Iris. She was walking out with a soldier living Marks Tey way. He went all through the war, Paschendale and that, and then, right at the end, he caught that awful flu and was dead in a week, along with half his platoon. He wasn't the only one to die from here, mark you. At the worst of it, every few days you'd see blinds down where folks had lost someone in the fighting. Thank God its over at last.

Bures, January 1920

Would you believe it? if Miss Fanny hasn't upped and gone to Burma too! She actually came up to the cowshed the other day when we were just about to start the milking, and told me she was going out there to look after her two brothers, and did I have any special message for Charlie. Of course I did.

46

Passenger List
HMS COLUMBUS

7 December 1920

Abercrombie, Matthew, Mr
Andrews, John, Mr
Andrews, Eliza, Mrs
Brinton, Jeremiah, Dr
Brinton, Annie, Mrs
Burroughs, Edith, Miss
Carter, William, Mr
- -
- -
Garrad, Charles, Reverend
Gudenheim, Fritz, Mr

Gudenheim, Greta, Mrs
- -
Mason, Frank, Mr
Mason, Isabella, Mrs
Maung Clit, Mr
Maunt Clit, Mrs
- -
- -
Wilberforce, Robert, Mr
Williams, Thomas, Mr
Young, Elizabeth, Miss

IT HAD BEEN AN EXCELLENT FURLOUGH. He had got home just in time to help with the hay-making. Then there had been the visits to the British and Foreign Bible Society to make firm plans for the Bible translation, and, later, work with Cardy in the Top Fields bringing in the harvest. The sun shone, the barley ripened to perfection with neither rain nor wind to flatten it, and the Suffolk countryside looked its very best. He missed Fanny, of course, but her absence in Burma would make his return that much easier. In any case, with so much ahead of him that was new and exciting, when the time came he was more than ready to go back.

~§~

THE PASSENGER LIST posted just inside the door of the lounge always seemed to attract a small crowd during the hours of waiting before the ship set sail. Who or what were people searching for, Charlie wondered? Old friends, turning up again unexpectedly? Long lost cousins, distant and forgotten? Perhaps they were simply curious. Or perhaps, like himself, they found the names themselves a kind of poetry. Perhaps they saw them in rhythms and patterns, those as yet unseen faces who owned them encircling them in a hazy halo, ghosts in reverse waiting to be firmed-up

No, nothing and nobody there to catch his attention. He left the lounge and made his way on to the passenger deck. It was at this moment an awful place. Visitors had not yet been turned away. They had not yet been instructed by the disembodied megaphone to walk down the gangplank and across the water that was to separate them form their loved ones for months, even years, to come.

All around him were tears and hugs and desperate embraces. As he wandered, scraps of conversation crept in and out of his hearing.

'... likes three lumps of sugar...'

'... my darling, I don't think I can bear it...'

And, as the rain started

'I do believe I've left the washing on the line.'

The booming voice pronounced its fateful message and the tearing apart began. Sad people trickled down the gangplank, back to their own dull lives. The intrepid travellers, their minds already turning to the excitements of all that lay ahead, rushed to line the ship's rail.

Charlie, caught up in the crowd, almost collided with a parting couple. The man, tall and muffled up against the rain, was holding the diminutive young woman's hand in both his own.

'Goodbye, my dear. Write soon – you're very brave, you know.' Letting her go at last, he strode away. The last call to leave the ship had been made. He was only just in time.

The girl looked after him and Charlie saw that tears were streaming down her face. Almost automatically, he began to feel in his pocket for his handkerchief.

Hang on, though – I can't treat her like my sisters. I wonder what's happening? Perhaps her mother's dying in some far-off place, and the husband can't go for some reason. He looks a bit of a rotter – maybe I should look after her, make sure she's all right ...

But at that moment the heavens opened and the rain descended in tropical ferocity. Everyone made a dash for cover and the bereft young lady vanished as though she had never been.

THERE WAS NO IMPROVEMENT in the weather. On the very first evening a notice was posted on each passenger deck:

'The Captain regrets to inform all passengers that violent storms for tonight, 7th December 1920, are forecast on the ship's radio. Room service will be available to those who feel unable to leave their cabins.'

Few slept that night, and even fewer ventured forth. Charlie, inured against sea-sickness by the voyages that were already behind him, sat almost alone in the dining-room for breakfast the next morning. But fried eggs and bacon were beyond even him. Up, down, backwards, forwards, upwards, sideways, up, back, and down again; the ship's stomach-churning roll in grotesque conflicting arcs defied even the most experienced of the staff to serve anything except dry toast. A trainee waiter's tray had tipped its offering of scalding coffee over his own hand. He was badly burnt and the ship's doctor took a welcome break from the stench of vomit to bandage the blisters with fragrant medicated dressings.

Cold water and the juice of any fruits that could survive the journey were the order of the day.

It was not until it had left the Bay of Biscay that life began to creep back into the belly of the ship. Wan passengers wended their wobbly ways up on to the decks, their pinched lungs joyfully exchanging the stale fug of cabins for great gusts of the salty air.

Charlie had taken up his favourite position in front of the foremost funnel, its plume of smoke blowing out harmlessly behind him. Idly watching and listening to the convalescents as they strolled past him, his own stomach took a sudden leap.

'... amazing that the ship could stand up to it!'

That voice! Whose is it? Where's it coming from?

The gusty wind was playing tricks with sound; it was difficult to pinpoint direction. She was almost out of sight again round the curve of the deck before he could locate her, a small figure in a thick coat, long, very long, strands of brown hair escaping from the plump bun at the back of her neck and blowing in his direction. He had the ridiculous impulse to run after her, to grab the hair in both hands and pull her back towards him.

You're insane! You don't even know who she is! And yet there's something familiar – yes, of course – that couple who were saying goodbye and the husband had to run to get off the ship before they pulled up the gangplank.

But what on earth's got into you? Whatever it is, it had better get out again pretty quick. Food – that's what you need, my boy.

And Charlie took himself off to the ship's dining-room.

But lunch, afternoon tea, dinner, came and went and, although he partook heartily of all three, he could not have told you afterwards what it was that he had eaten. Food seemed in fact to have made matters worse. Flowing rich brown locks insinuated themselves between his eyes and his plate, his book, his talkative companion; hair haunted his dreams that night.

At first, it was almost a comedown. There she was sitting opposite him at breakfast, her demure coiffure fitting her head like a gleaming swimming cap. Not one chestnut brown thread was out of place.

'Good morning.' Charlie held out his hand across the table. The small hand that met it halfway, immediately above the cruet, had a surprisingly firm grip. As its owner raised her eyes to his face, all thoughts of hair vanished.

Blue-bag! That's what her eyes look like, those bags of blue stuff Mrs Miller from the village puts in the boiler with the sheets and things to make them look white. How can anyone have eyes that colour and still be human? Perhaps she's not real at all. She must be an angel in disguise – and pretty poor disguise at that. Perhaps ...

'Excuse me, Vicar, but would you be so good as to pass the marmalade?'

The clipped upper-class voice coming from the lady seated to his left, every syllable soaked in disapproval, nearly made him jump out of his skin. Where was he? What world had he been in? Above all, what was he doing, holding a young married lady's hand right across the table in the middle of breakfast?

'I'm s-so s-sorry. I d-don't know what came over me.' He sat down with a bump, and it seemed to him that the little hand, so suddenly released from his, scuttled back to its own side and jumped for protection into its owner's lap.

Poor Charlie. Head down, he ate his porridge and toast as fast as decency would allow and with a scarcely audible 'please excuse me' left the table and almost ran back to his cabin.

THE WEATHER WAS STORMY STILL, and the hours dragged by. Deck-games no longer held any charm. The day's constitutional, round and round the deck ten times, was a tiresome routine to be got through. To both his relief and utter disappointment, the seat opposite him at his table was now occupied by a maundering old man, endlessly recounting his everlasting experiences in the Indian Civil Service.

'Miserable fellow, that vicar,' he would say later to his cabin companion. 'Telling him all my best stories, but can't get any reaction. Looks as if he's swallowed a tin-tack.' And he shook the smooth shiny bald head that led down to a face so astonishingly wrinkled that it had made Charlie think of a prune; he had half expected to see the stone propelled out with the torrent of words.

Of the girl with the blue eyes and chestnut hair there was no sign, no sign at all.

☙

'WHICH IS YOURS?'

He was standing by the passenger list again, for the hundredth time searching its columns of names for hers. Nothing seemed to fit. Men on their own there were in plenty but almost all the women were travelling with their husbands. Four were alone, but all of these had the prefix 'Miss.' To three of them he could now add a face, but not the fourth. And why was this youthful 'Mrs' not included?

But now, to his utter confusion, there she stood in the flesh, at his elbow and gazing like himself at the unrewarding list.

'This is mine,' she said. Reaching up with the very same hand that he had held over the salt and pepper, she pointed to the name of the faceless spinster.

'That's me,' she said. 'Rawson, Marjory, Miss.' And she laughed. 'Doesn't it sound silly written like that? All topsy-turvy,' and the laughter came again.

When there was no reply, Marjory tried again. This really was a very peculiar man, so friendly at the breakfast table that day, and hiding himself away ever since. She mustn't be too forward, but he looked so wretched and, after all, he was a vicar, so she supposed it was all right. Now, he was standing stock still, gazing down at her with a look of such bewilderment in those penetrating brown eyes that she had to work hard to suppress yet another giggle.

'Er – did you say Miss?'

Marjory looked puzzled.

'Yes – look – just like it says. Miss Marjory Rawson.'

'But you're married!'

'No, I certainly am not. What in the world made you think that?'

'Your husband was seeing you off ...'

'My WHAT? Oh, of course – no, that was the vicar from home.'

Then followed a long garbled explanation of all that had led up to the fond farewell on the boat deck.

'Are you sure? I mean, about not being ma ...'

'Of course I am, you goose!' and out came a little hand again to cover her mouth in embarrassment at being so forward with a strange gentleman, and a man of the cloth at that. This time the hand was the left one, and Charlie gazed, in total disbelief still, at the naked, ringless fourth finger.

'But you were crying so hard when you said goodbye – your face was all wet.'

'Of course it was – it was pouring with rain!'

Marjory was somewhat out of her depth. This was an entirely new sort of conversation, and to cover her unease, she pointed again at the list.

'So which is yours?'

'Er, that one.' Charlie's hand was shaking, and he brought it down again to his side – her side – so quickly that she scarcely had time to see where he had pointed.

'That one? Garrad, Charles, Reverend?'

Suddenly, simultaneously, to write people's names back to front seemed to both of them the funniest thing in the world and they both laughed so uproariously that passing heads turned to see what could possibly be so amusing on a dull passenger list.

'ALL TOPSY-TURVY.' That's what she had said when she first read out her own name.

Topsy-turvy – everything's gloriously, wonderfully, supremely, topsy turvy. How completely ridiculous I was to assume she was married just because she was being seen off by a man! When, after all, he was only just another vicar, an old friend of her dead father's, seeing her off because there wasn't anybody else.

Two whole weeks – two whole weeks to talk to her, have meals with her, play games with her, just be with her. How can I keep myself in – how can I pretend to all these amazing beautiful people on this amazing beautiful ship that anything is as it was before when it wasn't anyway, and certainly can't ever be again!

'Good morning! Isn't it a wonderful day!'

'How are your rheumatics today, Mrs Peters? Oh I am so delighted!'

'Did you ever see sea such a beautiful blue?'

Everyone he came into contact with felt better. The fact that it was actually raining, that Mrs Peters' rheumatism was certainly as bad as ever, if not worse, that in the general opinion the colour of the sea was not blue at all but a dirty grey, seemed neither here nor there. The radiant happiness of the Reverend Charles Edward Garrad gleamed in every corner of the great steamship and was reflected in the hearts of all.

THAT NIGHT, SLEEP FOR CHARLIE was out of the question. Was it possible that anyone else had ever felt as he did now, had ever been so blissfully bewitched? Could his old friend Matt have felt like this, for instance, when he married his beloved Annie? He couldn't quite picture it, somehow – Matt was so – well – solid. But he decided then and there to write to him, just the same.

Bures, England, 1920

I got a letter from Charlie today, and you could have knocked me down with a feather! 'Matt, old friend' he said 'you'll never guess what's happened,' and I couldn't have, not in a million years. Of course I'm that happy for him, but what can she really be like? A missionary doesn't somehow sound, well, a very comfortable sort of wife, does she? if it should come to that, of course. Does that sort of lady mend socks and cook and everything? Or perhaps they don't wear socks in those hot countries. Charlie needs looking after more than most, I'd say. When he was home on leave they were all clucking round him like a yardful of hens. Mind you, he did look ever so thin and pale under his foreign sort of tan when he arrived, but they fattened him up like a prize pig off to market and at the end he went back in good spirits. They were all ever so proud of him being offered that Bible translation job.

I wonder whether the family know about Charlie's young lady yet? I doubt he's told them, though Miss Fanny might have dropped a hint or two. Of course, it isn't as if he hasn't got Miss Fanny to look after him – she's bound to make sure the pair of them are all right, she's that kind.

Well I never.

47

AT LAST THE SUN REALLY DID COME OUT, and with it the rows of deck-chairs. It mattered not one jot that the only two left empty together stood right in the middle of the row; for Charlie and Marjory, the world belonged to them and them alone. But to everyone else, this delightful development was public property, and, though their owners would have strenuously denied it, long ears were stretched to the limit.

'... so terrible when Father died. But I know you understand, because of your poor mother ...'

'... my sister, you know, the one I told you about called Joe, made my life ...'

'... lived with Aunt B and Uncle Evie. That was all right for a bit, but I was longing to get away. Then I got this chance to go and stay with a couple in Weimar and go to finishing-school there – in exchange, I had to look after their daughter ...'

'What was she like – the daughter, I mean?'

'Spoilt to death. But the school was fun – only about twelve of us, from different countries.'

'In the holidays, though – what happened then?'

'Oh, mostly I had to put up with being a sort of skivvy. The couple I was staying with – he was a German army officer, like a colonel here – were pretty awful. She was a frightful snob and anybody who wasn't army was nobody. I did have one amazing holiday, though, with one of the German girls from the school on her family's country estate. Sounds terribly grand – which it was, I suppose. But we went riding and swimming and walking in the mountains – they were so beautiful, with gentians and waterfalls and marmots.'

'What on earth are marmots?'

Marjory looked at him.

'You're so clever with all that Latin and Burmese and Greek, and you don't even know what a marmot is?'

Charlie gazed down at her.

Marmots, whatever they might be, and mountains and gentians – of course, it's gentians that her eyes are like, not blue-bag! How could I think of her in the same breath as the laundry! She is so beautiful, so different, so amazing, so ...'

'Mr Garrad, are you listening? I don't believe you've heard a single word I've said.'

And Charlie had to admit that he still didn't know a marmot from a pot of marmalade.

TIME, THOUGHT CHARLIE, is a monster. The monster sleeps; the time drags. Suddenly something, some unexpected event, takes place to wake it from its slumbers and off it goes, careering through the days and nights, uncontrolled and unstoppable.

Faster and faster the time went, and now there was less than a week before their arrival in Bombay. No matter how much he told himself that this first arrival was unimportant, that they would be travelling on the train together to Calcutta and then on to Burma, that they would be working in the same country, in his heart he knew that nothing would be quite the same again. Here, the two of them, without duties or distraction, were insulated from the world by the confines of a tiny boat afloat on a mighty ocean. Hereafter, there would be none of this, nothing to keep them together but their own mutual attraction. For his part, he had no shadow of doubt, no breath of hesitation. But Marjory, his adorable, unbelievable Marjory? Could it be that she felt as he did, not so strongly, of course, but as a dim reflection? That was all he could possibly hope for, but was even that unattainable? How dare he even dream of her as 'his'?

She gave nothing away, and he simply was not sure.

Between the doubts was the continuing joy. They had discovered that each felt they had known the other all their lives. This, though patently untrue, was an astonishingly strong emotion and made confidences easy. Charlie poured out the story of his past:

'You know I told you about my mother dying just after she'd had my brother George? Did I explain how I climbed a tree to get out of going to the funeral?' And, when she shook her head, out it all came. And then, 'Father sent me off to boarding-school, in a sailor suit ...' By the end, he could swear there were tears in her eyes. The Clare College Fellowship, the struggles with his conscience about becoming a missionary, the family, the farm, his friend Matt. Nothing was left out.

'Now it's your turn again.'

This time they had found a shady corner of the deck. The weather was hot and oppressive; tropical wear was the order of the day, and Charlie's heavy cotton shirt was sticking uncomfortably to his back.

How in the world does she manage to look so deliciously cool?

He took the two glasses of pineapple juice from the attendant's tray and handed one to Marjory. She lay back in her deck-chair sipping her drink and smiling up at him, her thin flowery dress outlining her slender figure and allowing what breeze there was to play on bare arms and ankles.

'What d'you want to know?'

'I want to know everything – everything about my – my – new friend.' *My adorable, bewitching love.*

'That's a tall order!'

How can a laugh be so perfect?

And off he went into dangerous uncharted waters, into an unsuspected realm of fantasy hidden deep within his sterile scholar's soul. Plashing mountain streams, their banks overflowing with gentians; marmots in elegant fur coats roaming the hills (he'd looked them up, of course – they seemed to be some sort of mountain mouse, name derived from the Latin, but he still couldn't quite picture them)*;* dawn mists rising from alpine meadows; the music of distant cowbells, of yodelling herdsmen dressed in lederhosen; the scent of new-baked bread filling the crystal air ...

'... don't you agree?'

'Er, I'm so sorry. I didn't quite catch what you said ...'

Marjory shook her finger at him.

'I do believe, Garrad, Charles, Reverend, that you're day-dreaming again!'

And once again their combined laughter turned the heads of the passers-by.

She had so much to tell him, this solemn, beautiful man, with his high, clever forehead and his big nose, but half the time he didn't seem to be taking in what she said. Was it simply that he wasn't listening, or could it be that he had problems with his hearing? She had noticed that he always took trouble to sit on her right-hand side. Of course the ship was noisy; engines, people, sailors shouting commands at each other. But he was still young – well, anyway, not old – and he shouldn't be suffering from old men's complaints. One day she must pluck up the courage to ask him.

'I was just saying that telling the whole story of your life in just a few hours isn't easy. But I will try, if that's what you really want.'

'It's what I want more than anything in the world.'

'Well, after I finished at that school in Germany, I came back home and was a sort of governess to a family in Yorkshire. Then one day I got a letter with a stamp I didn't recognise. It was from a girl I'd been with in Weimar. She was Romanian – her parents were part of the Romanian court circle – Queen Carol was queen then. They needed an English governess, and they were offering me the job! Everything about it seemed perfect – good salary, first-class return ticket – luxuries I'd never dreamt of –'

'So you set off to seek your fortune?'

'No such luck. Poor Mother – she was as excited as I was. And then she began to have these awful tummy-aches. At first she said in her letters it was just indigestion, but I was worried somehow and came down from Yorkshire to see for myself. I got such a shock, she'd changed so much in such a short time. She was horribly thin and gaunt-looking, and then one day she was terribly sick and there was blood in it! At last she agreed to send for the doctor, and straight away he got a specialist to come and see her. They examined her together and then made me sit down and said they thought she'd got internal cancer – stomach cancer, they called it – but they'd got to do some tests to make sure. Anyway, after that she went downhill really quickly. My brother Edward did manage to get compassionate leave from the army which cheered her up a bit, but there wasn't anyone else in the family who could come and nurse her – in any case, I couldn't have gone abroad with her so ill.

So I had to write to the Romanian girl – I can't for the life of me remember her name – and that was the end of that. Mother just got worse and worse. It was awful to watch. In the end, she couldn't keep anything down, not even water. And then, one evening, she just slipped away – no sound, no anything. She just stopped breathing.' And Marjory's head went down into her hands, and the tears that crept between her fingers made round dark blobs on the pale green background of her summer dress.

They sat together, not speaking; it seemed that the whole ship, usually so noisy, was muffled by her grief.

Then at last Charlie's quiet voice cut gently across the silence.

'You mentioned Edward. Did he manage to extend his leave, to be with you for a bit? After all, he is your only brother.'

'Was.'

'How d'you mean, was? Was what?'

'Was my only brother – he was killed in the war.'

Charlie was dumb-struck.

'Do you know what happened?'

'Not really, not at the end. He'd had rather a sad life, you see. He was always supposed to be going to be a great scholar like his father, but he didn't do well at school. Actually he left early – enlisted in the army when he was just seventeen – probably desperate to get away from home and everybody's expectations. After our mother's death he emigrated to Canada. – I wish to goodness he'd stayed there. I only saw him once more – he'd spent his life feeling guilty and this time it was about being safe when everyone else was fighting. So he came home to get a commission and he was killed in France in 1918.'

48

London, England, 1920

'MISS RAWSON, YOU MUST understand that we at SPG have stringent, very stringent, conditions which must be fulfilled by any missionary aspiring to do God's work under our banner, and ...'

The first crashing chord of 'Onward Christian Soldiers' burst into the room through the open window. The speaker rose to her feet to pull down the sash and managed a frosty wave to the Salvation Army troop below.

'Where was I? Ah yes – stringent conditions. The Society for the Propagation of the Gospel is a highly respected and long established organisation that prides itself upon its ability to choose only those candidates who have the very particular Christian faith and the skills and personality needed for this kind of work.'

The elderly lady had looked over the rim of her round spectacles at this newest recruit and her heart had failed her. The heart itself was warmer than most, but its owner had had to turn away so many enthusiastic and totally unsuitable candidates that over the years it had built itself a protective layer of steel. The pair of bright blue eyes across the office table were drilling holes in the tough casing at such painful speed that the Dragon of the Desk felt herself in danger of losing this initial skirmish and, sitting up even straighter in the hard office chair and bracing back her shoulders, she returned stare for stare.

Marjory had been told that this first interview was crucial to her success, and had come prepared. She had made up her mind; that was all there was to it. She was going to be a missionary, and it would take more than one old lady sitting in comfortable London to stop her. But she knew she must be circumspect.

'It's extremely kind of you to spare time to see me when I know how busy you must be with far more important things ...' and on she went. It seemed to her that the dragon's fiery breath was cooling as she spoke, and when she paused the questions that came back at her were surprisingly gentle.

'So tell me, Miss Rawson, what is your background? And why do you think it prepares you for such a difficult life?'

So Marjory told her. She stressed her father's calling to the Church and his early death and made the most of their resultant difficult childhood. She skated over her time at finishing-school except to point out, with due modesty, that she found learning foreign languages easy. She talked at length about her various teaching jobs, as it was in this field that she felt she would be most useful abroad. Lastly, she explained that over the last months she had been nursing her mother throughout her terminal illness, and that this experience had taught her a great deal about life, and death, that she hadn't known before.

She had no more to say. There was silence inside the office, but the busy city sounds of traffic, horses' hooves and the snort of motor cars, came clearly through the closed windows.

'You have given me a very clear, and at times I have to say moving, account of your life so far.' The last wisp of smoke had disappeared now, and the voice was kind.

'It seems to me that you have had a great many experiences, some very difficult ones, for one so young. What is your exact age?'

'I shall be thirty-four next November.'

'Ah – I had thought you younger. But the extra years are in your favour. You seem very sure in your own mind that this is what you want to do, and of course this too is in your favour. I shall recommend to our clerical committee that they interview you with regard to your Christian beliefs. If the outcome of this is successful, then I see no reason why SPG would not welcome you in its midst. I shall make the necessary arrangements, and you will hear from us very soon.'

They rose, smiled, shook hands, and parted.

'So far so good,' thought Marjory, as she closed the heavy front door behind her and joined the rest of the world on the busy pavement.

THE LETTER, WHEN AT last it came, held both the fewest words and the greatest significance of any that Marjory had ever received.

Dear Miss Rawson

Please attend SPG House for a further interview at 10am on Monday 10th January,

Yours sincerely

AG Hubbard, Dean

For a week, she worried. She might not pass; that would be dreadful. But on the other hand she might pass and that would be dreadful too, for then she would be committed, and she was suddenly not at all sure that this was what she wanted. She got up each morning, washed, dressed, brushed her long hair fifty times as Mother had always made her, and said her prayers. The prayers always made her feel better; it seemed then that this was 'meant'. Each day the same, until, at last, the day of the interview came. She went. She got the job.

She was urgently needed in Burma, to teach at the girls' school in Rangoon. She was examined by the SPG doctor, inoculated twice against typhoid (the second one made her arm ache); bought three lightweight summer dresses, including a green one with a pattern of flowers, packed her trunk, and sailed from Liverpool, escorted there by her vicar. It rained as they set sail, and the weather in the Bay of Biscay was atrocious, as everyone had said it would be. She was sicker than she had ever been and thought that she would die.

49

'CHARLIE LOOKED EVER SO WELL AND JOLLY.' Sister Fanny's diary again.

The entry was written late on New Year's Day 1921, the day of her brother's return from England. Fanny had come to the port to meet both him and the new lady missionary.

Charlie, later, clearly remembered making the introduction.

'Fanny, I should like you to meet Miss Rawson. Miss Marjory Rawson, Miss Fanny Garrad, the sister I've told you so much about.' But the diary remained stubbornly silent on the subject. 'Charlie and I walked to the goods station after tea & found C's heavy luggage. Unpacked it at our lodgings by the light of lanterns with a crowd of little Burmese boys looking on & helping unwrap. C unpacked his cycle.' That was all.

Nothing whatever about an event which must have been enormously important to Fanny, the arrival of an addition to the intrepid band of Englishwomen. Was there a hunch, a premonition of a profound change in their lives? That nothing would be quite the same again?

TWO WEEKS LATER, on the same day that, unbeknown to them, their father died on his peaceful farm in faraway Suffolk, Charlie finally left his Mandalay home and took the train to Maymyo, just forty miles away. Bible translation was to begin in earnest. The scholar's mind must set aside all memories of modern mermaids with russet locks and eyes of a deep sea blue. Instead, it must travel back thousands of years to the thoughts and inspirations of the holy men of the ancient world, inscribed on reeds and the skins of animals and handed down from generation to generation until it reached this place and time. Now, those ancient documents, endlessly copied and rewritten, had come to rest in modern guise in his own hands. It was his hand that must rewrite the ancient truths and make them come to life for those around him, to give them in their own language and idiom the teachings from God that were at the very centre of his own being. How could he possibly rise to this challenge?

THERE WERE THREE OF THEM in the official team appointed by the British and Foreign Bible Society but of the trio, only one was foreign. The Reverend W. Sherratt, a Wesleyan minister, and the Reverend C.E. Garrad, a solid down-the-middle-Anglican, both classical scholars, were British to the core. Mr Sherratt had been in Burma the longer of the two and so was appointed leader. The remaining member, the Reverend George Kya Bin, otherwise known as Saya (Teacher) George, was Burmese. When Saya George was told that the translation into his own language would be not from English but direct from the Hebrew and Greek in which the two Testaments were originally written, he shook his head in disbelief. He had three questions.

'Why Hebrew?'

'Because the Old Testament was written by Jews and that was their language.'

'But why Greek for the New Testament? Greece is a long way from Palestine, where Jesus lived.'

'Because Greek was the language spoken by the Palestinians in Jesus's time. There was a famous Greek warrior called Alexander the Great who conquered the whole of the Middle East from Egypt to India three and a half centuries before Christ, and for hundreds of years after that the whole lot spoke his language.'

'But you have already got English translations from Hebrew and Greek. Why do it all over again? It would surely be much easier from the English?'

'Indeed it would. But they contain a lot of mistakes. This new Bible for your people is to be as perfect as we can make it, and so we must start from the originals.'

Saya George's head shook from side to side in solemn uncomprehending agreement.

The whole enterprise was scheduled to take four or five years. It was a mammoth undertaking.

'WHAT ON EARTH ARE YOU fellows up to, working at this time of night?'

Sherratt had left their 'office' at what he considered a sensible time, but had come back to retrieve an important letter. He found Charlie still writing, his answer to the question swallowed up in a huge yawn. The Burmese teacher and scholar sat with his head in his hands. It was dark in the little hut; just one candle flickered in the draught coming through the mat walls.

'It is all right, Father,' said Saya George. 'My head aches, that is all.'

'But what in the world are you doing here at eleven o'clock? Of course you've got a headache – what can you expect? It's nearly five hours since it got dark, you've got one candle, some of those Hebrew hieroglyphics are almost impossible to decipher even in daylight, AND you've been working since six this morning! For goodness sake ...'

'Please, Father, please do not be angry!'

'I'm not angry, just it's so stupid.'

'But look at what Saya George has achieved to-day.' Charlie came to the Burman's rescue, holding up a single sheet of paper, and Sherratt brought the candle close. He could just make out that the document was closely written from top to toe in Saya George's neat Burmese hand.

'So how many verses does this represent?'

Charlie turned to a worn Bible lying open on the table and ran his finger from right to left along the rows of square Hebrew letters.

'At least twenty, I should think. Saya George has done a wonderful job in correcting my clumsy Burmese – the final effort is near perfect, I believe.'

Despite himself, Sherratt was impressed.

'All in one day? That's a tremendous achievement! At that rate, we'll have the whole of Isaiah finished within the month!'

'SO WHO DO THESE ENGLISH fellers think they are?'

'Well, we know for certain that they're great scholars, specially Charles Garrad. He's the one that's deaf – you really have to yell at him pretty loud. Big nose. Thin as a beanpole. Fellow of Cambridge University. Don't know too much about the other Brit. The Burmese guy seems with it, too – a deacon, whatever that is, in the C of E.'

'OK, so they've got a good pedigree. But that doesn't give them the right to do Judson down, does it? After all, his Bible translation's been around for at least eighty years. Stood the test of time. Just because he's been to the most famous university in the world, Garrad seems to think Judson's ... yeah, come in!'

The Americans were sitting in their pretty English sitting-room inside their pretty English house in the centre of Maymyo. They were Baptist missionaries; when the knock on the door came, the discussion on their own new proposed translation of the Bible into Burmese was just getting into full swing. The newcomer, a lad of about twelve, went and stood by his father's chair.

'Sorry to interrupt, Dad. I really came because Mom wants to know if you'd like cold drinks, but I heard you talking about Judson. Is he a famous Christian? We've got to do an essay on one for our scripture prize next term – an important American preacher, I mean. D'you think he'd do? D'you know him?'

The three men laughed.

'That would be tricky – he died about fifty years ago. But I do know quite a bit about him. Want me to tell you? Now? That is, if the others don't mind?'

Sensing general agreement, his son took the remaining chair.

'Well, he sure was quite a guy, this Judson. Even his name was spectacular – christened Adoniram – how d'you like that?'

The boy laughed.

'Anyway, he wanted to be a missionary, same as your Dad. There were no missionary societies in the States then, so he had to go to England. On the way, everyone on board his ship was captured by French pirates and imprisoned in Bayonne, in France. After a bit they let Adoniram out, and he wasted no time in getting married to a girl called Nancy and then priested the very next day. A couple of weeks later they were on their way to Burma. That enough?'

His son shook his head, fair hair flopping into dark brown eyes.

'No, it's good. Go on – what happened next?'

'Well, Ad and Nancy worked very hard at learning Burmese, and then started to try and convert the Burmese to Christianity. Trouble was, the Burmese king sentenced to death anyone who changed religion, which made it all pretty tricky. Progress, I guess, was extremely slow.

Poor old Ad was sent to prison again for a year or more when the English were fighting the Burmese. Soon after, his wife and their third child died – they'd already lost the other two. The poor father took himself off into the jungle for a whole year to mourn, I believe. After that, he concentrated on translating the whole Bible into Burmese, and made a pretty good job of it, too. He got married twice more, and had nine children altogether, though three of them died early. He converted hundreds and hundreds of people in the end – he was a missionary for getting on for forty years.'

'So what happened to him in the end?'

'Even that was dramatic. He'd had an awful chest for some time, and the doctors prescribed a sea voyage as a cure. Sadly, it didn't work, and he died on board ship in the Bay of Bengal, and was buried at sea. He was round about sixty, if I remember aright.'

One of the other men spoke.

'I must say I didn't know all that,' he said, and his companion shook his head. He turned to the boy.

'What your Dad hasn't told you is how famous he is – not just here in Burma but home in the States too. He was really the founder of the Baptist Church in the US of A – there's no end of Baptist churches named after him ...'

'... not forgetting Judson College in Illinois, and that other one, in Alabama, I think, named after Nancy ...'

'... so I think he would be an excellent choice for your prize essay. He's really a bit of an icon in American Baptist circles, as well as with the older people here.'

'Thanks, Dad. Nobody else at school will know anything like as much.'

'Better go and write some of it down then, before you forget.'

Bures, England, January 1921

How I wish Charlie was here. When Miss Edith came down to the cottage and said 'Matt, I have some sad news for you' I realised straight away what it would be. Old blind Mr Garrad had passed peacefully away in the night – he'd been poorly for some time, you see, so it didn't come as a surprise. I think they'd quite like me to go to the funeral, as a kind of stand-in for Charlie I suppose – although they never did understand why we were such friends. So I shall go. There'll be the five spinster sisters of course – only Miss Fanny away, in Burma. Though maybe Miss Daisy won't go to the church, as she's not quite right in the head. Then there'll be John and George – they run the farm – and Frank the doctor and Bob who's a clergyman up north.

Charlie and Will and Fanny won't know yet – not for at least a fortnight. So I must do what I can.

50

'SO, WHAT ARE WE GOING TO DO about the Americans?'

Sherratt had called a meeting of his own team in his house, and for a long moment there was silence in the airy room. Saya George sipped his coconut milk and the rattan chairs creaked as the men shifted uncomfortably, disturbed by the directness of the question. At last, Charlie spoke.

'Well, the fact is they are colleagues and they've come here to do exactly what we're doing, to make a new translation of the Bible. So far, we've all gone our own way. But it's becoming more and more obvious that it's a gigantic task, and the more of us that work on it the easier and quicker it should be. In theory.'

Sherratt spoke again.

'Exactly. In theory. They're all good scholars with excellent teaching behind them, but it's going to be an uphill struggle to move them very far from the Judson translation, I can tell you. As a non-conformist myself, I do know what store my American brothers set by Judson. Of course, he was a fantastic man and a fantastic missionary, but that doesn't mean that his translation was perfect. Quite extraordinary that he found time to do it at all, of course, in the middle of everything else, but he simply couldn't give it the necessary time.'

'But surely, at least we should meet them and see if we can't pool our resources. It would be madness not to.'

'All right, Garrad, if you say so. But I think it will be you who'll suffer the most. You're a perfectionist – it's obvious from the work you've already done. The Americans will find that very difficult to cope with.'

'You may be right, but I still think ...' And so the discussion went on until at last Charlie won the day and a messenger was sent to offer a date and time for Round One.

❦

'WELCOME!'

The red-haired American could not have been more friendly or more gracious. (Did he have a trace of an Irish accent? Charlie could not be sure.) The Englishmen were ushered into the same sitting-room where the essay on Judson had been launched. Seduced, if only for the moment, by the relative luxury of the room, they settled back into the long chairs and gratefully accepted glasses of cold tea.

'My houseboy will have boiled the water for a good twenty minutes, I can assure you.'

The wool rug on the floor and pretty chintz curtains at the windows could have belonged in any well-to-do English home, and Charlie felt his spirits lift. Here was a reassuring comfort that transported him back where he belonged; such harmony surely boded well for the friendship between the two groups.

After some general conversation, their host brought the meeting to order.

'Well, folks, if you're ready, I suggest we move next door. We can sit round the table for our discussion – much more practical, as I see we've all got paperwork with us.'

Settled once more, he turned to Sherratt.

'Mr Sherratt, I understand you're the leader of your team. What are your feelings about combining our efforts? D'you think it's a good idea? And how do you suggest we set about it?'

'I will be blunt. I have to say that I have doubts, grave doubts. I know that my colleague here, Mr Garrad, will not be content with anything that falls short of a near-perfect translation, and that will mean changing, or even destroying, a great deal of Judson. And I think that would upset you greatly.'

'It surely would. But perhaps you're painting the picture too black. Sure, Judson didn't get everything right – but neither will any of us, if Mr Garrad will forgive my saying so.'

Charlie smiled and shook his head.

'If we can rearrange things a bit, I believe a lot of Judson will stand. After all, he has been used for nearly a hundred years, and the proof of the pudding...'

Charlie interrupted him.

'... is not so much in the eating as in the digesting, surely. The pudding may taste delicious, but if it's made with faulty ingredients, it may do a lot more harm than good.'

'OK, but let's not get too hasty here. My friends and I have come up with a simple experiment. Why don't we pick a chapter of something not too obscure, but not too easy either. Each group studies it and translates it, and then, when we're both done, we meet again and compare, with each other and with Judson. How does that strike you?'

It struck them all, in principal, as a good initial solution. But what should they pick? Too easy, and there would be little to choose between them. Too complicated, and they might well have differences of opinion as to its meaning even in their own language, let alone Burmese. Passage after passage was suggested until Charlie finally banged his fist on the table in frustration.

'This is ridiculous. If we can't even agree on a test chapter, what hope have we got for the real thing? I think this is counter-productive – we're simply irritating each other before we've even started. I propose we close this meeting and make a date for another in which we start work properly.'

'Seconded!' All hands but one went up, and the meeting was brought to a rapid close.

How could I lose my temper so quickly! Reverted to childhood – must have. All these years in this difficult country and I've never even been near it. Till today. That red-headed fellow – Abe, they seem to call him ... silly name, short for Abraham, I suppose – he manages to put the needle in every time. No excuse for me being rude, though. Make amends somehow. Give him lunch, perhaps.

But Abe beat him to it. A general invitation to both teams, with wives, sisters, children or any other hangers-on, was issued and rice and an excellent chicken curry were served in more than generous proportions. Charlie, always economical and therefore always hungry, for once allowed himself to eat to his limit and accordingly felt better.

Until the next meeting.

'Look here, Garrad – I'd rather call you by your Christian name, but I guess that would make you feel awkward; you Brits are funny that way – you were pretty critical of Judson at our last meeting. Why is that?'

And Charlie proceeded to tell him.

'Judson is full of holes. Again and again, the meaning simply is not there. It never unfolds in consecutive sentences – only tumbles out in scraps, one after the other ...'

The face under the carroty hair was getting redder.

'That may be your opinion, but it certainly isn't mine. What do the rest of you fellows think?' He scanned the faces round the table. Discomfort and embarrassment were universal. The anger was American.

For a few moments, nobody spoke. This time it was Sherratt who broke the silence.

'I don't know how your team goes about its translation sessions, but this is the way we do it. We all sit round the table. Garrad and I have the original Hebrew in front of us – Saya George has the Bible according to Judson. A lot of it's perfectly straightforward, of course. One of us reads out a sentence he's just translated into Burmese and Saya George, who's following along in Judson, nods happily. The two translations are the same. Then we get to a sticky bit. Garrad conquers it first – reads out the meaning in his best Burmese. Astonishment on Saya George's face – you tell him, George ...'

The Burman blushed. He was not used to speaking in public, and certainly not in his limited English, and had no wish to do so now. But his word was needed, so speak he must.

'Yes, Father, I am surprised. The words in Father Judson's Bible I have understood – the words, yes, the meaning, no. Now, when the two English Fathers change the Hebrew into my language, I see the meaning. Then it is easy for me to change the little mistakes the Father has made in his Burmese.'

'We owe a huge amount to Saya George. His gift with words is astonishing.'

The Burman blushed again.

'See here, fellows.'

This time it was one of the two younger Americans who spoke. Plainly dressed in white shirt open at the neck and pale grey shorts, his quiet voice demanded immediate attention. Charlie's hand cupped his left ear, a pose that was to become increasingly characteristic and familiar as the time went by.

'See here. We are all here for the same purpose, to do the Lord's work. St Matthew tells us to 'go and make disciples of all nations' – I believe it's in chapter twenty-eight. There's another verse in Mark that says much the same thing. The Lord has brought us together so surely we must swallow our pride and our differences? Of course we can go our own ways and make as good a job of it as possible. But between the six of us we've got the brightest and the best...'

'OK, OK – of course you're right.' Red-head spoke again. 'Garrad, I sure am sorry if I've upset you. Compromise – that's got to be the order of the day if we're ever to agree. So let's just start and see if we can't come up with something that satisfies the both of us.'

Compromise, thought Charlie. *How can you compromise on something as important as this? Either it's correct or it's not – and if it's not, it has to go. Of course, in some ways they're right. We are here to preach the Gospel to the nations – well, this one, anyway. But this is the Gospel, the Truth – not some smudged affair that's meant to please everybody. This is going to be very difficult, very difficult indeed.*

.

51

My dear Miss Rawson

It is now just a month since we came ashore in Rangoon, and so I am taking the liberty of writing to you to enquire as to your health and general well-being. At least I hope that it is well-being; illness is horribly frequent in newcomers to Burma, before they have had time to get accustomed to so much that is new and strange. I hope, too, that the time has not played its tricks and dragged its feet as it is wont to do when one is plunged into a strange new place where everything is unfamiliar. I try hard to think back to my first arrival in Burma, but it was so long ago that I can scarcely remember! I know that it seemed unbearably hot and humid, that there were a great many insects that took particular pleasure in biting me, that I longed for the green-ness of the English countryside and oh so many other things beside. No doubt you are feeling all these things and many more. But I do hope you are well. If you are well, life is an adventure; if you are ill, it becomes an adversary.

All is well with me. I have a nice little house with a palm roof and mat walls here in Maymyo, and we have started in earnest on our Bible translation. By coincidence, there is an American Baptist team here as well, also translating the Bible. We all feel that we should be working together, and we have met twice to discuss it, but I do not think that it will be possible. Their ideas are so very different from ours. But for the moment we must persist.

I do hope that you are not offended by my writing to you.

Yours very sincerely

Charles Garrad

Rangoon
16th February

My dear Mr Garrad

No, I'm not a bit offended that you wrote to me – I think, though, that I would have been if you had not! I had begun to wonder if you had forgotten me already.

I am well, thank you, and beginning to recover from the shock of living in such a different country – every single thing here seems to be strange. The other teachers in the Mission School are overwhelming me with kindness, so you need not worry that I have no-one to look after me. I only hope that you are faring half as well – your house doesn't sound very comfortable and I do wonder whether you eat enough.

Do you know what happened to me the other day? I ventured out into the street alone, meaning to go to the bazaar...

I have written for far too long – you will be bored with all my little adventures. Write again if you have time in your busy life.

Yours sincerely
Marjory Rawson

Maymyo
21st February

My dear Miss Rawson

The sky was grey and dismal when I woke up in my little hut this morning, but as soon as the boy brought me the post and I spied your handwriting the sun came out and the sky turned a brilliant blue. I should be preparing for the day's work; Sherratt and Saya George will be arriving soon, and I am not ready for them. But your letter has knocked everything out of my silly head and I fear it will stay empty until I have written a few words back. Only a few, mind; Jeremiah is proving a hard nut to crack, and there are Hebrew phrases left over from yesterday which demand the dictionary.

I have to own up to laughing when I read of your exploits in the bazaar. Don't worry; you will get used to bargaining, and no doubt you made the stall-holder immensely happy by your unintended generosity. It's a great mercy that you were only buying candles and not a ruby necklace! That really would have been cause for dismay.

The Americans continue to irritate, try as we will to love our neighbours as ourselves. It is a hard lesson, and one which I fear will be more difficult to learn even than the last chapter of Burmese for the Englishman. In the meeting with them yesterday – oh, but they have arrived. Sherratt and George, I mean, not the Americans, thank goodness. They will think I am being particularly studious writing away already, so early in the morning. (It is not yet 6.30; it is best to do most of our work before it gets too hot.) I shall not confess; I have no wish to share our 'conversations'.

Goodbye for the moment.

Yrs. affectionately

Charles Garrad

Rangoon
16th March

My dear Mr Garrad

Thank you for another letter – it is very kind of you to write so often when you are so busy with such important things. But it is lovely to know I have a friend in this extraordinary country, even if he does live more than a hundred miles away, and your letters do make me feel less lonely. Not that I am unhappy – far from it. It is just that every single day is full of surprises. Everything is so very different, isn't it?

I am getting braver, but that can make it even more alarming. Today I wanted to go from the blind-school to SPG House – something to do with my papers that they were worried about. I decided not to waste money on a private gharrie, so I hailed one of those enclosed double ones. I could see there was someone else inside, but when I got in I got a terrible shock! I could scarcely see the other passenger's face for the pussy spots all over it! I've never seen a case of smallpox, but he looked exactly like the horrid picture in my medical book. I felt like jumping straight out again, although the pony had started to move, but it seemed so terribly rude. So I sat tight, trying not to look as if I was leaning away from him as far as I possibly could in such a small space. Luckily it was only a short ride as you know, and I can tell you I was mightily relieved when we got there and I could climb out. Of course I shall be all right, because I was vaccinated before I came out. Otherwise I think I would have been bound to catch it. Poor man – he's not so lucky.

I am so sorry you're having such a difficult time with the American Baptists. I'm sure you know how to do it better than they do.

Yours very sincerely
Marjory Rawson

Maymyo
20th March

My dear Miss Rawson

I was horrified when I got your letter this morning; what a beastly experience. But of course you are right. As you have been vaccinated, the chances of you catching smallpox are exceedingly small. Even so, I shall still worry about you until the time of danger has passed. I believe the incubation period to be exactly twelve days, so we must wait for nine more, or perhaps even a little longer to be absolutely certain. In the meantime, be sure you do not get overtired. Eat well, sleep well, and please take care of yourself in general. And next time, do spend a few more annas on a private gharrie!

Be sure and write to me again on 29th.
Yrs. affectionately
Charles Garrad

The 30th March came, but the post-boy did not. When he had still not called at the hut on the 31st, Charlie was convinced that Marjory's encounter in the double gharrie had had the worst possible outcome. At the very best, she was in the infections ward of the Rangoon Hospital; at the worst, she was – but that thought was simply not sustainable. Instead, he cycled to the station to find out when the next train left for Rangoon.

'Very sorry, Sir, but you have missed it for today. Tomorrow it will go at 10am.'

He packed his bag. That took five minutes. He went for a walk. That took ten, for it was midday and the temperature was still rising. He waited.

Next day, the post-boy met him as he was wheeling his cycle to the front of the hut.

'For you, sahib,' said the boy, holding out a letter. It would have been hard to decide which face, the brown or the white, shone with the wider smile.

Rangoon
31st March

My dear Mr Garrad

It is all right! I looked in the looking-glass this morning and I have not got a single spot! I waited another day or two before writing, to be quite certain.

What a relief! Now I feel that I have been spared for a reason, and I do believe the reason to be all these dear little blind children. They need looking after so desperately, and I do love them so.

Yrs. very sincerely

Marjory Rawson

The post-boy would surely have been astonished had he known just how narrowly he missed a mighty English pat on the back. But Charlie's delight was short-lived.

How ridiculous I am. Instead of being pleased that she hasn't got smallpox, I'm just plain jealous of the children! If only it were me and not them that was her reason, and me that she loved! When I was about ten, I remember everything seemed unfair, and that's just the way I feel now. They're not the only ones who need looking after – why should they have her and not me?

Maymyo
31st March

My dear Miss Rawson

I cannot tell you how relieved I was to receive your letter. As I had heard nothing after the nine days, I must admit I was beginning to worry, or rather worry even more. But you were right and sensible to wait. Your big family of blind children are exceedingly fortunate to have such a devoted friend and teacher; perhaps I could swallow a dose of Alice-in-Wonderland's shrinking mixture and come and join them! Only I am deaf and not blind.

Compared with yours, my life here is very dull, or at least I believe you would think it so. It is made up of translation, more translation and even more translation, day after day, week after week. I take some services, but otherwise have few pastoral duties. But I love my little hut, and my boy looks after me very well. My bicycle is a good friend and takes me for long rides when I feel the need of exercise. There is quite an English community here, and I get asked out to tiffin and even dinner quite frequently. People are very kind, for I have no space here to return their hospitality.

Work goes on apace, and our little team of three get along very well together. But whether my decision to try to reach agreement with our colleagues from across the Atlantic was the right one is quite another matter. We continue to irritate each other nearly to death, and I think the time is approaching when we should finally give up and part company. It seems that they are simply unable to appreciate that Judson so often misses the point as to be not worth having. Today we had yet another argument when I lost my temper again.

You will be bored by my long rambling letters. But I was so delighted by your good news and even writing to you soothes me. Half an hour ago, I could only scowl at my poor boy; now he looks pathetically grateful for the smile that I have just given him.

Yrs. affectionately

Charles Garrad.

Rumour had reached Charlie that the new lady missionary was to make the eighteen-hour train journey to Mandalay, just forty miles from Maymyo, and was going to visit the new children's hospital and, while there, his sister Fanny. He declared a three-day holiday from translation work. He oiled his bicycle, and had the brake-pads replaced at one of the many cycle 'stalls,' men who squatted at the roadside with a spanner or two and a bucket of water to detect the endless punctures from the rough stony roads. He had made the journey several times and found it easy. He had his hair cut, but decided that a new shirt was an unnecessary extravagance.

Would Marjory be the same? Was she actually real, or a figment of an incandescent imagination? He was almost frightened to put it to the test, but on the 3rd April, in the cool of the early morning, he pedalled off to visit his sister Fanny.

Fanny's diary, 4th April:

'Miss Patch (Matron of the new children's hospital) thought Miss Rawson was coming, & made her a fruit salad & then found it was a mistake, so she brought us the fruit salad instead.'

5th April:

'Miss Patch arrived with more fruit salad, for again Miss Rawson did not come!'

POOR CHARLIE. NO WORD came from Rangoon. Why had she not come? He could not refrain from writing again.

> Maymyo
> 6th April 1921

Dear Miss Rawson

Where were you? Are you ill? I am constantly concerned for your health, now that the hot weather is upon us. My sister and I were so looking forward to meeting you again and then you did not come! Please write and tell me that you are not ill.

Your affectionate friend

Charlie Garrad

> Rangoon
> 20th April 1921

Dear Mr Garrad

No, I am not ill. Two new children were accepted at the Blind School just the day before I was due to travel to Mandalay, and as we are short-staffed and the two new little ones were very upset at having to say good-bye to their parents, I decided that I must stay. I am sorry if you and your sister were upset by my decision. I liked her so much when we met briefly at the docks, and look forward to meeting her again before too long.

Yrs. sincerely

Marjory Rawson.

Nothing about being disappointed not to see me. Of course, she's getting busy, like the rest of us, and not needing so much support. But oh! how I hope that I haven't been living a dream. I simply do not think that I could bear it. I'm writing too often – that must be it. Mustn't overdo things. Better wait a few weeks before the next letter.

But how can I?

ꞏ⸎ꞏ

SOMEHOW HE MANAGED IT. The weeks went by and no more letters were written. The post-boy called and no more letters, of the right kind, were received.

He tried to forget everything except his work. Sleep, once a restful escape from days spent in translation, became instead an exhausting marathon of dreams. In one, giant Hebrew characters formed themselves into a flimsy ladder and he was climbing, climbing, almost falling, higher and higher, reaching up for something that, struggle as he might, was always just beyond his reach. In another, he was trapped in a goldfish bowl. His colleagues swam round him, their mouths soundlessly opening and shutting in a silence so complete that he thought himself dead. He would wake exhausted, relieved that he could hear a dog bark in the darkness but stricken by the realisation that the tick of his clock, once irritatingly loud, had vanished, the hands moving noiselessly round with no apparent motivation. The boils that had plagued him recently swelled in number and size, his appetite disappeared and, with it, pounds in weight that he could scarcely afford to part with.

Still he struggled on. Meetings with the Americans came and went, each one bringing yet more discord. He simply could not bear their slapdash translation nor their sentimental obsession with Judson's Bible. He had always respected Judson; now he found himself beginning to hate him. Sherratt and Saya George, deeply concerned, tried their best to make him take more rest. They put his ill health down to overwork.

Charlie had not taken them into his confidence over Miss Rawson.

And then, at last, a letter came.

Mandalay
June 1st 1921

Dear Mr Garrad

Why haven't you written to me for so long? Your last letter was so short and it didn't tell me anything. I shall try to make up for it by writing you a really long one.

I'm sure you have heard of Father Jackson, or perhaps you have even met him. He's an English missionary who is completely blind and came out here a few years ago to set up this blind school. He lost his sight when he was about two years old, but most of the time you'd never guess that he can't see. He's such fun – I love to hear him laugh! Such glorious pluck and joyousness! He has this club for the blind boys that he calls his Night-Club, and waltzes his boys round the school hall until one or other of them almost drops. He plays cards with them, runs races, does comic turns – he even manages to invent completely new games, and very good ones they are too. So you see my time is never dull, especially when he's around.

The new little ones are settling nicely now, though we still have tears sometimes at bed-time ...

Of course! Father Jackson! Yes, yes, yes, I've met him, of course I have. What a fellow – everything that a man, and a missionary, should be. He's so warm and funny and friendly and strong – you feel when you're with him that everything and anything's possible. I've never known a chap so full of enthusiasm – never seems to be 'down,' like the rest of us. Inspirational. Blind as a bat, but after a bit you don't even notice.

Poor Charlie. He was not normally given to envy, but in his weakened and emotional state jealousy overwhelmed him. Marjory, his own Marjory, worked with Jackson in the blind school every day – saw him, talked to him, sat with him. In his own mind what hope had he, deaf and dull and ugly, against such a paragon?

It was intolerable, insufferable, impossible, insupportable. It was beyond bearing. And yet, what could he do? He was so tired, so very, very tired.

⚜

Fanny's diary, 31st August:
'We had a whole holiday for the opening of the Children's Hospital.'

CHARLIE DRAGGED HIMSELF down to Mandalay for the occasion; after all, it had been part of his project in the early years. It was he who had been asked to set it up, to find funds, to search for suitable staff. He would go a day early and stay the night with Fanny. This time, he didn't even consider going by bicycle; forty miles in this heat, not to mention a large boil in the one place that mattered, made it out of the question.

Fanny met him at the railway station. She looked so trim and pretty, and so happy.

'Dear Char – it's wonderful to see you! But whatever's the matter? You look so ill! Have you got malaria again?'

When he shook his head, she took his arm and led him to the waiting gharrie.

'It's all so exciting! The Bishop's coming to make a speech, and the Lieutenant Governor will make another one, I expect, when he opens the hospital. And there'll be crowds of people there. A group of missionaries are coming all the way from Rangoon, I'm told, and probably from lots of other places as well. I believe all the Girl Guides and Boy Sc ...'

But Charlie had stopped listening. Rangoon! Why had he not thought of that before? If missionaries were coming from there, was it possible, just possible, that Marjory ...

'... and I believe Miss Linstead and Miss Rawson are coming to call on us the next day. But whatever is the matter? You look as if you've seen a ghost!'

'No, Fanny, not a ghost – just a wonderful, wonderful vision!' And, to the astonishment of the gharrie driver as well as his sister, he gave Fanny the biggest hug she could ever remember.

52

PUNTS ON THE CAM. Dinghies on the Norfolk Broads. Sculls on the little river that ran through the village at home. Boats had always been an important part of Charlie's life.

After the crowds, the heat, the interminable speeches; after the band had played, off-key, the last chord of God Save the King; after the paint-smelling wards had reabsorbed the young walking wounded, dressed in their best despite their tuberculous coughs, their blindness, their paralytic limps; after all this came the new boat. Moored on the Irrawaddy, it was the proud possession of one of the teachers in the school and, out of the kindness of its owner's heart, was made available to any of the missionaries and their children. That very evening, Miss Wilson spoke.

'Mr Garrad. Forgive my saying so, but you do look tired – I dare say you could do with a change. Why don't you and Fanny take out my boat for an hour or two? I believe you have already made the acquaintance of Miss Rawson. As she's new to the area, why not invite her to come too?'

Marjory, unaccustomed to the water, stepped into the little boat too near its edge; the rescue that followed was not simply gallant but essential if the evening were not to be the wettest of wash-outs. As for Charlie, he flew straight to Heaven. Whether preceding death took place he neither knew nor cared; in either case, it seemed irrelevant. Surely she clung on to him a fraction longer than was strictly necessary? Surely the look she gave him held more that the requisite quota of gratitude? As he settled to the oars, every problem in his world flew skywards to the full moon, gathering up his spirits on the way and raising them so high that he felt he would explode with happiness.

Fanny, sitting in the stern, her eyes and heart wide open to her beloved brother's feelings, kept her own counsel.

53

WHEN THE TEAM MET FOR BIBLE translation on his first morning back, Charlie opened the proceedings with a little speech.

'You know I've been struggling lately. My health hasn't been good, and I've had personal worries. I'm very sorry to have failed you both, but all that's over now, I'm glad to say. I think we should have a new beginning. I suggest that we say farewell to the Americans – we're never going to agree anyway, and it's a complete waste of all our time. And if we work hard, we surely can finish Jeremiah. The sooner we get on to a more optimistic book, the better we shall feel.'

And they all agreed.

FROM THEN ON, the team moved at a great pace. There were still difficulties and disagreements, of course. The quarrels were between the two Englishmen; commas and colons, semi-colons and full-stops, all the squiggles that secretly seemed to Saya George to be so unimportant, could hold them up for hours. But, on the whole, translation moved swiftly and accurately enough to please all three men. Jeremiah gave way to the Book of Lamentations, Lamentations to Ezekiel, Ezekiel to Daniel. Daniel in the Lions' Den had always been a favourite of Charlie's; how could he foresee that years after his own death that particular story would figure so largely in the resurrection of his life's work?

So the months went by. There was parallel progress in postal communication between Maymyo and Rangoon. Letters went to and fro with reassuring regularity and, on Charlie's part at any rate, increasing warmth. At last:

'... how I yearn to talk to you again. The voyage from England was the happiest time I have ever had, and I think back on it with longing. There remains so much to talk about and letters are such a poor exchange for the real thing. Of course they are a great deal better than nothing; our regular correspondence is a great joy to me, and I dare to hope that it gives you at least some pleasure. But I must see you ...'

And so it came about that, six months after the momentous day of the opening of the children's hospital, Fanny's diary for 17th April 1922 read thus:

'C went to Kalaw by afternoon train, & took a tent. They worked all the morning & he went off in a bustle. I went to the station.'

What Fanny's diary did not relate is that Miss Marjory Rawson had also taken a holiday, for a week, in the old-established British hill station of Kalaw to rest from her labours in Rangoon.

It certainly had been a rush getting to Mandalay in time to catch the Kalaw train, but, once aboard, there was plenty of time for Charlie to marshal his thoughts. His thoughts, though, refused to be marshalled. They were not rows of dry Hebrew characters to be arranged in straight lines. In fact, they were not really thoughts at all. They were a motley assortment of feelings; of joy, fear, longing, excitement, wonder, desire and a considerable measure of guilt. All his life, Charlie had been bound by a steely thread of guilt; never, since the death of his mother, had he been able to escape it completely and enjoy himself as everyone else seemed to do. Never, that is, until those fantastic weeks on the voyage from England.

But that felt right – more right than anything I have ever known. There's no sin in happiness, surely? Real happiness, that is – the sort of happiness that Marjory and I could – can – give each other – perhaps it's the guilt that's wrong...

And off his thoughts went again on their, to him, shamefully undisciplined wanderings.

He stretched out on the carriage's long empty seat, the train's hypnotic hammering rhythm, *Mar*jory, *Mar*jory, *Mar*jory, sending him to the very edge of slumber. But it was not to be. At the next station, a family of seven climbed into the carriage, talking at the tops of their voices, and any thought of sleep vanished. He was too tired and too excited to read, but his overactive brain would not, and could not, rest. Words were both his work and his pleasure, and for the rest of the journey his mind once again took refuge in their addictive challenge. Sorting them, teasing out their meaning, choosing the best; these were pastimes of which he never tired.

'Falling in love' – never really thought about it before. 'Fall' – much too

tame. Tumble, crash, plunge, nosedive – better, none of them right, though. Overbalance – what about that? I've 'overbalanced into love.' Sounds odd, but it's true, true, true! I'm just plain drunk, out of my mind on happiness, and I've hopelessly overbalanced into love!

All this, this part of himself that had shaken free, that even he had not known existed, he had confessed to no-one. It was so overwhelming, so breathtaking, that sharing it was utterly out of the question. With nobody to talk to, no previous experience, no solid platform under his feet, he found himself groping in a world so strange that he simply had no idea how to handle it. On board ship, the two of them had been cocooned, isolated from the outside world. But gone was the fun, the light-heartedness, the sheer joy of the voyage. Now, instead, the challenge of the real life to which they were both committed put a strain on the relationship which neither had expected.

The week careered by in a precarious switchback ride. Admittedly, there were some wonderful times. On the third day, Marjory tried her skill at cooking on the camp fire outside Charlie's tent.

'This,' he declared, manfully attacking his tin plate of burnt, dried-up bits of scraggy chicken, 'is absolutely delicious!' And the sudden duet of laughter was loud enough to send the group of scavenging mynah-birds pecking round their feet fleeing for their lives. There were walks in the twilight, with the half-moon rising behind the shoulder of the eastern hills; there were snatched moments of conversation sandwiched between the various activities of the day. But always there were tensions.

'We must get back; what will people say?'

Never could they completely escape from their persona as respectable unmarried missionaries.

But the real tensions were seated far more deeply. Both knew the purpose of this week, knew where the hurried talks, the exchanged glances, the casual hand-touching, were leading. Charlie had found no problem all those years ago in asking his theology student, Gertrude, to marry him. But that had been, for him, a mere formality, based simply on shared interests and the convenience of marriage. This was as different as fire from water. This time, he realised that his whole life's happiness hung in the balance, and he simply could not summon up the courage to put it to the test.

It was the last day of the holiday, and he had still done nothing, said nothing. To add to his misery, he woke up that morning in severe pain. He had been sleeping with just a ground-sheet between him and the hard earth. That night he must have lain awkwardly, for when he woke his right leg was buckled under him, the pain in his knee excruciating. Eventually he was able, slowly, to hobble to the guest-house where Marjory and her group of friends were staying. On this, their last day, they were all to go for a long walk together, taking a picnic lunch; it was clear to everyone that Charlie's knee made joining them an impossibility.

Marjory set out with her colleagues; duty, as always, came first. After they had covered a mile or so, she asked their leader if they could stop for a rest.

'Well, if you must, we'll have a five minute break. Then we really have to go on, or we shall never get back before dark. And I expect you've all got packing to do. We've an early start tomorrow.' He looked more closely at Marjory.

'It's not like you to want to stop, Miss Rawson. Are you all right?'

'I'm so sorry, but I have a really bad headache, and I think it would be best if I went back. I'm entirely happy to go alone – there really is no need for anyone to come with me.'

In the end, it was decided that the boy would take her home, and so the two groups parted.

CHARLIE SAW THEM COMING and hobbled to meet them. He peremptorily dismissed the boy, who, for his part, was delighted to have an unexpected day off.

'Will you marry me?'

It, the question, the impossible demand, had come out totally unexpectedly to them both. Both had pictured romance, a moonlit assignation on the banks of the stream, or, at the very least, two comfortable chairs in the shade of the palm trees, cool drinks beside them. Charlie would leap up, bad knee forgotten; he would kneel on that same knee at her delicate feet and proclaim in an elegant speech his undying love. Then, and only then, would come the impassioned request.

The boy was giving a running commentary from the open door of the cookhouse to an invisible presence within.

'Saya Garrad has said something to the memsahib. They are just standing there, staring at each other, like strangers.'

'What now?'

'Still there – not moving at all.'

'Well, go on!'

'Ah, now they're moving off. The memsahib has taken Saya Garrad's arm

– he can hardly walk. She's supporting him. They're heading towards the veranda – no, they've changed their minds – they're going round the back of the bungalow.'

Then, with regret, he added:

'I can't see them any more.'

Perhaps Charlie had been aware of eyes on his back. The two of them found a shady spot out of sight of the buildings and settled themselves on the ground. They began to talk properly for the first time in that frenetic week. Out flooded all Charlie's pent-up feelings and then Marjory had her say. It was a deeply loving say, but, unlike Charlie's, it was a say with reservations.

'... so you see, I really don't know how to answer you. Work's my main problem. I've come out here to do a job, like you. Mine isn't nearly so important, of course. But the poor little blind children need so much mothering, and Father Jackson says ...'

'So what about Father Jackson? Do you – are you in – do you care for him?'

Marjory just sat and looked at him, and then burst out laughing.

'You silly goose! Of course I care for him like everybody does, but I'm certainly not in love with him, if that's what you're trying to say! How could I be, when I've got you? Whatever gave you that idea? Yes, of course he's a fantastic man – he's so funny, and he's got this incredible knack of making everybody feel better as soon as he walks into the room. I admire him tremendously, but that's all. I couldn't possibly marry him even if he wanted me to, which I'm quite sure he doesn't. Anyway, he's years younger than me.'

She laughed again, and shook her head.

'Whatever put that in your poor jealous head?'

Charlie took her hand and laughed with her, in sheer relief.

It was then that the boy appeared, as if from nowhere. Tip-toeing melodramatically towards them across the grass as he pointed over his shoulder.

'They're almost back!' he said in a stage whisper, and disappeared as quickly as he had come.

When the walkers came through the bungalow's front door, they found Charlie sitting comfortably reading in the sitting-room, his injured leg up on a stool. Marjory was nowhere to be seen.

'I'll write to you,' she whispered in Charlie's ear as they said goodbye the following morning.

Fanny's diary, 25th April:

'Rain cleared up just in time for me to meet Charlie at 10.45. His knee was stiff.'

28th April:

'C had a letter from Kalaw at tea-time. He was sad.'

54

MISS FARMER'S ARRIVAL AT THE BLIND SCHOOL was no surprise. A missionary of a number of years' standing, she was visiting the new Christian communities scattered throughout the countryside and her travels had brought her to Rangoon. She knew that her old acquaintance, Father Jackson, was working there and sent word that she hoped to call in on him if time permitted.

A special welcome was hastily put together for this important visitor. Marjory's children were dressed in their best, and under her conductor's baton a ragged performance of Father Jackson's loudest songs raised the thatched roof. They danced, they recited, they did conjuring tricks and, finally, Father Jackson himself herded them all into the school's big hall and settled them down to the best feast that the cook could produce at such short notice.

Miss Farmer wished to be introduced to the new missionary.

'That was splendid, my dear. You're obviously doing great work with the children – as you know, this is a project very close to Father Jackson's heart, and he's so pleased that you are putting so much effort into it. But I gather you haven't had the chance to see much of the real Burma yet, and I wonder whether you would care to come with me tomorrow when I go and visit one of the nearby villages? It would give me great pleasure – I've been here so long that home seems a very long way away, and I'd love to talk about it. Strange that I still think of England as home after all this time!'

TWO DAYS LATER, Marjory sat down and wrote to her sister Agatha.

The Blind School
Rangoon
3rd May 1922

Dearest Agatha

Thank you very much for your letter. I'm so grateful that you keep me in touch with home – it's hard to believe that the two worlds, yours and mine, actually do co-exist. Letters really do help enormously – please write as often as you can.

I can't wait to tell you what I have been up to! At last I feel like a real missionary – I have been out on tour! It was, I must admit, a very short tour – just one day – but I do believe it has made me see why we are all here.

My companion was a Miss Farmer, who's evidently been out here for ages. Clearly a missionary of the old school, if you know what I mean. Anyway, we started out early in the morning with Miss Farmer's boy and two of her men helpers. We went by gharrie as far as possible, and then strode across dry, stubbly paddy-fields in blazing sun, passing buffaloes, some bullocks with large wooden clappers round their necks, and women sifting paddy and then shovelling it into heaps. We had to cross a stream on a very wobbly, rickety bamboo bridge – the boy walked just behind me, to give me confidence. After the bridge, we were met by a flock of about a dozen queer little objects, all in their Sunday best, clean longyis, clean jackets, their hair newly oiled, in the charge of their teacher. They all wore huge grins, but still examined us very critically. We were strange beings of a like rarely seen, so we had to be made much of. We all went in procession to a little bamboo thatched building which they said was the Church. It was built entirely of wood, on piles several feet high. A primitive ladder led to the entrance. There was no door, no windows, only the openings where they might be. Walls and floor were made of strips of bamboo with spaces between to let in the air and the insects. Inside at the east end was a piece of rough wood fixed across the corner to form the altar. A cross was set on the roof for all to see who passed that way. A little Church, but the villagers were proud of it.

The Headman's house was our next port-of-call – the only house in the whole village more substantially built than the Church. Karens (that was the tribe we were visiting) don't use chairs, they just squat. Anyway, they seemed to realise that it was not our custom to rest in like manner, so two old deck-chairs had been cleaned and re-covered with canvas. We sat down. The boy disappeared to get breakfast ready. People from the near villages came to gaze at us, shake hands and continue to gaze. No work was done that day; how could they grind paddy when there was a show on? Lots of dogs, puppies innumerable, pigs and piglets, hens and chickens, children and naked brown babies, to say nothing of grown-ups, swarmed round us. About 10.30, breakfast was announced and while it was being brought the children flocked in with presents for us, Saya Ma said. From their pockets they carefully drew out new-laid eggs. We looked for somewhere to put them and finally decided to use our topees (those funny pith sun-helmets). It was amusing to watch the children as they put them in, to make sure that we both had equal shares. Our breakfast consisted of porridge, eggs and chicken, which our wonderful boy contrived to serve almost as at home. After breakfast we visited all the houses in the neighbourhood, queer places they were, more like sheds than houses. All up on stilts, they generally had one room with open door or window, a floor of bamboo strips and a roof of bamboo thatch. There was no furniture, only mats, with a rug or blanket here and there; water chatties and cooking pots, here a Karen basket or the strips to make one. In the centre of the village is a well; the women draw water in a long bamboo and sling it on their shoulders.

At noon, a boy went towards the Church sounding a huge Burmese gong. Sixty-five of us gathered inside. Miss Farmer and I sat in our deck-chairs, the rest, from three or four villages, just squatted on the floor. Saya Saw Dee, the teacher of the village, took the service. There were no books, the people know the words of canticles and hymns by heart – in their own language, of course. As they didn't often get the semitones, the tunes varied at times. I could not sing in Karen, but I sang lustily in English, to the intense satisfaction of all present. Miss Fisher spoke to them, and said she hoped they would send their children to school and if their eyes were bad go direct to Hospital so that they might be spared blindness. So many of the Karens go blind. The only ailing person we found in the village was a blind woman.

Now it was one o'clock, and dreadfully hot. Back in the headman's house, we flopped in our chairs which had been carried before us. We had tea, and while we rested we took our knitting. Knitting had not been seen before, though some of the women do very fine sewing, so once more crowds gathered round us and gazed. As the boy was packing up, he threw away a sheet of paper which happened to be a coloured cover from Punch. Some little boys seized it and went into raptures over the picture of a little pink baby in a bath, an advertisement for Pear's Soap, I believe. The little stolid lumps of brown humanity got so excited over it that their parents would have been alarmed had they not also been excited. We gave a piece of paper to as many as we could. Before leaving we shook hands all round again, and escorted by at least half the villagers, began our homeward tramp across the awful paddy fields. We reached home at 5 p.m., very hot, very tired and very very dirty but very pleased with ourselves. I had done a real missionary trip!

I hope that gives you just a little idea of what Burma is like. It is so hard to describe things as they really are, so that you can see in your mind's eye what I'm up to.

Your affectionate sister
Marjory

Of what she was really up to, of the trip to Kalaw and her dreadful indecision over her possible marriage, she gave no clue. In her letter to Charlie, she had asked him for a little more time to make up her mind. But she mustn't keep him waiting for ever, and it would take too long, six weeks or more, to ask her sister's advice and to get an answer. In any case they had not been close for a long time.

55

1922–1924

BEFORE HE HAD COME TO BURMA, the word 'Rangoon' had conjured up all the mystical magic of the East. How strange, then, that ever since he had been there, it had brought him nothing but misfortune.

It was there that Charlie had been stricken with his first bout of homesickness, there that he had been ill, so ill that in his sick mind the label 'unwanted here: return to sender' had already been tied tightly round his skinny neck. And now it was in Rangoon that his beloved Marjory was somehow slipping away from him.

'My dear Mr Garrad,' the letter had said. 'Thank you, thank you, thank you for asking me to marry you. That someone as clever and important and good as you are should even consider such a thing is extraordinary and wonderful. But I don't know what to say. For one thing I don't think I'm up to it, I don't believe that I could rise to your standards. And for another, to be honest, I'm a little frightened. I don't think my brain always works properly in this heat and strange atmosphere. I might be making a huge mistake, for both of us. So please just give me a little longer.'

And that was it.

So this time it was to Rangoon that he must go. He simply could not carry on like this. Everyone and everything was suffering. A decision must be taken. Fanny's diary, 9th June 1922:

'I had dinner at the station with Charlie. He was going to Rangoon for a fortnight.'

⁂

WHEN HE WENT INTO the sitting-room, she was sitting by the window, needle in hand and an untidy pile of 'mending' on the bamboo table beside her. In front of her, stark naked, stood a diminutive figure, his hands rushing downwards to cover himself as the door opened. Marjory looked up and the smile in her brilliant blue eyes struck so deep that Charlie's bare feet glued themselves to the floor and he could go no further.

With perfect teeth, she bit off the thread from her needle and handed the boy a grubby longyi.

'There,' she said to him, 'that's the best I can do. Off you go.' And off he went, at top speed, winding his skirt round him as he felt his way through the open doorway with scarcely a hesitation.

'He won't have understood a word, but he will be able to play football better without the hem of his longyi hanging on by a thread.'

Arrived in the safety of the playground, her small client grabbed hold of his friend.

'There's a strange man in there with the mem-sahib,' he whispered, and both heads turned towards the window, blind eyes staring, pricked ears cocked, sharper than Marjory's needle.

At first the conversation was awkward. Charlie had pulled up a chair beside her, and it took time to move on past the weather ('what a glorious day' – but then of course it was always a glorious day in this season) to matters relating to their work. At last, Charlie could wait no longer.

'You know why I've come,' he said.

'Yes, I know why you've come.' Marjory got to her feet, the next tattered garment falling forgotten from her knee. Automatically, Charlie bent down to pick it up and put it with its fellows on the table.

She took a step towards the window and stood with her back to him, staring out. Playtime at the blind-school was over, and the bare earth outside was empty of everything except a couple of the mynah-birds that seemed to haunt their meetings. Charlie, too, got up and stood behind her, so close that he could smell the cleanness of her hair.

'Will you marry me?' he asked.

There was no reply.

He waited for an eternity. Still nothing. He tried again.

'Marjory dear, you've got to marry me. The fact is that I simply can't go on without you.'

'But I just said I would, you goose! Didn't you hear?' Turning, she threw her arms around him.

Perhaps it was only then that both of them realised just how dangerously deaf he was.

Fanny's diary, 12th June 1923:
'HAD A TELEGRAM TO SAY THAT C WAS ENGAGED TO MARJORY RAWSON.'

Of the fourteen days Charlie had allowed himself, only one had been needed. He had achieved his impossible goal and Marjory was to be his wife. Though of course no such thoughts entered his mind, it would not be long before together they would add a limb to the family tree, a budding branch that continues to grow and divide to this day. And although the outer leaves of the new side-shoots may look so different, their inner strength stays solid to the core. Charlie would have approved of that.

But still he could not quite believe his happiness. In a letter to his beloved a couple of months later he wrote:

'It's still a dream, such a fantastically impossible dream! How can I possibly wed a fairy?'

Fairy or no, wed her he did eight months after their engagement. It was a major event in the Burma expatriate community. The service took place in Rangoon Cathedral and was conducted by the Bishop himself. In attendance were the Governor of Burma and his wife, a statuesque lady in a very fashionable hat. All the ladies wore white. The bride herself was decked out in an ankle-length white dress, the train following several feet behind and evidently requiring the support of no less than four grown-up bridesmaids, all recruited from the Burmese staff of the blind school, and a single small English child. On the bride's head was a waist-length veil, moored by a circlet of white flowers. A beautiful posy completed the picture. Not to be outdone on this the happiest day of his life, Charlie had splashed out on a frock-coat, its skirt hanging just below his knees.

No-one from either family had made the long crossing. There is no doubt that Fanny, had she not been there already, would have quietly booked her own passage and come. Even brother Will was missing; his furlough home had long been booked and to change it would have upset too many plans. 'Of course I'm sad to miss the fun,' he'd said, 'but you'll both still be there when I get back, and I'll drink to your health and happiness with the family at home.'

The honeymoon was a tour of the jungle in a bullock-cart. Honeymoons are private affairs; the only comment that goes down in history was Marjory's answer to the inevitable question on their return:

'Yes, thank you, we had a wonderful time. Only Charlie did keep going to sleep.'

'GARRAD,' SHERRATT HAD SAID, 'when you're married, you will simply have to move. You cannot expect a wife to live in a shack. As you know, my time in Burma is almost at an end and, if I might make a suggestion, I think my house would suit the pair of you very well. For the first half-dozen children there will be plenty of room. After that you will have to think again.'

Marjory was already thirty-seven, Charlie ten years older. By almost any calculation, that point was unlikely to be reached, so Charlie duly thanked his colleague and in due course the transfer was made.

Bures, England, 1924

'Miss Marjory Rawson and Mr Charles Edward Garrad request the pleasure of the company of Mr Matthew Gissing at their wedding at 2 o'clock on 2nd February 1924 in Rangoon Cathedral, and afterwards at Bishop's Palace, Rangoon '

Of course I can't go. But I shall try and be in Bures church at 2 o'clock that day and say a prayer for them. The trouble is every time you go to the church your mind jumps back to the war – you can't help seeing the War Memorial cross. It's been up several years now with 43 names on it, all men and boys from just around here. I knew every one of them. I can't believe how lucky we were – apart from poor Iris, of course.

But this is a wedding, not a funeral. Up at Brook House, they're all of a dither, though of course they've known about the engagement for some time. They've completely changed their tune about Miss Fanny, though. When she first said she was going out to look after her two brothers the other five sisters couldn't believe their ears. Violet said that the six of them was arguing morning noon and night, but Fanny's mind was made up. She was going, and that was that. Now they're only too pleased she's there, to keep an eye on things. 'This Marjory's bound to be a thoroughgoing bluestocking' – that's what they keep saying, according to Violet.

There's been a lot of talk about someone going out there for the wedding, but it's all come to nothing, Violet says. Too expensive, too busy, too far away – puts me in mind of that feast in the Bible when all the guests made excuses not to go. Anyway, Miss Fanny'll be there, even though Mr Will will be home on leave. Couldn't he have put it off for a bit?

56

1925–1929

THE TWO EYES, ONE RED, ONE BROWN, stared fixedly along the length of the bed from its foot to its head. When Marjory, propped up on the pillows, curled the toes of her right foot, the dragon winked; when she curled the left ones, the lamb slept. She smiled, tried it again and laughed out loud.

For her, this moment was perfection. It was not just that, at last, she could see her feet, in their odd slippers, for the first time for months; not just that she was cool and comfortable, lying on her bed with her wonderful husband fussing about beside her. To make sure that she was not in some dream world, she leant over the edge of the bed yet again and gazed down into the wicker basket beside it. No, she was still there, her little round, red face sticking out incongruously from the tightly-wrapped swaddling clothes, shiny black hair catching the rays of the hot afternoon sun. Baby Anne, a mere four pounds six ounces, was no longer an increasingly awkward encumbrance, something to be borne patiently through heat, sickness, exhaustion, sleeplessness and a multitude of other discomforts. She was, without doubt, the most beautiful being in the whole wide world.

'My darling, do be careful!' Charlie took his wife gently by the shoulders and pushed her back on to the pillows.

Fanny, sitting on the other side of the bed, could wait no longer.

'Which do you like best?'

She had been shopping for the slippers, and, dithering from one to the other, had finally bought both pairs, pink ones from Witeways and Chinese ones from Hok Eangs. She had fallen in love with the lambs embroidered on the pink background, with their great big brown eyes, but she supposed the Chinese ones were more stylish; her sister-in-law was, in her view, exceedingly and rather alarmingly stylish. Char couldn't choose either, so they had brought both to the hospital and let Marjory decide. Standing respectively to her right and left, they had fitted one from each pair on to the small, neat feet.

Marjory wiggled her toes again, more violently. She bent forward to listen.

'No,' she said, shaking her head sadly. 'For a moment, I thought I heard the dragon roar. But I can't possibly choose. I shall wear the dragons on Mondays, Wednesdays and Fridays, and the lambs on Tuesdays, Thursdays and Saturdays.'

'What about Sundays?'

Baby Anne squawked just in time.

Marjory's slipper-clad feet were not allowed to touch the ground for sixteen days from the birth, which had been entirely normal.

THUS BEGAN FAMILY LIFE. In October 1925, when Anne was fifteen months old, Charlie set sail for England yet again for a year's furlough, but this time with the good old days firmly behind him. No longer could he just pack his bag and go. Now, there was Baby Anne; her luggage, which occupied more space than all the rest put together; Fanny, who was coming with them to help; and of course his own beloved Marjory, whose life must be made to run as smoothly as possible.

The eruption into the world of Anne's baby brother three months after their arrival in England was a second cause for rejoicing, but it cannot have made the return passage to Burma nine months later any easier. Yet Charlie was happier than he had ever been. Gone, finally, was the loneliness that had haunted him, even amongst eleven brothers and sisters, ever since the death of his beloved mother. Not only had he found his heart's desire but, to his own utter amazement, he seemed somehow to have become the father of not just one but two lovely children.

Even after years of marriage and when parted for only a few days, he would write love-letters to his beloved:

'Walking along the street in the middle of the day yesterday I came across a funny old fellow with his head all in a whirl; he said that he was going to the P.O., but he was going the wrong way and he didn't seem to care in the least. He was tramping along the road but his feet were in the clouds, as well as his head. And what do you think it was all about? Simply that half an hour earlier he had had two letters from his wife, from whom he had been parted just three days. Of course, I told him he was an old silly, but he only laughed, and said that he felt perfectly delicious inside, because an angel had come to him and was waiting for him at home. Oh my darling, I do love you such a lot. And now there are only two days before I shall be back ...'

There were inevitable sadnesses. Marjory had a miscarriage, the sudden and unexpected end to a life as yet unlived. At the opposite extreme came the demise, both anticipated and prepared for, of King Mindon's beloved church.

Right from the start of his time in Mandalay, Charlie had been worried about it. He knew that an invisible and invincible army of termites was hard at work and that the days of the old wooden church were numbered. When he found the sturdy teak supports chewed through at ground level to the width of a young bamboo, it was clear that its time had come.

Brother Will took on the major burden of the design of a new Christ Church, and after its consecration on October 28th 1928, Charlie wrote:

'We have not felt the break with the past that seemed inevitable. The site is the same, the furniture is the same, much of the carving of the church of King Mindon Min and Dr Marks has found a place within its walls, and we feel in the new church as if we were still in the old, only with substantial brick walls instead of decaying timber, and with much greater nobility of design and proportion. My brother Will thought out every detail and saw it carried through. For this, we must emphatically say Laus Deo.'

How much more deeply he must have felt these words when, a year later, he was able to post to the office of the *Rangoon Times* the following announcement:

'On 14th September 1929, to Charles and Marjory Garrad a daughter, sister to Anne and Douglas.'

As they lay side by side in the big bed, protected from the world by the folds of their mosquito net, Charlie took his wife in his arms.

'What can we possibly have done to deserve such happiness?'

But there was no reply. Even the movement had not wakened her. Exhausted by a life of infinite intensity, of birth and death, of steaming heat and drowning rain, misery and enchantment, wonder and despair, of total impossibilities turned paradoxically on their heads, Marjory slept as if never to awake again.

Charlie smiled into the darkness. His wife, he knew, would be up at dawn, facing the day with all the excitement and enthusiasm of a new beginning.

Bures England 1929

I remember it all so clearly – the first time we all met Mrs Charles, when they came home on leave four years ago. As soon as she could get away, Violet came running down to our cottage.

'Matt', she said 'You'll never believe what a lovely lady she is!' Violet was that excited. 'She's going to have another baby soon, but even so she's ever so small and neat, and she's got the bluest eyes you ever saw, and a beautiful smile. The sisters can't take their eyes off her – they're all sitting round her in a circle with her in the middle, and she's telling them stories. Mr Charlie and Miss Fanny aren't getting a look in!'

The sisters found baby Anne a bit of a handful – she'd just learnt to walk, and was into everything. But when the new one came you never saw such a fuss! He was certainly a beautiful boy, and everyone was happy. Miss Fanny was always there to make sure things ran smoothly, and when they all went back to Burma at the end of their leave there was enough for the sisters to talk about to last them for months.

And now of course there's the third one – Elizabeth, they call her. I wonder when they'll all come home again?

57

1930–1932

ONE AFTER THE OTHER the garments were displayed. The police officer, tall for a Burman, held each out at arm's length, spreading it out to its full width so that no detail would be missed by the company assembled in the local police station. One thick, brown lisle stocking, full of ant-holes that some unseen hand had attempted to repair with bright red thread; one pair of voluminous knickers, equally afflicted; one pretty summer dress, so torn and dirty that its pattern of bright spring flowers was scarcely recognisable. With each demonstration came the same question, and always to the same person:

'Is this yours?'

And always, from Fanny, the same scarcely audible reply:

'Yes, I'm so sorry, I'm afraid it is.'

Poor Fanny. Never in all her life had she been so embarrassed. Oh how she wished she had kept last month's theft of her tin trunk to herself. If only the boy had caught the rascal so that she hadn't had to report it to the local police. Now that strangers had seen her most intimate underwear, always kept so scrupulously neat and tidy and today almost unrecognisable, how could she ever hold up her head again?

And when she saw the thief, so skinny, so poor, how could she blame him anyway, when she had so much and he so little?

'SAYA GARRAD! How wonderful to see you again! We thought you had forgotten us!'

The two men, the priest and the farmer, settled themselves in the shade of a banana tree and caught up with the news. It was a long time since Charlie had visited this particular village and the farmer had heard nothing of his marriage and his three wonderful children. Even here, life did not stand still, and it was some time before the flow of local gossip ceased. At last came the fateful words:

'Now you must have a drink.'

Charlie had dreaded this moment. His stomach, always sensitive, was no longer accustomed to rural germs, but he knew he must accept or cause lifelong offence. His relief, then, was great when his host picked up a fresh coconut from the pile inside his doorway. No harm could come from the sterile milk sealed within.

The farmer tested the edge of his long knife on his finger, and then expertly sliced through the top of the nut's thick shell. He took from a shelf the only glass and wiped it round with his skirt. Charlie's stomach churned, but bravely he held out his hand for the glass.

'No, no – please wait a moment. The milk may be dirty.'

The longyi tied round the old man's skinny waist clearly came in handy for a variety of tasks; dusting the crockery, wiping the sweat from his face, even beating off the flies from the back end of his one and only cow. Now, to Charlie's horror, it was spread across the top of the glass and every drop of the pristine milk carefully filtered through it.

The farmer beamed as he handed it to his guest with all the ceremony of a waiter in the best hotel.

'There – now it is quite safe for you. I know, you see, that every precaution must be taken to protect the reverend Fathers from ill-health.'

And Charlie had to sit there and drink it – every drop.

THE STORMS WERE WEATHERED and much of life went smoothly. Bible translation came to an end and first drafts were sent off to publishers and to the promoters, the British and Foreign Bible Society. The children grew and prospered, and Marjory set time aside to start to teach the two older ones their letters. Elizabeth, the baby, possibly had the best of it. She spent a great deal of time with her Ayah and her Ayah's friends. There were frequent visits to the market, first in the pram and, later, on her own two legs. She listened to the bargaining and the gossip with ears that grew daily in size and sensitivity. By the time she was two years old, she could speak not only English but seven local languages as well. The Burmese are a mixed race and this one small brain readily adjusted itself to the dialects of its owner's companions.

⤳

WHETHER IT WAS THE longyi-filtered milk that started his downfall will never be known for certain. But it was not so very long after that particular episode that Charlie's health started to deteriorate. The comments became more and more frequent.

'Mr Garrad, are you quite well? You are getting so thin!'

'You must be so worried about your husband, Mrs Garrad. He doesn't look himself at all. Have you had the doctor?'

And from the victim himself:

'No thank you, Marjory. I really can't face curry today,' followed by yet another rapid rush to the latrine at the far end of the compound.

The children, playing quite close to the primitive 'WC' as their father insisted on calling it, would act as informants, relaying the latest symptoms to their mother.

Little Douglas reported:

'Daddy's making those beastly sick-noises again.'

Anne, nose firmly pinched between finger and thumb, asked her mother:

'Yuck! Why is Daddy so smelly? It's really, really stinky out there,'

And Marjory would chide her children for their language and lack of sympathy, knowing full well that it was time to act.

Doctors were called, examinations made, authorities consulted. But both Marjory and Charlie were fairly certain of the outcome. After all, hadn't he been in almost exactly the same position when he had first come out and been so sick? He remembered feeling just as ill as he did now, and quaking in his bed at the very idea of the ignominious retreat ahead of him, of the return home with his tail between his legs. But that had been more than twenty-five years ago, when he was young and strong and full of good, solid Suffolk nourishment. Now, it was very different. His work was almost behind him; any remaining aspirations were blunted by fatigue. He was just so tired. Everything, every single thing, had become an insuperable task. It seemed to him that he was finished, done for.

The two doctors, the soldier and the missionary, came to see him together. They sat one on either side of his bed as he rested in the heat of the day.

'I'm afraid we have something to tell ...'

'There's no point in beating about the bu ...'

They had started to speak at the same moment and stopped in perfect unison. One looked at the other; which of them was to break the news?

But the patient spared them the difficulty.

'You want to send me home,' he said. 'That's what you've come to tell me, isn't it?'

Their diagnosis was tropical sprue, an illness for which in 1932 there was no medicinal cure. The only way out was to leave the tropics. Otherwise death from sheer weakness and dehydration would almost inevitably follow.

IN A LETTER HOME, Charlie's brother Will wrote:

March 1932

Packing is a thankless job and thoroughly bad for the temper. And yet, quite honestly, there is something worse for the nerves than packing; and that is, being unable to do it oneself.

Packing for an ordinary furlough is bad enough in all conscience; but for Char it was a goodbye for always, which makes it worse, and it was under doctor's orders, which makes it quite the worst possible. Being ill makes one short-tempered; packing is apt to make one short-tempered; but being ill and having to watch another pack one's things would easily take the prize for short-temperedness.

All one's treasures are treated disrespectfully; our books, that have become our friends, lose all their personality; it seems profane to see them being treated so unceremoniously by an outsider. And for a person to lie still and watch others pack for him without ever a word of complaint says, I think, a very great deal for the genuineness of his religion.

What is going to happen when one gets home? To oneself, one's job, one's future? No, this is no ordinary packing.

Everything must be organised and catalogued, or there will be chaos at the other end. If the fifty cases in the hold have to be undone before the one with baby's crib in it can be located, there is going to be trouble. There must be method and a scheme, and we all have our own methods and schemes, and think other people's methods and schemes perfectly futile.

And to have to lie back and watch other people making muddles with one's things must be very trying for the temper; and yet from start to finish not one single hasty word was heard. Some silly ass must have packed the vaccination certificates, to be shown to the shipping authorities, in the heavy luggage, but no-one called him a silly ass. The very labels themselves only just escaped being packed, but never a word of complaint was heard.

Despite all difficulties, and after an endless series of farewells, the Garrad family, entire apart from Will who had so much more to give to his beloved Burma, got themselves on to the boat and homeward bound for the last time. And for the last time, too, little Elizabeth spoke Burmese. After saying goodbye to her beloved Ayah, she could never again be persuaded to say a single word of any of her seven languages.

Bures, England, May 1932

Mr George, Charlie's youngest brother, saw me in the yard today. 'Matthew', he said, 'I thought you would like to know that we had a letter from Mr Will today, and that he said Mr Charles is very ill and is being sent home, with all the family.'

I'm that worried about him. Mr George didn't seem to know too much about it, but I could see he was worried too. Violet says everything is upside down and none of them know what to do with themselves. Well, there's nothing to do, only wait until his boat docks. There's to be a special service for him in Church on Sunday. The vicar's good at praying.

September 1932

It's all right – Charlie's going to be all right! He's got one of those tropical diseases – sprue, I think it's called. Sounds more like a kind of tree. Anyway, he's in a big hospital in London where the doctors know all about it. It'll take a long time, but they think he'll recover completely. Then I suppose he'll have to look for a job over here. They won't let him go back, thank goodness. So maybe we shall have a chance to meet once in a while. I should like that, very much.

BOOK THREE

ENGLAND

58

'I'M AFRAID WE SHALL HAVE TO keep you in hospital for some time. We have done the necessary tests, and the results show conclusively that your doctor's clinical diagnosis in India ...'

'Burma,' muttered Charlie,

'... was absolutely correct. You have a condition called tropical sprue. It only occurs in hot countries, and there is no known treatment for it except a temperate climate and a diet almost totally free of fat. For months, you have not been absorbing fat from your food, and that is why you have lost so much weight. It is essential that we keep you here until we are confident that you are gaining weight and strong enough to lead some sort of independent life.'

'Pompous ass,' thought Charlie. 'I knew all that before we left' – and reprimanded himself for gross ingratitude.

THIS HAD BEEN THE START of the family's homecoming. As soon as the ship docked, both families had rallied round. SPG and the Bible Society had done their best with hospital admissions and accommodation, but it had been an unsettled time. The children had been happy enough; the rented flat found for the family in Malvern was spacious, with plenty of room for their games, but for the adults, it was a different matter. This was no furlough, with the joy of seeing their families and friends all the greater for the knowledge that Burma was waiting for them at the end. In Burma they had been needed, loved and respected by their many colleagues and dependants, Burmese and English alike. Now, they were nobodies, two curiosities with three noisy children. There, it had in many ways been a good and easy life, the low cost of living well within their means and with servants only too pleased to wait on them in return for extra money for their own households. Here, the two women, Marjory and Fanny, tried their hardest to cope with forgotten ways and future uncertainties, but it was far from easy.

∽

AT LAST THE LETTER CAME. The postmark was indecipherable, and Charlie opened it, along with the two brown envelopes that contained, in his opinion, ridiculously large bills, with little thought as to its possible content.

'Dear Garrad' at the head. At the foot: 'Yours sincerely' and a scribbled 'Bath and Wells,' with, underneath: 'The Right Reverend Bishop of Bath and Wells' in typescript.

Charlie took a deep breath, and read the words between:

A living has become available in the village of Barrow Gurney, in Somerset. It is within the benefice of the squire of the village, who lives there and owns the land. Your details have been passed to him, and he, like myself, is of the opinion that this would be an ideal appointment for you in your fragile state of health. The work is not hard, as there are only two hundred inhabitants, almost all of them employed in farm work. There is no industry of any kind.

In addition, it should give you plenty of time to complete your life's work of Bible translation, which I expect to be your main ambition.

The stipend, I fear, is small, as one would expect from a parish of this size. It will, however, be enough for you and your family to live on.

I urge you to give careful consideration to this offer. There can be few livings that will fit your particular requirements so closely.

'MARJORY! MARJORY! We've been offered a job!'
And when she came running, he handed her the letter. She read it in silence before handing it back.

'Are you disappointed?' was all she said.

'I can't hear you!' and up went the hand to the ear.
Marjory gave a deep sigh. The deafness was getting worse and there were times for her of near despair. She looked at him and, just for a moment, thought of

what might have been. The Bishop of Rangoon was due to retire before too long. She pictured a comfortable summer residence, in the Shan hills perhaps, where she and the children could have spent the hot weather, with tennis and swimming and bridge and congenial company; if only he had not been ill. She thought of the preferment he deserved here in England, of the senior prestigious appointments he would surely have had; if only he had not been deaf. And then she looked at him again, and read the appeal in his eyes – and loved him more than ever.

So he never knew that the thought of disappointment had even crossed her mind.

'MORNING, VICAR!'

Charlie could see the tractor driver's lips move as the clumsy machine lumbered past, and he raised his own hand in greeting. Now, which of the Vowles clan was that? Was it John, or Gilbert, or the one whose name he never could remember? No matter; he would soon have them all sorted out. After all, there were only two hundred souls in the whole village, and it was early days. Three weeks, just three long weeks, since the furniture van had ground up the lane to deposit their few bits of furniture in the dilapidated white house at the top of the hill where the road ran out.

Now, who was this fellow on a push-bike? He looked as if he was going to stop. Yes, the long leg swung back over the saddle and landed on the road beside him.

'Morning, Vicar! Hot enough for you? But then you be used to it after Africa, I daresay.'

Charlie smiled and raised his cap

'Good morning. I'm sorry, but I didn't quite catch what you said. Would you mind repeating it?' And, leaning forward, he cupped his left ear with his hand.

The young man propped his bicycle against the hedge. He rather wished he hadn't embarked on this conversation, but there was something about the skinny, clever-looking fellow with his dog-collar and wrinkled face that appealed to his sympathies. The new parson whom the Bishop had seen fit to give them was, after all, a bit of a curiosity and a bit of a celebrity, too; he'd heard tell that he'd rewritten the Bible in whatever lingo it is that all them black men speak. And to cap it all, he was deaf, by the looks of things.

'TIS TOO HOT FOR MY LIKING! A BIT LIKE AFRICA, I DARESAY!'

'Yes, I daresay it is. I've never actually been there. It was Burma we were in. But, my word, I think Barrow Gurney's every bit as hot as either of them! We can't get a single one of the vicarage windows to open – it seems as if they've been stuck shut with paint for ever. Do you know of a builder who'd come and get them moving?'

'I reckon you'd best leave well alone, Vicar. T'ain't often hot like this, not in this part of the world it ain't. If you get them windows open, you'll have draughts for ever more, up on top of the hill, like. But if you does need a builder, ask Edward Chapman up on the Bridgwater road. He do all the building work round here.'

Charlie thanked him and, raising his cap once more, saw the boy turn, wheel his bike across a bridge over the little river and deposit it against a brick building. As he watched, someone appeared in an open hatchway above. His hair was completely white, and yet he moved like a man in his prime, pushing out on to the hatch's horizontal door a large sack, tied at the neck.

'Lower away! And look sharp about it!'

Immediately, a rope with a strong hook on its end swung out and within moments the heavy sack had been lowered to the ground to join its fellows, half-a-dozen bulging bags neatly stacked together.

'Morning Vicar!'

Even Charlie could hear that voice, accustomed as it was to shouting commands above the hum of the mill. With his bird's-eye view, the miller had seen Charlie standing there, and within seconds had run down the invisible stairway and out through the door. Now he was striding towards him, dusty hand extended, a cloud of flour rising from his jet-black hair.

Charlie was in no hurry. This was his first voyage of exploration of his new territory, and he was delighted to meet and talk to as many of the residents as possible.

He gave a deep inward sigh of utter relief.

How strange. Here I am, in a completely new place and as far as can possibly be from everything that has happened in the last twenty-five years, and yet I have come home.

The miller was a busy man. He couldn't stand about like this chatting, not for long he couldn't. But it was a good ten minutes before he finally drew breath and turned back into the dark building. There was very little now that Charlie didn't know about flour mills and dairy farming – the mill's herd of Dairy Short-'orns should've won first prize at the Bath and West Show, but one of the silly

————s 'ad gone and bin and broke off the tip of 'er 'orn on the way – got it caught in the truck's door-frame some'ow. But what can you do? He heard about the miller's three sons, two grown boys working with him and young Brian, his pride and joy. Brian had had his twelfth birthday just last week but already he was top of his form at Bristol Grammar School. He'd go far, that one, and his father's lungs filled themselves with a great breath of floury air laced with deep pride in this prodigy who was to change the world.

As they talked, the two men had turned their backs on the mill, and were looking up the steep hill opposite. This was one of the miller's meadows, and at the top of it perched the big white vicarage with its sealed windows and its peeling paint. The grass was ankle-deep, glowing a brilliant green in the early afternoon sunshine. For a fraction of a second, as the miller boasted about his son, a black shadow flitted across Charlie's mind and instantly was gone. Imagination, he thought. Too hot, too much to do. But somehow the beautiful field had lost its charm.

Fourteen months later, in the midst of the villagers' shocked grief, that moment would come back to him.

59

'Shall I light the Reverend's fire in his study, ma'am?'

'No, Iris. He doesn't like it lit until the evening. Besides, I believe he's just going out.'

Marjory didn't confess to their new little maid that there was only just enough coal for the one fire that they all sat round and that they couldn't afford to have the coalman call again until next month. The builder had answered Charlie's summons to make the windows open; now the wind whistled interminably through the cracks whilst the family crouched over the 'Cosy Stove' in the dining-room, rueing the day that Mr Chapman had been asked to take his chisel to the window-frames.

'I should have taken Maurice's advice and left well alone. I'm sorry.' And Charlie took his overcoat from the hook in the hall, put on his cap, and wound a thick knitted scarf round his neck. Iris, peeping from the kitchen, was surprised to see him go, not out through the front door, but into his study where he settled at his desk, an orderly pile of papers covered with the Burmese script in front of him. The grate stood black and empty. One big hand, tinged blue and with a tiny scrap of stamp-paper stuck over a gardening scratch on the knuckle, stretched out for the pen; a drip settled on the end of the big Garrad nose. The cold was forgotten; concentration became ferocious. Charlie was doing what he loved most.

'The boys at my school aren't very good at reading, I don't think.' Douglas was snuggled up on his mother's knee, close by the Cosy Stove. He looked down at the small book on his lap.

'They can't even read *Peter Rabbit!* Once upon a time there were four little rabbits, and their names were Flopsy, Mopsy, Cottontail and Peter. They lived with ...'

'For goodness sake read it to yourself! I can't concentrate!' Anne was there too, book in hand.

Elizabeth, the youngest, was on the hearthrug.

'Stupid bricks! It's not fair – they keep on falling down!' It was left to Fanny to abandon her mending and come to the rescue. The laying of solid foundations was a skill for which their aunt had an invaluable talent.

CHARLIE SEEMED HAPPY ENOUGH. He took the Sunday services, did his very best to preach sermons that were both helpful and within the reach of his tiny congregation, and worked on the correction of proofs for the Burmese Bible. In the afternoons, he visited the old and the sick amongst his parishioners, or tackled the vast area of ground elder that did its best to overwhelm the vicarage shrubbery.

Fanny settled quickly into the multiple rolls of nanny, housekeeper and grandmother ('proper dogsbody,' Iris would say). In many ways it was she who, without fuss, became the hub of life at the vicarage.

Marjory joined, and then ran, the Women's Institute. She joined, and then ran, the Mother's Union. She conducted the local choir, and at a mass performance in the Albert Hall had a footstool placed under her small feet by Sir Adrian Boult. She was the leading lady in amateur dramatics. With the help of *The Home Doctor*, she tried to spare the local GP, usually knowing before he did what was wrong with his patients.

'Mrs Garrard, I be that frightened – I be coughing up blood!'

'Goodness me, Maria! How much? A pint?'

'Oh no, not so much as that.'

'Half a pint?'

'Nor that neither.'

'A tablespoon? A dessertspoon? A teaspoon, then?'

'Oh no, Mrs Garrard. Just a little on me 'andkercher!'

They both laughed and the old lady went to bed happy. If Mrs Garrard thought nothing of it, then why should she?

Maria was ninety-one, and she never could get the last bit of the vicar's surname right.

IT WAS IN JUNE that it happened. The winter had passed at last; the sun came out and warmed the earth into life.

'Mrs Garrad! Mrs Garrad! Can you come quick? There's been the most terrible accident!'

Marjory was in the garden, snatching great armfuls of weeds from the border round the top lawn. The frantic messenger shouted her message from the hill below the house where, fourteen months earlier, Charlie had stood deep in conversation with the miller.

Tucking wisps of her long hair behind her ears and wiping the soil off her hands on to her gardening skirt, she ran through the kissing-gate into the field and together they flew across the upper gentle gradient, too breathless to talk. At first, when they came over the brow, Marjory could not make out what she was looking at. It was haytime, and the lower half of the field was already cut, wide stripes of the new-mown hay lying neatly across its slope. The grass at the top was still long, the bright reds and yellows of poppies and buttercups shining out against the uniform green. Where the two halves met was a heavy piece of farm machinery unlike any that she had seen before, with four men bending over it. What could it be?

And then the truth struck her with shocking force. This was not some monstrous new invention but a farm tractor that had overbalanced on to its side on the steep slope, the great blades of the attached mower gleaming behind it in the afternoon sun.

There was only one way the tractor could have got there. So where was the driver?

'Oh Mrs Garrad – thank goodness you've come!' The miller straightened from his task and ran to her side.

'I should never have let him do it – kept on and on at me after school, wanted to so much and I thought it would be all right – he's a good driver, see – but I should never have let him, never!' And he ran back to his colleagues straining over the machine.

Brian was lying with his head down the hill, his body trapped by the heavy tractor. As Marjory hurried to his side, she almost slipped and fell; looking down, she saw that she was standing on a spreading stain of dark red blood that covered the grass. Oddly, though her mind grappled with the horror of what she saw and must act upon, later it was the image of the buttons on the growing boy's new grammar school jacket straining in their buttonholes that she remembered most vividly.

A sudden tiny movement of the tractor startled her, and she took a quick step back. But the efforts of the four men to lift the great machine off the body had only made it slip a fraction further down the hill.

Brian's eyes were shut as Marjory stooped over him. The lids were flickering in an ice-white face, his lips scarcely more coloured than the skin. She felt a deep hopelessness – surely they were too late. She picked up his hand, the ink on his plump first and second fingers showing through the blood. Desperately she tried to find a pulse. For a moment, she thought she could feel a tiny beat, but then it was gone.

Brian was dead.

CHARLIE CAME TO HIM where he lay. Kneeling down beside him on the crimson grass, he said a prayer for the safe passage of this young and unstained soul.

60

September 1939

'I HAVE TO TELL YOU NOW, this country is at war with Germany. You can imagine what a bitter blow it is to me that all my long struggle to win peace has failed.'

The wireless, carried across the fields from the vicarage to the church for this very purpose and plugged in to the only power socket in the vestry, blared out its message as the eleventh stroke of Big Ben died away. Enid Peters, the church choir's leading soprano with a vibrato of Richter scale eight proportions, collapsed into the arms of the very same Edward Chapman who had let the four winds into the vicarage and was the only tenor. The vicarage children, all in the choir and robed accordingly, stood bemused by the whole performance. Mr Chapman had a perfectly good wife already – what was he doing clutching Enid?

The news, at eleven in the morning on September 3rd 1939, of the outbreak of the Second World War was of course deeply shocking, and Enid had fainted clean away. But Charlie was already marshalling the choir for its normal procession into the church, and a shaken Enid took her rightful place. The vicar took the unprecedented step of marching straight up the steps into the pulpit.

Looking down at his congregation, and clearly deeply moved himself, he spoke to them.

'It has just been announced on the wireless by our Prime Minister, Mr Neville Chamberlain, that we are after all at war with Germany.'

꧁

NEARLY FOUR MONTHS LATER, Douglas wrote to his father's youngest brother:

Barrow Gurney Vicarage
December 27th 1939

My dear Uncle George

Thank you very much for Biggles of the RAF. Lots of the boys at school have got Biggles books and they're really good but Ive never had one before. I cant wait to start it but Ive got to do my thankyou letters first.

We had a nice Christmas, I hope you did. We had turkey and plum-pudding as usual because they put off rationing for a bit after all. I think that was very nice of them, doing it because of Christmas.

Here is a sort of riddle for you. When Daddy goes out at nights now he wears a cushion on his head. Please write and tell me if you can guess why.

With best love from

Douglas.

The shrill bell in the hall rang and rang and rang again. Charlie started up in his chair, placed immediately below the bell so that it would wake him should he fall asleep. He stood up and, making his way to the dining-room, lifted the receiver from its hook and held it against his 'good' left ear.

'Hullo.' He spoke loudly and carefully into the separate mouthpiece on its long stalk. 'This is Flax Bourton 70.'

'Hullo? Is that Mr Garrad?' The telephonist in their local exchange had been married in his church. 'I'm ever so sorry to ring you up in the middle of the night, Vicar, but it's them air-raid people again and they wants to talk to you. Just a moment, and I'll connect you.'

Charlie waited.

'Hullo? Is that the Barrow Gurney air raid warden?'

'Yes, Charles Garrad here.'

'An air-raid is imminent. You should get to your post immediately.'

Charlie carefully hung the receiver back on its hook. He went to the drawing-room, took a cushion off the sofa, put it on the top of his head and tied it there with the piece of string kept in his pocket. Careful to keep his head upright, he put on his overcoat and a pair of trouser-clips, and went out through the front door, shutting it behind him. His bicycle was leaning against the wall. Meticulously, he turned on first the front light, hooded to conform with blackout rules, and then the back, swung his leg over the saddle and free-wheeled down the drive. With the intervening gate and cattle-grid safely negotiated and the steep descent of the lane behind him, he cycled, cushion firmly on head, along the silent empty village road, past the mill and the mill cottages, until he reached St Anne's Chapel.

St Anne's was the air-raid post, chosen for its central position in the village, for its thick stone walls, and for its bell in case of emergencies. It had been fitted up with a telephone, and here Charlie sat until he was released by a second call from the authorities.

'The air-raid is over.'

'Thank you,' said Charlie, 'but while I have you on the telephone, have you any news about the tin hats? Of course if they're still in short supply I must stick to my cushion. No doubt other people's needs are greater than mine. But it is a very clumsy alternative to the real thing.'

Charlie's stint was over now and he could go to bed. But, because of his deafness, whenever he was on call he had to sit in his chair in the hall; otherwise he could not hear the telephone.

'MUMMY! EVERYBODY! Come and look! Call Daddy, somebody!'

Elizabeth and her family stood in a row in front of the dining-room window, curtains drawn back. In the darkness it seemed to the horrified watchers as if the top of the next hill across the vast intervening valley had erupted into one enormous bonfire. Strung out along the ridge, flames stretched for miles, the stars above extinguished by their smoke. The beams of searchlights roved the sky, reaching out towards the half-moon and criss-crossing through the murky air in sweeping arcs of brilliance. Two met at their points and for a second held there a tiny shining jewel; it vanished in a puff of orange cloud, and several seconds later the deep boom of a gun reached the spectators as they stood transfixed.

'Watch out! I think they're coming!' A dull distant roar, scarcely audible at first, was getting louder, and the group made a dive for the floor under the sturdy oak dining table.

'I don't think those are German.' Douglas's just-broken voice came out unnaturally loud. In his new status as a man, he stood aside with his father to give more space for the women and children in their makeshift air-raid shelter. The fear inside him urged him into speech. 'There's no throb. The sound's steady.'

'No – listen! Can't you hear?' Even as Elizabeth spoke, the pulse of the

German engines forced itself upon them. They held their breath.

'Get down, both of you!' Marjory groped for the men's ankles.

The first explosion was sufficiently loud to send their hands flying over their ears. Even Charlie did not feel left out. The next one came within seconds. Glass shattered; the whole house shook. Anne and Elizabeth screamed in unison. Marjory grabbed randomly at whatever part of her family's anatomy she could find in the pitch dark.

'Is everyone all right?' Fanny did not even have to raise her comforting voice for the thrum of the engines was fading fast. The sound of more explosions disappeared into the distance as the heavy German aircraft unloaded their bombs, chased away from Bristol by the fierceness of the anti-aircraft fire.

CHARLIE WROTE TO HIS ELDEST SISTER:

Barrow Gurney Vicarage
January 20th 1941

Dear sister Mary

Just a note to let you know that we are all right. You may have heard on the wireless that there was a very heavy air-raid over Bristol last night; they are after the docks, of course. We had a bird's eye view from our dining-room window, and it did look as if the whole city must have been destroyed. However, as warden I have been informed that the destruction is not total, though extremely serious. Fortunately Elizabeth's school appears to be undamaged; up on the Clifton hill, it is well away from the Centre. She was hopeful of a few days holiday!

I understand there is some slight damage in the village, tiles off rooves and that sort of thing, but somehow the bombs landed between the houses, thank God, and no-one was hurt. But I must get on my bicycle and see if there is anything I can do to help. At least my fellow wardens and I have been issued with proper tin hats at last!

Thank you for your last letter, in particular for telling me about my great-godson. Dear old Matt; he must be bursting with pride. I'm sure he never thought all those years ago when we sat on milk churns in the yard and compared our different lives that one day his own grandson would be going to Cambridge! You don't say which college; could it possibly be Clare? His admission will of course have to be deferred until after his call-up into the navy; it certainly is an anxious time for the family. Please give my congratulations to the proud grandfather. I hope the good news will do a little to make up for the worry about his son, though now they know for certain that Charles is in a POW camp the strain must be less. I will write to Matt soon – letters must be doubly important now that he is laid up with that wretched arthritic knee.

Please look after yourselves in these dangerous times.

Yrs. affectionately

Your brother Char.

For a few months, the raids on Bristol continued, but by the end of April 1941 they were dying out. The Germans had done their worst, and were turning their attention elsewhere.

W/1 – THE VICAR'S WIFE was W/1! She had joined the Auxiliary Territorial Service, ATS for short, and had been allotted this memorable number. When her friends said, 'oh Marjory, you really are amazing! Fancy being the very first woman to join the army!' she had had in all honesty to shake her head and tell them that there had been many before her but the authorities had only just got around to assigning numbers. But still, when her daughter Anne joined her in the Service a year or two later, a great deal was made of it in the press:

'W/258922 joins W/1.' It made an excellent story.

Marjory's own job was a desk one, from home.

Anne's war was very different.

LITTLE WINNIE WHIMPERED in her sleep, and once again Marjory climbed wearily out of bed to try and comfort her. The smell of urine rising from the big mattress on the floor where the two children lay was almost overpowering, and she found it hard to pick up the child in her wet nightie and give her the love she needed. She thought back to Burma days when her own children had been small and it would have been the Ayah who had left her bed to tend to her small charges. But how thankful she was that they were not in Burma now. In a recent letter from brother Will he had sounded desperate. What was it he had said? A lot about the Japs and the awful things that had happened to various friends and colleagues as they tried to flee the advancing Japanese army, and then ...

'Food is becoming difficult, and we are running out of salt.'

What could he mean? Why would they run out of salt? She and Charlie had decided it must be a sort of code for rice, in case the letter fell into enemy hands; perhaps the authorities did not want the Japanese to know what real difficulties they were in. But why?

Winnie was asleep now, and Marjory climbed back into bed beside Charlie, sleeping peacefully and protected from disturbance by his failing ears.

WINNIE AND LENNY, evacuees from the east end of London, were unhappy at the vicarage. It was too big, too cold, and they hated the toffee-nosed vicarage children. So after a few months another billet was found for them in the village. Not so with their two teachers, however. Miss Aggie and Miss Mabel took up what seemed to the family near permanent residence in the absent Douglas's bedroom, having meals with them and innocently causing a great deal of private, but ribald, amusement at their irritating eating habits. Mr, Mrs and Baby Fonseca deprived the normal residents of another bedroom for the best part of a year. Dorrit Weissova, daughter of Jewish Czech escapees from Nazi Germany, grated along side by side with Elizabeth; they went to school together, catching the bus to Bristol every morning.

'Mummy, why does that man always wear his bowler hat? D'you think he wears it in bed?'

Marjory had often wondered about that herself, but did not feel it was polite to ask him. He was one of the half-dozen or so refugees from Bristol who were encamped in the vicarage attics. Mr Abercrombie, unfailingly polite, only removed his bowler in order to raise it in greeting to one of the family, wherever they might be. Coming downstairs or emerging from the one lavatory, it was always the same. They were an ill-assorted bunch up there, who lived not with but alongside the family, emerging from their attic roost early in the morning, walking the mile to the point where the Bristol bus stopped, and reappearing just in time to climb the two flights of stairs to bed.

At the time, it didn't seem particularly strange.

THE END OF THE WAR came at last, first the fighting in Europe, then the very different hostilities in the Far East. Life did not return to the 'normality' of pre-war Britain, but cows still needed milking, fields ploughing, grass mowing for hay. Charlie, relieved of his duties as chaplain to the nearby naval hospital and to the forces' temporary convalescent home in the Big House, went back to his Bible. Marjory picked up the pieces of her former life as best she could. Auntie Fanny finally left to look after a sick brother. Anne came home from her war in Italy unscathed but with a lifetime's experience behind her. Douglas went into the navy and captained a minesweeper clearing the mines left behind by the Germans. Elizabeth went peacefully off to university.

61

'LET ME DO THAT – IT'S TOO HEAVY FOR YOU.'

Charlie took the big hod of coke from his wife and tipped it into the innards of the hungry kitchen range. It was a Saturday, and Mr Speed, the verger-cum-gardener, had taken the day off to go and visit his grandchildren in the next village.

Charlie and Marjory had stuck to the old arrangement of lighting the range on Mondays for the washing, on Wednesdays, and on Saturdays for Charlie to have his weekly afternoon soak in the bath in time for the Sunday services. On Tuesdays, Thursdays, Fridays and Sundays the water was cold, but there was an electric cooker tucked up the corner of the big kitchen for the preparation of meals.

Charlie's attacks of lumbago were getting more frequent, and Marjory watched him anxiously as he handled the heavy coal. The task safely accomplished, they each pulled up a chair to the scrubbed table and looked at one another.

'I think,' said Charlie, 'that the time has probably come.' Marjory nodded, strands of grey hair escaping their hair-pins on the nape of her neck.

'I saw an advertisement in the *Western Daily Press* yesterday for a small house in Crewkerne, down in the south of the county. What would you think of that?'

❦

A WEEK LATER, they were on their way, estate agent's details in the glove compartment, picnic lunch in a basket on the back seat of their old maroon Hillman Minx, its door still bearing the scars of Elizabeth's early driving efforts.

It was almost impossible to talk in the car. Charlie had not driven since the terrible, unforgettable evening years earlier when he had run into a young father on a bicycle. In the failing light, the over careful driver had given a stationary van too wide a margin, and had not spotted the oncoming cyclist. At the inquest into the man's death, he had not been prosecuted but upbraided for careless driving. He had never enjoyed it; since that day it had become intolerable.

So it was Marjory who was at the wheel, with her husband's stone-deaf right ear beside her.

'Have we got a Somerset guidebook anywhere?' she asked before they set out. Charlie nodded.

'Can you bring it, then, and read it to me on the way?' So now, book in hand, he read to her over the noise of the old engine.

'Crewkerne has been an important town since pre-Norman Conquest times – and so on and so on. Ah, this sounds rather more interesting: The 15th Century parish church, Georgian town houses and streets of old stone cottages stand alongside the busy shopping centre. The town centre reflects a prosperous cloth-making past – the sails for Nelson's flagship Victory were made here.'

Marjory nodded and smiled. It sounded promising, she thought. The vicarage was too much for both of them now and, in any case, the village was changing, with 'incomers' from Bristol buying up the old farms and turning them into smart new homes. It was time, she thought, for a smart new vicar to match.

THE VERY YOUNG MAN in the wide-shouldered suit and lurid tie unlocked the front door of the bungalow. Behind his back, Marjory caught her husband's eye and shook her head. They went through the pantomime of visiting each small dark room in turn, but both had known at once what the outcome would be. So when, in answer to their question, the very young man took them to see a second never-to-be-repeated offer, a desirable property the like of which would not be seen again for many years, they fell into the trap. The comparison with the first was so immensely favourable that they put down a deposit on it there and then.

'YOU MEAN YOU'VE actually bought it, without even going back to have a second look?'

And when they heard about the three flights of steep stairs, the basement study, the second bedroom in the attic and, above all, the forty-five degree slope of the garden, the outcry from their three children was unanimous.

'No, you really can't. It sounds hopelessly unsuitable. You'll hate it.'

But their parents were not listening.

'It will do us very nicely. And, in any case, the deed is done.'

The very young man had made it all too clear that the deposit was not returnable under any circumstances whatsoever.

PROOFREADING PROGRESSED SLOWLY. There was not so very much more to do now. Admittedly, the light in the semi-basement study was poor, but at least the electricity in Crewkerne was a great deal more reliable than it had been in Maymyo. If the occasional visitors found their bedroom under the tiles scorchingly hot in the summer and freezing in the winter, they did not complain. The steep little garden at the back, unlike the vicarage one, was limited in size and had been well cared-for by the previous owners.

'So what do you think? Did we do right to come here? I find the house perfectly comfortable, don't you?'

Charlie was sitting in the window of their front room; Marjory had just carried in the tea tray. It was the first anniversary of the move, of the day when they had finally finished clearing out the big vicarage with all its clutter of battered furniture, Buddhas, reminders of Burma that they could not leave behind, books, toys, broken china glued together with Secotine – everything that had made up almost twenty years of busy life. There had been a party for them in the WI hut. The old folk had turned out in force, the farmers bringing their children, now grown up and taking over the land from their parents. Some had left for city jobs, but came back in deference to the departing vicar and his wife. A few of the newcomers were there, out of curiosity more than anything else. There had been speeches and a presentation, a painting of the vicarage by an artist from the next village, expensively framed and paid for from a secret house-to-house collection, calloused hands digging deeply into capacious pockets.

'Goodbye, Vicar. Goodbye, Mrs Garrad. We shall miss you.'

That was all that was said, but it was repeated over and over in the familiar voices that belonged here and here alone, and in tones that meant so much more than the written word.

It had been the second painful wrench in their joint lives, and the last parting that Charlie would have to bear.

MARJORY MADE FRIENDS, as she always did. Charlie, living now in an almost silent world, felt wanted; locum clergymen were hard to come by and he was kept busy on most Sunday mornings. At least the small payments received kept them warm. Sentence by sentence, the Burmese translation of the Bible was sieved through the intricate wiring of his brain, but the process was slower now and sometimes he despaired of reaching the very last words of the Bible, the words that summed up the enormity of the task his team had set themselves:

'For I testify unto every man that heareth the words of the prophecy of this book, if any man shall add unto these things, God shall add unto him the plagues that are written in this book: and if any man shall take away from the words of the book of this prophecy, God shall take away his part out of the book of life, and out of the holy city, and from the things which are written in this book.

'He which testifieth these things saith, Surely I come quickly. Amen. Even so, come, Lord Jesus. The grace of our Lord Jesus Christ be with you all. Amen.'

62

13th–21st December 1958

HE WAS TIRED, SO VERY TIRED. To his failing blood-starved brain the road ahead seemed to be tilting, tilting, rearing ever more steeply upwards, its unyielding tarmac threatening to tip him backwards at every laboured step. But reach the corner he must, where the scarlet pillar-box stood. That was where he turned back for home, back to the warmth and welcome that were always waiting for him. That was where he went. He must.

And then, somehow, he was seven years old and at the top of the pine tree at Brook House. Once more he was falling, but things seemed to have changed. The pins-and-needles he had felt before, the cramps from sitting still too long, were magnified a thousand times until, suddenly, his leg was numb. There was no feeling. Nothing. He tried to move, and there was no movement. He put out his hand, but his hand stayed motionless on the road beside him. Perhaps it was someone else's hand, but what was it doing there, where his own should be? And the people, all the people. All the white faces, turned towards him. Why were they looking down at him when he was high in the sky, up there with the squirrels? Ah, but after all something was the same. The same strong arms stretched out to hold him, the same smell of outdoor sweat and soil, the same reassuring voice.

'It's all right, Mr Garrad. We've got you. We'll take you home.'

CONFUSION. MUDDLE. A precise and ordered life turned backwards, inside out. Headache. Backache. Bewilderment. Faces, faces, looming down to peer at him, their great lips moving, mouths opening and closing like ugly fish. Ice-cold hands invading, pulling, pushing, lifting. Clumsy, so very clumsy. A nasty smell, and more hands, kinder this time, more gentle.

But he should be in his study. There was more work to do on that final draft. It wasn't finished; it couldn't go back to the publishers like that. There were still mistakes in the punctuation, in the syntax. Not perfect; must be perfect. But how could he go downstairs when he was floating on the ceiling? Up there it was peaceful, watching, just watching, not taking part. The old man on the bed below was thin, oh so thin. He felt sorry for him; they would not leave him alone. They were crowded round him, turning him on to his poor bony side. He knew they must be hurting him; could see his mouth open in a shout of pain. But he could hear nothing, nothing at all.

Now, the picture flipped and he was the old man once more, back on the bed. And at last, blessed relief; the face that was bending over him, so close to his own, was Marjory's. How he did love her still. Her cool hand stroked his face, smoothed away the creases. The smell was her smell now, her soap, just her. Passion had shrunk to a single glowing cinder, but love welled up in him in an overwhelming flame. How could he tell her? No need; she knew. The flame grew and grew until it encompassed everything. The Peace of the Lord be always with you. He smiled.

'HE'S GONE, DOCTOR,' she said when the running footsteps, stairs taken two at a time, had slowed at the door and the young man, bag in hand, had walked into the room. 'You know, he could not sing to save his life, but he was humming when he died.'

PART EIGHT

Postscript

England, 1958

THEY WERE LYING ON THE HALL TABLE, unnoticed and neglected since the postman had delivered them three days before. Both were addressed to the Rev C.E. Garrad and now, in the sudden blank and awful silence, these two small envelopes seemed the only link with the man whose body had just been carried awkwardly down the steep little stairs and hurried away in the undertaker's van.

Marjory snatched them up and almost ran to her usual chair in the front room. She sat for a long time with them on her lap, perfectly still. How strange, how impossible, that the eyes for which they had been intended would never, ever, read the letters they contained. Those eyes, so bright and clear when they had first met and now, with their old man's ring of white half obliterating the brown, would never again peer out from below their wrinkled lids to make sure she was still near him. They had been so important to him as his hearing failed more and more. And those funny little round glasses with their silver wire frames – she smiled, despite herself.

But the letters must be opened. Charlie would not want bills to go unpaid, letters unanswered. She tore open the brown envelope first.

'To: Sundry groceries during the month of November 1958, 16 pounds, 5 shillings, & 8 pence. Prompt payment welcomed.'

And, underneath the printed bill:

ME AND MRS JAMES was ever so sorry to hear of your illness, and hope as how you will make a speedy recovery. We send our respectful and fond wishes to Mrs Garrad.
Yours truly
Sidney James

It was some time before Marjory's own eyes were dry enough to allow her to open the second envelope. Of thicker paper, this one, and, in her state of increased sensibility, something made her hesitate before unfolding the single sheet inside. Ignoring the heading, she turned straight to the letter itself; and could scarcely believe what she read:

> Dear Mr Garrad.
>
> I fear this letter will come as a sore disappointment to you. After a great deal of thought, discussion, and the exchange of many letters with the Bishop of Rangoon, it has been regretfully decided that your translation of the Bible has not after all been adopted for use amongst Burmese Christians. It is generally thought to be too erudite and insufficiently colloquial for general use, although of course it remains an exceedingly important book of reference, which I am quite sure will be turned to on many occasions when accuracy of meaning is under discussion.
>
> From my own point of view, I am deeply saddened by this decision ...'

Marjory could read no more. All his work wasted, all to no avail. She must surely have misread the letter, for this just could not be. She forced herself to go through it again and again, and when her daughter came into the room she found her mother collapsed in her chair, her blouse soaked with tears, scarcely able to speak. Anne gently took the letter from Marjory's hand and read it. After a moment, she put her arms around her mother and held her against her breast.

'Thank God we didn't open it before Daddy died,' she said.

And then, less with conviction than to comfort them both, she added:

'I have a feeling that, in the end, the Garrad Bible will come into its own after all.'

Epilogue

Burma, 1989

THE COLD WOKE HIM. Pyau curled up into an even tighter ball and put out an unwilling hand to feel for his blanket. Ah, there it was; his fingers closed on the cloth and he gave it a tug.

'What the f— d'you think you're doing?'

The soldier lying next to him pulled his loose shirt more tightly round him.

'Keep your f——— hands to yourself, can't you,' and the young soldier humped himself over on to his other side.

Pyau, faced with an angry antagonistic back, was wide awake now. The early morning breeze ruffled the leaves of the great tree arching above them and, stretching the cramp from his arms and legs, he lay still and gazed up through the branches at one faint star.

Early morning is the best time, but then it's always been like that. Just for a moment I thought I was back at home, back high in the hills where everything was perfect. Though I suppose it can't have been really – nothing ever is. Of course, I didn't realise then how lucky I was – I thought everyone was like me, free as air and with the countryside in my bones. Townspeople seem to have something lacking – some primitive potion that flows in your mother's milk. Mind you, this is a hard test for all of us. Even I haven't come across jungle quite as dense as this – half the paths seem to lead nowhere, or back to where you started from.

It was so difficult to keep a sense of direction. He had been a good tracker as a boy, patient and painstaking in following the spore of wild animals, and he had gained a reputation for his skills amongst his army colleagues. Now, always, this meant that he took the lead whenever they were out of town. Their present quarry was immensely skilful, taking enormous pains to cover its tracks. Despite himself, he was impressed, for it left so few clues that time and again he and his party had had to retrace their steps and start again. And all the time the gap widened and the pursuit became more difficult.

'Come on, get up, lazybones!'

'What's the hurry?'

'Nok Lek has just turned up, and says he and Lu moved on last night by moonlight – gives me the shivers, thinking of them out there in the dark with only the evil spirits for company, but they did it, and survived. They say that from the top of that next hill they caught a glimpse of our friends not too far ahead. So we've got to get a move on.'

Pyau rolled over and got slowly to his feet. He was so tired. The last bout of malaria had been a bad one and had delayed his start, so that his own platoon had gone on without him, leaving him to come on later with soldiers who were strange to him. When the malaria finally departed, it had left him washed out and weary, prone to other ailments, and now he had to make a dash for the bushes, getting there only just in time. The bouts of diarrhoea had become almost continuous, and each time the bleeding got worse. Today's offering was no exception.

He filled his water bottle with the brown stream water, shouldered his grubby pack and picked up his rifle. All round him cursing, swearing men were gathering their few possessions and pulling off the leeches that had dined on them during the hours of darkness. It had been a mistake to camp so near water as he knew it would be, but the choice had not been up to him. At last, the straggling group moved off with the self-important Nok Lek at its head.

'Fall in and follow me,' he'd said, shouldering Pyau out of the way. 'I know where they were last night, and they can't have moved far.'

It was he, Nok Lek, not some trumped-up stranger dumped on them, who would lead them to victory. At long last his moment of glory had come.

At the back of the group now, and relieved at last of the burden of leadership, Pyau let his thoughts wander.

What on earth am I doing?

I'm certain that some of these 'rebels' we're chasing are the people I was at university with only two or three years ago. The government seemed OK to us then – after all, we'd all been taught endlessly at school about our wonderful new ruler, Ne Win, and how he was going to turn our country into the best in the world – and we believed it!

We scarcely noticed the change, it was so gradual. And then, as more and more people understood what was going on and broke away and then simply disappeared, the penny began to drop. Nobody ever actually knew what happened to them, but we never saw them again. So now we weren't just brain-washed, we were frightened too. Even so, a lot of us went on believing what we were told – we simply didn't dare do anything else. The fact is, their brainwashing had been so complete that they'd got us exactly where they wanted us.

And then the demonstrations started, hordes of people quietly marching through the streets of the big towns, holding up anti-government banners. I'd joined the government army by now, the Tatmadaw, mostly so as to get enough to eat after they'd devalued the currency for the second time. To start with we were told to disperse the crowds by firing above their heads. That didn't worry me – I hadn't had a chance to use my issue AK47 before, so I have to admit I quite enjoyed it. But gradually more and more people gathered and the Party must have taken fright. They issued orders that we were to aim straight into them, straight into thousands of ordinary people walking along in families, with grandmas and babes in arms, and I knew that I simply couldn't do it. At last I had to face the fact fair and square that the country was in the grip of a group of evil, power-hungry dictators, and that in my weakness I had got caught up in what they were doing. I don't think anyone noticed that when I pointed my gun and fired like the rest the ammunition stayed in my pocket. There were probably others that did the same – I hope so, anyway. But most of the soldiers were in real earnest, and in a couple of the biggest demonstrations literally thousands of ordinary people died.

Still I stayed on, too scared to leave. But a lot of people took the decision to take up arms against the junta, including several of my university friends. After a while I heard they'd joined up with one or other of the local tribes that have never wanted to be ruled by any Burmese government anyway, let alone this one.

It's amazing how even secret news spreads – someone knows someone who knows someone else. Finally, it has come to my long ears that my fellow students have realised at last that they're risking their lives for nothing because there aren't enough of them to do much good. So now, with the help of the tribesmen, they're trekking through the jungle trying to escape into Thailand.

And here am I, dressed in Burmese army uniform and armed with Burmese army guns, using my tracking skills to hunt my best friends down.

'Look where you're going, you fool! Sorry, brother – didn't see it was you.'

So engrossed had Pyau been in his own thoughts that he hadn't noticed the straggling group had stopped suddenly, and he cannoned into the sweat-soaked back of the soldier in front.

'What's up? Trouble?'

The private grinned.

'No – they're just missing you up front. Nok Lek has lost the way.'

Should he go and offer to help? Probably not – they didn't want him, and the longer the delay the more chance the others would have of escaping. So he smiled at the lad and said nothing.

They were soon off again, though noticeably more slowly and hesitantly, Pyau thought. As his trained eye automatically searched the bush on either side, he spotted a splash of brilliant turquoise, a butterfly wing lying just off the track. His mind went back to the expeditions of his boyhood, and the great flocks of huge butterflies, wing tip to wing tip and in brilliant luminescent blues and greens, that clustered wherever there was water. But what was that, beyond the wing? There was something unnatural about that group of leaves – surely it had been disturbed? Muttering the true excuse of an urgent call of nature, he left the trail made by the soldiers' feet and branched off towards the east, making careful mental note of his direction. Yes, surely more than one person had passed this way, and recently. His heart was beating fast as he attended to his needs. His tracker's eye seemed even keener than usual, and as he moved quickly from clue to clue, a decision burst inside his head. He would not go back to the path and tell them he had found the trail; he would leave them blundering off in the wrong direction and would follow it himself, alone. They would not miss him, an unwanted interloper. He would try to catch up with his true friends, friends from the old days when the world was still the right way up, and warn them of their danger.

For the first time in years, his conscience cleared and he felt truly free. The spirits of the butterflies had released him.

HE WALKED INTO THEIR CAMP with his hands held high above his head. He had taken off his army shirt and left it, with his rifle and pack, up a marked tree half a mile back. The reflection of the sun glaring from the barrels of a hundred pointing guns shone in his eyes and almost blinded him. He had come fast, with little water, and he was almost done.

'Friend' and 'Pyau' was all he managed, and then, in front of them all, gradually, very slowly, slipped on to his knees and down on to the dusty ground.

Hands came and picked him up, cool on his hot arms and legs and body, and carried him into the shade of a great tree. A water bottle was held to his lips, and taken away long before he had slaked his desperate thirst.

'Steady on, old chap – we don't want to drown you!'

Surely the voice was familiar? He tried to peer through the crimson mist in front of his eyes. The outlines of human shapes began to appear, and then a face – a big smile, full of white teeth, a nose cheekily angled, perhaps from a schoolboy fight. There was only one person in the whole world who could own that face – Ping, his greatest friend from student days, the man whose courage in the fight against the government he had come to admire more than anything in the world.

There was no time now for rest or talk. They gave him medicine for his dysentery, and they gave him water and a little food. Ping believed his change of heart, but the rest were mistrustful and thought he was a spy. He told Ping where he had left his kit, and because they were short of firearms they made him lead them back to the marked tree. But there was no doubt that he was their prisoner, and it was they who reclaimed the gun and carried it.

They kept him in their sight for every hour of the three days and nights that he travelled in their company. Once his tracking skills saved them from attack by a tigress separated from her young, and slowly he gained their respect, if not altogether their trust.

On the fourth day, they reached a larger encampment in a clearing in the forest, protected on all sides by the densest jungle they had seen. This was the headquarters of the rebel group befriending the students, and Pyau was taken at once to their leader. It was evening, and there was mosquito netting stretched across the open door of a palm-leaf hut. One of the rebels pulled it aside, and pushed Pyau through the doorway so hard that in his weak state he actually fell at the feet of a man sitting on a crudely made seat, reading by the light of a hurricane lamp.

Now what's going to happen? Here am I, an officer in the Tatmadaw, sprawled on the ground in front of the commander of the one tribe dedicated above all others to end the rule of the evil junta that I work for.

When he looked up, the commander was actually laughing.

'It's not normally my way to have my prisoners chucked at me like Daniel thrown into the Lions' Den – do you know that story?' and he held up the book he'd been reading.

'N -no, Sir, I'm afraid I don't.'

And then I looked at the title. It was written in the Burmese script; big gold letters standing out boldly against the black cover spelt out the words 'Holy Bible,' and a huge flood of relief spread all over me. Although I've been brought up a Buddhist, I've always had the greatest respect for Christians, who seem to be good people. And I know that this is the book they set great store by. I've heard all sorts of stories about my great-grandfather who was an ardent Christian. He was a countryman, too, and lived in a little village called ...

But the commander had put out his hand and was hauling Pyau to his feet. 'Sit down, Daniel,' he said.

I wondered whether to correct him, but decided it was probably more politic not to. Anyway, he soon went on:

'I know your real name is Pyau, but I shall always think of you as Daniel after that spectacular entry. Remind me to tell you the story one day –

'So, Daniel, I hear you've just saved our troops from a nasty accident with a tigress. Some of my men say you're a spy, and some that you truly have changed sides. What do you say?'

It was the strangest interview I have ever had. He made me sit on another chair, and sent for some coconut milk. After a few minutes I told him just what I had been thinking on the way, and a bit more. He was so easy to talk to, somehow, just sitting there listening and nodding from time to time.

'... so you see, Sir, I've come to try to warn you that the Tatmadaw are not so far away. There's no reason why you should believe me, I know, but what I am telling you is the tru ...'

'I know. My trackers have been out to spy out the land and confirm what you've said. Our enemies are heading off in the wrong direction. You could have stopped them, but you didn't. That's good enough for me. I suggest you stay with us – you're a deserter, and I don't need to tell you what'll happen to you if you're caught. When you've rested and recovered we should be glad of your help in the war. Now, this is the general plan ...'

But a flustered orderly had come to the door.

'Excuse me, Sir, but Htoo wants you in the hospital hut urgently.'

I was left alone in the commander's hut and was just about to make my own way out when I caught sight of the Bible again, lying on the table. It was an old tattered copy, and when I picked it up it opened at the marker between its pages. A pencil line had been drawn against a certain passage, and this is what I read:

The wolf also will dwell with the lamb
And the leopard shall lie down with the kid
And the calf and the young lion and the yearling together
And a little child shall lead them.
And the cow and the bear shall feed their young ones that lie

down together
And the lion shall eat straw like the ox
And the sucking child shall play on the hole of the asp
And the weaned child shall put his hand on the cockatrice's den.
They shall not hurt or destroy in all my holy mountain;
For the earth shall be full of the knowledge of the Lord
As the waters cover the sea.

I was mesmerised. It was not just that the poetry of the passage was so beautiful, but the hope that it conjured up was overwhelming. If this was what the Bible taught, then I must read more. Suddenly I was excited. Everything had seemed so hopeless, so awful, so impossible. Men were killing each other for nothing more than greed, for power over each other. Perhaps the answer lay in this ancient book – perhaps the people of a bygone age knew better than we do how to live in harmony and peace.

I longed to read more, and was so absorbed in my thoughts that the commander was back in the hut before I realised.

'I'm sorry, Sir, it's very rude of me to read your book.'

I think he could see I was excited and patted me on the shoulder.

'I'm delighted to see you're interested. Are you a Christian?'

'No Sir, but I've heard a great deal about Christianity. There are all sorts of stories handed down about my great-grandfather, who apparently gave up everything for your Jesus Christ.'

'There are more Christians in my tribe than in yours, I think, I learned about it from my father, and then, when I went to Rangoon University, I studied religion – theology, they called it. That was where I learnt to love the Bible – so many good stories, so much common-sense, so much brilliant teaching, so much love.

'If ever there was need to love your neighbour, it's now. I've just been visiting our newest patient in the simple little hospital we've made here. He's a porter for your army, the Tatmadaw, and some of my men just happened to come across him in the jungle when they were searching for the Tatmadaw column. He was barely alive, chained to another porter who was clearly very dead indeed, with one leg blown away by a land-mine. Both were covered in sores from the heavy weights they'd made them carry. Your 'friends' *(and he looked at me)* 'had left him to die, no longer of any use to them. They hadn't even cut him loose from the corpse that had been his partner. But I think he may pull through.'

I was sickened beyond measure.

'If you want to borrow my Bible while you're here, you're more than welcome. This is an interesting copy, and the best translation that I've come across. There are a couple of others, one much earlier and one later, both by Americans. But our professors at the university told us that this English one was far the nearest to the original. Take care of it.'

He opened it once more. On the fly-leaf was written:

Holy Bible

and, underneath, in smaller letters:

Translated by

and then three names, one below the other – and it was the top one that hit me in the eye:

Charles Garrad

and the name, like the butterfly's wing, took me straight back to the stories of my childhood:

'Once upon a time, more than a hundred years ago, in the year 1885, my great-grandfather Pyau was born and brought up in a village called Bootalet, not so very far from Mandalay ...'